To J.M.S.

Some Books are to be tasted,
others to be swallowed,
and some few to be chewed and digested.

FRANCIS BACON, *Essays*, 1625

RONALD E. SCOTT, *Department of Electrical Engineering, Northeastern University*

ELEMENTS OF LINEAR CIRCUITS

ADDISON-WESLEY PUBLISHING COMPANY, INC., READING, MASSACHUSETTS

This book is in the

ADDISON-WESLEY
SERIES IN ELECTRICAL ENGINEERING

Consulting Editors
DAVID K. CHENG · WILLIAM A. LYNCH

ADDISON-WESLEY

PUBLISHING COMPANY, INC.

READING, MASSACHUSETTS
Palo Alto · London
NEW YORK · DALLAS · ATLANTA · BARRINGTON, ILLINOIS

PREFACE

The *Elements of Linear Circuits* is in one sense an abridged version of the author's two-volume *Linear Circuits*. In another sense it is designed to stand on its own as a shorter introductory course in electric-circuit theory. Some knowledge of physics and calculus, while not an absolute prerequisite, is recommended for those using the book.

The material covered falls into four sections of roughly equal length.

1. Resistive circuits
2. *R-L-C* circuits

3. Steady-state AC circuits
4. Transform circuits

Circuits are introduced as mathematical models which follow well-defined laws. The first section on resistive networks allows the student to attain some facility with circuit theory within the realm of simple algebra. The second section on *R-L-C* circuits introduces the student to the exponentials, sine waves, and damped sine waves which constitute the allowable natural behavior patterns of linear circuits. The third section covers phasor networks in the frequency domain, and the final section is devoted to Laplace transforms and transform networks.

The purpose of the book is to provide a strong foundation of linear circuit theory at the beginning of the engineering program, which can be used in all of the subsequent courses. Electronics becomes the circuit theory of active and nonlinear elements, energy conversion becomes the circuit theory of time-varying systems, field theory becomes the circuit theory of distributed parameters, and communications theory becomes an extension of signal analysis.

The criterion which has been applied to the selection of material for this basic text is that the methods included should be in general use by the engineering profession and not merely inherently interesting. More specialized and more speculative methods can be taught in subsequent courses.

It is a pleasure to acknowledge the continuing support of Northeastern University for my writing projects and the continuing help of the staff of the Addison-Wesley Publishing Company.

R.E.S.

CONTENTS

CHAPTER **1**

INTRODUCTION

The goal of science is order. Science is constructed from facts just as a house is constructed from stones, but an accumulation of facts is no more a science than a pile of stones is a house.

HENRI POINCARÉ

In the year 600 B.C., Thales of Miletus, one of the Seven Sages of Greece, rubbed amber with a cloth and observed that it would then attract light objects. The phenomenon was called "electricity," from the Greek word amber. The first recorded use of electricity was by Anteus, a freed-man of the Emperor Tiberius of Rome, who stepped upon an electric eel and was immediately cured of his gout!

Since those early years the knowledge of electricity has multiplied endlessly and so have its uses. Virtually all the conveniences of modern life depend in some way upon electricity. The subject is so comprehensive that a student cannot discover all the facts for himself. In the interest of efficiency he must learn the subject as an ordered science.

Circuit theory is the basic discipline of electrical science. It concerns the transfer of energy from one device to another. It has no regard for the internal structure of the devices nor for the location of device A with respect to device B. It considers only the amount of energy which passes from one device to the other. Since the principal function of electricity is the transfer and control of energy, it is not surprising that circuit theory plays a key role in electrical engineering.

1-1 Model theory

Every branch of science has its own collection of "models." When the physicist talks of an atom or an electron he does not pretend to be dealing with physical reality, but only with a model whose mathematical equations he understands and whose behavior he can predict with precision. The economist who analyzes the fluctuations of an economy also deals with models. His models are less precise and the conclusions which he draws from them are correspondingly less reliable. Indeed, the "exactness" of a science is a measure of the degree of correspondence between its models and physical reality.

There are two points of view regarding models. The first is that a model is a mathematical representation of a real physical device. For example, a wheel may be described mathematically as a circle of radius R. The second point of view is that the model is an idealized physical device. An "ideal" wheel would be perfectly round and might have zero mass, just like its mathematical counterpart, the circle. Both points of view are useful. Electric circuits are the idealized models which represent electrical devices.

If the student is disappointed to learn that circuit theory is not "real" engineering, he will also be overjoyed to learn that neither does it become obsolete. As he becomes a more proficient engineer he will use more complex models to represent a given device, but the rules for manipulating them will remain the same. As new physical devices are invented, they too will be reduced to models and treated by the same circuit theory.

The ideas of stimulus and response are basic to our concept of a physical world. A block diagram of a typical situation in electrical engineering is shown in Fig. 1–1. The input stimulus represents energy supplied to the system by an external source, and the output response represents the utilization of the energy at some other point. The idealized system itself is called a *circuit* or a *network*.

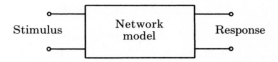

Figure 1–1. The stimulus-response relationship.

In many networks the output response is directly proportional to the input stimulus. For example, if the input is doubled, the output also doubles. Networks which possess this property are called *linear*. The implications of linearity are far-reaching. One of them is the *principle of superposition* which states that the response for a large number of sources acting at once can be obtained as the sum of the responses produced by each of the sources acting alone.* Therefore it is never necessary to consider more than one source at a time. The single stimulus-response relationship shown in Fig. 1–1 represents the most general problem for a linear network. It is the central theme of this book.

The first third of the book discusses a particularly simple type of network in which the response is equal to the stimulus multiplied

---

* For a mathematical proof of linearity and superposition, see Chapter 3.

by a constant.* This constant, which summarizes the effect of the network in producing a response from the input stimulus, is called the *response function* of the network. In the second third of the book the response function is no longer a constant but a function of time. In the third section the stimulus and the response are sinusoidal in character.

1–2 Circuit variables: current and voltage

If we were interested in the flow of automobile traffic in a country, we would undoubtedly concentrate on the movements along the trunk highways and ignore the exact distribution within any single city. Similarly, in the realm of electric circuits we are often interested in the flow of electricity from one device to another and not in the distribution of the energy within any one device. Under these circumstances we are justified in taking the basic building blocks of our model theory as "lumped" elements in which the electrical behavior is summarized by the effect produced at the *terminals* or trunk lines entering the device. The simplest devices have a single pair of terminals. Electricity enters at one terminal and leaves from the other. A typical lumped element and its associated terminal pair are shown in Fig. 1–2. The actual physical device is pictured in Fig. 1–2(a) as occupying some region of space. The network model shown in Fig. 1–2(b) has one pair of terminals with an idealized mathematical connection between them. It has no physical dimensions and no preferred orientation in space; it can be moved around and rotated at will.

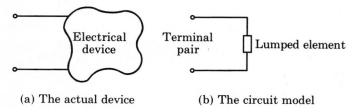

(a) The actual device   (b) The circuit model

Figure 1–2. A lumped element and its terminal pair.

Energy itself is not a measurable quantity. To keep track of energy in an electrical system we define a new measurable quantity called *electric charge*. Historically, charges were first observed by rubbing dry substances together. For example, when cat's fur is stroked with rubber, charges appear which cause the fur to stand on end. By contact with the cat's fur, charge can be transferred to other light bodies,

---

* These networks are sometimes loosely called direct-current, or dc, networks. The correct requirement is that there should be no energy-storage elements in the network. There is no restriction on the type of stimulus.

which then repel each other. In 1747 Benjamin Franklin called the charge on cat's fur positive, and the charge that appeared on the rubber negative. In modern times atomic physicists have pictured electric charge as being one of the building blocks of the universe. The ultimate unit of electric charge is the electron, with a mass of 9.107×10^{-31} kg and a small negative charge.

Electrons move in orbits about the nucleus of each atom and many of them break loose and move at random in the interatomic spaces. An excess of electrons in a body represents a negative charge, and a deficit of electrons a positive charge. The practical unit of charge is *the coulomb*, which is 6.24×10^{18} electrons.

In the year 1819, Hans Christian Oersted observed that a flow of electric charge produced a force on a magnetic compass needle and that the force was proportional to the rate of flow of charge. The measurement of this magnetic effect is a great deal easier than the measurement of the forces between charges. For this purpose a new variable, current, which is equal to the rate of flow of charge, is defined in terms of a unit called the *ampere:* 1 ampere = 1 coulomb/second. Current, rather than charge, is the basic variable of circuit theory. It is represented by the symbol i or I. In summary,

$$i = \frac{dQ}{dt}, \qquad (1-1)$$

where i = current in amperes, Q = charge in coulombs, t = time in seconds.

Two additional comments need to be made about currents. First, they have direction. In a traffic analogy, charge represents the number of automobiles in a city. In the same analogy current is the number of cars entering or leaving per second. Clearly, the number of cars per second has direction. By the same token, the number of coulombs per second, or the current, has direction. *Because current has direction, it is customary to consider it as "flowing" around a circuit.*

In order to keep track of the direction of a current, it is convenient to assign an algebraic reference direction. In the traffic analogy we might assign a plus sign to all traffic entering the city and a minus sign to all traffic leaving the city. A net plus count for the traffic would then mean a movement of cars into the city, while a negative count would mean a movement out of the city. In electric circuits the reference direction for the current is marked by an arrow on a figure. A current of positive charge moving in the direction of the arrow is considered to be positive and in the opposite direction to be negative. Note particularly that *a reference direction may be chosen arbitrarily, and the actual physical current will be either positive or negative, depending on the choice.*

The second comment concerns the nature of current. In most good conductors of electricity the current consists of a motion of free electrons. In other materials, however, it may be a motion of positive charge, or of positive charge in one direction and negative charge in the other direction. The magnetic effect produced by a flow of positive charge is equal to that produced by a flow of negative charge in the opposite direction; that is, the current is the same in either case. Since we can make no distinction between the two cases, *current is always considered to be an equivalent flow of positive charge.*

The flow of electric current is different in one essential respect from the flow of traffic or of water. As a consequence of the two kinds of charge the current into a device at one terminal is always equal to the current out at the other terminal. Currents are thus associated with terminal pairs as shown in Fig. 1–3.

In our quest for a method of measuring energy in electric circuits we have introduced the concept of electric charge and have defined an electric current as a flow of charge. We still cannot keep track of the energy. An additional variable is required which will measure the amount of energy gained or lost by each element of charge as it passes through a device. This variable is called *voltage.* It is represented by the symbols e, E or v, V. The unit of voltage is the *volt:* 1 volt = 1 joule/coulomb. In summary,

$$v = \frac{dW}{dQ},\tag{1–2}$$

where v = voltage in volts, W = energy in joules, Q = charge in coulombs.

If it is to be useful, voltage must be a readily measurable quantity. A direct mechanical measurement can be made in terms of the force between two charged bodies. More often, however, voltage is measured in terms of the related current it produces in a known circuit.

From the definitions of current and voltage given in Eqs. (1–1) and (1–2), it is apparent that the product of current and voltage is the power associated with an electrical device. Power is measured in joules per second, or watts, and has the symbol p. Thus

$$p = ei,\tag{1–3}$$

where p = power in watts, e = voltage in volts, i = current in amperes. The dimensions associated with Eq. (1–3) are

$$\text{watts} = \text{volts} \times \text{amperes}$$

$$= \frac{\text{joules}}{\text{coulomb}} \times \frac{\text{coulombs}}{\text{second}} = \frac{\text{joules}}{\text{second}}.\tag{1–4}$$

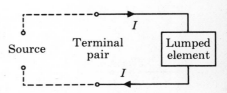

Figure 1–3. An exact definition of current in a lumped element.

Voltage does not possess direction in the same sense as the current. It does, however, have polarity, since energy can either be supplied to the electrical device or be received from it. A plus sign for the voltage at the terminal where the current enters indicates that energy is absorbed in the device, and, conversely, a negative sign at that terminal indicates that the electrical device is a source of energy. In terms of our traffic analogy the positive voltage represents a hill and the negative voltage a valley. If cars enter the city from a hill and leave by way of a valley, they supply a net amount of energy to the city. On the other hand, if they enter through a valley and leave from a hill, the city must supply energy to them! *It is convenient to regard voltage as potential energy and voltage levels as elevations or heights.* *

A pair of signs, plus and minus, are used at a terminal pair to give a reference direction for the voltage, as shown in Fig. 1–4. In terms of potential energy, the positive sign represents an elevation above the negative sign. However, it should be carefully noted *that the polarity marks for voltage,* as for current, *are for algebraic reference only.* If an actual voltage has the same polarity as the reference signs, it is a positive voltage, and if it has the opposite polarity, it is a negative voltage.

Consistent signs must be assigned to current and to voltage if the algebraic sign of the power is to have meaning. Usually current directions are assigned at random and the voltage is made to agree. *A plus sign for the voltage is assigned at the terminal where the current enters the device.* If this convention is followed, a positive sign for the power will represent energy lost in the device. The voltages are then *voltage drops* produced by the flow of current. As the coulombs "roll downhill" they lose energy to the device.

We shall not discuss the use of actual meters in this text, but it will be convenient to define ideal meters for the measurement of current, voltage, and power. An ideal *ammeter* placed in the path of the current gives a reading proportional to the current passing through it. It must absorb no energy from the circuit and thus has no voltage across it. An ideal *voltmeter* is connected across a terminal pair in parallel with a lumped element. The reading is proportional to the difference in the energy levels of the two terminals. Since no energy can be absorbed by the meter, no current must flow through it. An ideal *wattmeter* measures the power entering a terminal pair. It is a combination of a voltmeter and an ammeter and gives a reading

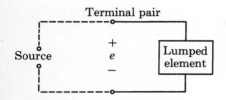

Figure 1–4. An exact definition of voltage in a lumped element.

---

* Voltage *is* potential if terminal-pair definitions are used. In circuit theory there is no need to distinguish between the potential (the static, conservative field) and electromotive force (the nonconservative field component).

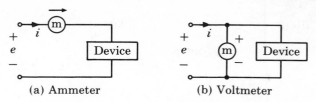

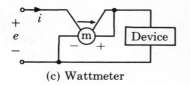

| (a) Ammeter | (b) Voltmeter | (c) Wattmeter |

Figure 1-5. Ideal meters.

that is proportional to the product of the voltage and the current. These three types of meters, with their symbols and connections, are shown in Fig. 1-5. All three have reference directions marked on them, so that a positive reading will have algebraic significance.

1-3 Circuit parameters: resistance, inductance, and capacitance; sources

In the preceding sections we have seen that the energy associated with an electrical device is specified in terms of the current through it and the voltage across it. The relationship between current and voltage is determined by the nature of the device. If we force a given current through a device, the energy which we must supply will be determined by the device. Alternatively, if we supply charge with a given amount of energy, the number of coulombs which will pass through will be determined by the device.

There are three basic types of linear circuit elements. A *resistor* is an element which dissipates energy (as heat or in some other way). An *inductor* stores energy by virtue of a current through it. A *capacitor* stores energy by virtue of a voltage existing across it. Sources that supply a given number of coulombs per second, regardless of the energy required from them, are called *current sources*. Sources that supply coulombs with a given energy, regardless of the number of coulombs required, are called *voltage sources*. We shall discuss the parameters and the sources in turn.

Resistance. Electrical elements which dissipate energy are called *resistors*. The idealized circuit models are called *resistances*. Typical examples of resistors are the heating elements in stoves, the filaments in electric light bulbs, and the copper wires used to bring electric power into our homes. In a sense all materials are resistors since they all conduct electricity to a greater or a lesser extent. It is convenient, however, to divide them into three classes: conductors such as metallic elements, which conduct electricity easily; semiconductors such as germanium and silicon; and insulators such as wood and glass, which conduct electricity with great difficulty. Because of the range of materials available, the resistance parameter is truly remarkable. Physical units of approximately the same size can be created over a parameter range of 10^{18} or more. A given material offers more resistance in proportion to the length of the conducting path and less resistance in proportion to the cross-sectional area of the conducting path.

The theory of electrical resistors was given by Georg Simon Ohm in the year 1826. He clarified the concepts of current and voltage and showed that for a resistor *the current is proportional to the voltage*. His contemporaries thought so little of his work that he was not made a professor until twenty-two years later. The verdict of history is kinder. The volt-ampere relationship of the resistance element bears the name of Ohm's law, and the unit of resistance is the ohm. For the ideal resistance element

$$e = Ri, \qquad (1-5)$$

where e = voltage across the element in volts, i = current through the element in amperes, R = resistance in ohms. An alternative form of Eq. (1–5) is

$$i = e/R = Ge, \qquad (1-6)$$

where $G = 1/R$ = conductance in mhos.

The symbol for resistance and the sign convention associated with it are shown in Fig. 1–6. If this sign convention is adopted, the resistance and the power dissipated in the resistance will both be positive. The power is

$$p = ei = i^2R = e^2/R. \qquad (1-7)$$

The first form of Eq. (1–7) is convenient when the current and the voltage are both known, the second form when only the current is known, and the third form when only the voltage is known.

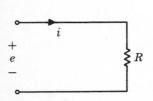

Figure 1–6. The resistance parameter and its sign convention.

Inductance. The electrical element which stores energy in association with a flow of current is called an *inductor*. The idealized circuit model for the inductor is called an *inductance*. Inductance was first discovered by Michael Faraday in 1831. (Faraday began as a janitor in the Royal Institution of London, but he later rose to become its director.) He observed a magnetic effect in the air surrounding a wire carrying a current and noted that a compass needle always pointed in the direction of a circle around the wire. Faraday explained the effect in terms of magnetic "lines of force" in the "ether" surrounding the wire. He postulated that the lines of force were stretched into place by the current in the wire, somewhat as though they were elastic bands, and that the energy thus stored in the ether returned to the wire in the form of a generated voltage when the current decayed to zero.*

---

* The lines of force were called *flux linkages* by Maxwell, who justified Faraday's concepts by more rigorous mathematics.

Practical inductors are usually made of many turns of fine wire wound in a coil or a helix to enhance the magnetic effect without greatly increasing the size of the device. Often the wire is wound on magnetic material, which is capable of storing more energy per ampere than is air. Because of their shapes, inductors are called *coils*, and because of the energy required to establish a current in them, they are called *chokes*.

For the ideal circuit model of an inductor, the voltage is proportional to the rate of change of the current. The proportionality constant is called the *inductance*. It has the symbol L, and the unit is called a *henry*, after Joseph Henry, an American investigator who obtained many of Faraday's results independently. The mathematical volt-ampere relationship for an inductor is

$$e = L\frac{di}{dt}, \tag{1-8}$$

where L = inductance in henrys, e = voltage across the element in volts, di/dt = rate of change of the current in amp/sec.

An alternative form of Eq. (1–8) is obtained by integrating both sides with respect to the time. To include all possible magnetic effects we must integrate from minus infinity to the present time. Thus

$$i = \frac{1}{L}\int_{-\infty}^{t} e\, dt. \tag{1-9}$$

The power entering the inductor at any instant is given by

$$p = ei = Li\frac{di}{dt}. \tag{1-10}$$

When the current is constant, the derivative is zero, and no additional energy is stored in the inductor. The "elastic bands" maintain their form and the energy associated with them is fixed. When the current increases, the derivative of the current has a positive value, and the power, as given by Eq. (1–10), is positive. Additional energy is stored in the inductor. The total energy in the inductor at any given time is the integral of the power from minus infinity to that time. It is expressed by

$$W_L = \int_{-\infty}^{t} ei\, dt = \int_{-\infty}^{t} Li\frac{di}{dt}\, dt = \int_{0}^{i} Li\, di = \tfrac{1}{2}Li^2, \tag{1-11}$$

where W_L = energy stored in the inductor at time t in joules, i = current in the inductor at time t in amperes.

Equation (1–11) shows that the *total energy in the inductor depends only on the instantaneous value of the current* and not on the

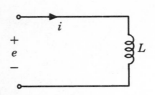

Figure 1–7. The inductance parameter and its sign convention.

manner in which it is established. In order for the energy stored in the inductor, as given by Eq. (1–11), to be positive, the current and the voltage must have consistent signs, as shown in Fig. 1–7.

Capacitance. A *capacitor* stores energy because of the voltage across the device and independently of the current through it. The idealized circuit model of a capacitor is called *capacitance*.

Historically, capacitance is the oldest of the three circuit parameters. In 1745 van Mussenbroek of Leyden performed an experiment for the purpose of preserving static electricity from the decay which it experienced in air. He placed an insulator between two metal sheets, charged it by rubbing, and handed it to a friend, Cunaeus, who received a violent shock! For the first time a method of accumulating electric charge and intensifying its electric effect was available.

A mathematical discussion of the energy storage on a capacitor was given by Simeon Poisson to the French Academy in 1812. He likened the forces between charges to the gravitational force between a mass and the earth and the energy of the stored charges to the potential energy of a mass at rest above the earth. As the conducting plates of a capacitor are made larger, they contain more charge and hence more energy at any given voltage. The closer the plates, the greater the force between the charges and hence the greater the energy stored per unit charge. Thus capacitance is a parameter which is proportional to the size of the plates and inversely proportional to the spacing between them.

Sometimes the material between the conducting plates is air, and sometimes it is an insulator such as glass or mica which will store more energy per unit volume. In "electrolytic" capacitors the oxidized surface of a metal such as aluminum or tantalum is used for the insulator.

In the ideal circuit model of a capacitor, the voltage is proportional to the charge or to the integral of the current. The constant of proportionality is the reciprocal of the capacitance, in farads. The total charge on the capacitor is the sum of all the charges which have entered the capacitor since the beginning of time, and therefore the integral of the current must be taken from minus infinity to the present time. The voltage across the capacitance is given by

$$e = \frac{1}{C} Q = \frac{1}{C} \int_{-\infty}^{t} i \, dt, \qquad (1\text{–}12)$$

where e = voltage across the capacitance in volts, Q = charge on the capacitance in coulombs, i = current in amperes (coulombs per second), C = capacitance in farads. The current i is said to "flow" through the capacitor, since a positive charge entering one terminal repels a positive charge at the other terminal.* The derivative of Eq. (1–12) gives an alternative form for the volt-ampere relationship of the capacitance:

$$i = C\frac{de}{dt}.$$ (1–13)

The power entering the capacitance at any time is given by

$$p = ei = Ce\frac{de}{dt}.$$ (1–14)

When the voltage is constant, the derivative is zero and the power expressed by Eq. (1–14) is zero. Only by increasing the voltage can additional energy be fed into the capacitance. The total energy in the capacitance is

$$W_C = \int_{-\infty}^{t} ei\,dt = \int_{-\infty}^{t} Ce\frac{de}{dt}\,dt = \int_{0}^{e} Ce\,de = \tfrac{1}{2}Ce^2, \quad (1\text{–}15) \qquad = \tfrac{1}{2}QV = \frac{Q^2}{2C}$$

where W_C = energy stored in the capacitance at any time t, in joules; e = voltage across the capacitance at any time t, in volts.

In order to make the energy stored in the capacitance [as given by Eq. (1–15)] positive, we use the sign convention shown in Fig. 1–8.

In electricity, as in mechanics, there are two types of energy storage. The energy stored in an inductor is associated with the motion of electric charge and in many respects is similar to kinetic energy in mechanics. The energy stored in a capacitor is associated with a force between stationary charges and is like potential energy in mechanics. Many of the interesting properties of electrical devices stem from the existence of these two types of energy storage. Wave motion, for example, exists only when energy can alternate between one form and the other; the same is true of resonance phenomena used in tuning radio and television sets.

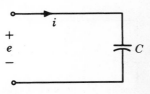

Figure 1–8. The capacitance parameter and its sign convention.

Sources. In addition to the passive circuit elements which store and dissipate energy, we must define ideal or model source elements that can supply energy to our circuits. Idealized sources fall into two categories, *current sources*, which supply a given number of coul/sec regardless of the energy required of them, and *voltage sources*, which supply an arbitrary number of coulombs, each possessing a fixed amount of energy. Ideal sources in conjunction with resistance represent typical physical sources.

––––––––––

* Maxwell postulated a real physical current, which he called the *displacement current*, in the region between the plates. The existence of a real displacement current makes possible the propagation of radio waves.

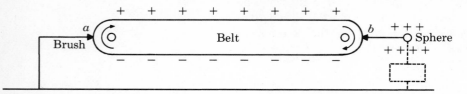

Figure 1-9. Electrostatic (van de Graaff) generator.

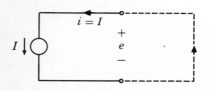

Figure 1-10. A current source.

Historically, *current sources* were discovered first. The earliest electrical effects were obtained by rubbing two materials together. A modern version of the frictional generator, called a van de Graaff generator, is shown in Fig. 1-9. A moving belt transports the static charge produced by friction at point *a* to point *b*, where it is transferred to the inside of a sphere. The amount of charge deposited on the sphere per second depends on the speed of the belt and the amount of charge produced at *a* and not on the external circuit connected to the sphere. Such devices are used as current sources for nuclear research.

The ideal circuit model of a current source produces a fixed current no matter what voltage is across it. If the external circuit presents infinite resistance, the voltage rises to infinity and the power supplied must also become infinite. An ideal current source is capable of supplying infinite power and for this reason is not physically realizable. Physical sources can, however, behave like current sources when the power drawn from them is small. The symbol for a current source, and its volt-ampere relationship are given in Fig. 1-10. It is necessary to suppose that the current source is connected to some external circuit to complete the path for the current.

The earliest *voltage sources* were discovered by Luigi Galvani in 1791. In the course of dissecting frogs he noticed a peculiar twitching and an electric spark when he touched a nerve with a scalpel. He rightly attributed the effect to electricity, but it remained for Alessandro Volta to explain the origin of the electricity. Volta showed that electricity was produced whenever two dissimilar metals were immersed in a conducting fluid. (Galvani's frog merely acted as the "fluid" connecting the scalpel and the metal table.) By 1800 Volta had constructed cells of copper and zinc and observed the first continuous electric currents ever produced by man. The electric variable *voltage* was named for him, in honor of this achievement. Modern batteries and storage cells are similar in principle to Volta's original devices. The energy is released by chemical action in the cells, and the amount obtained per coulomb is fixed by the nature of the chemical reaction.

In the ideal circuit model of a voltage source the voltage across the terminals is constant and independent of the current drawn from it. The symbol for a voltage source and the volt-ampere relationship are shown in Fig. 1–11. When an open circuit is placed across a voltage source, the current is zero and no power is drawn from it. The strain on a voltage source occurs when zero resistance is placed across it. The current then rises to infinity and with it the power delivered by the source. Physical sources can behave like voltage sources only for a range of small currents.

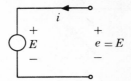

Figure 1–11. A voltage source.

1–4 The circuit laws $\sum e = 0$ and $\sum i = 0$

All of the basic circuit elements discussed in the previous section have two external terminals. Electric circuits are constructed by connecting these external terminals in various ways. The connections are assumed to have zero resistance and to pass currents without absorbing any power; they are called *short circuits*. Conversely, if there is no connection between two terminals, an *open circuit* is said to exist between them. An example of a circuit is shown in Fig. 1–12. Circuits are related to the mathematical science of junctions and elements, called *topology*. The exact location of the elements is of no consequence. The shapes and lengths of the short circuits joining the elements have no significance. In our mathematical model the elements can be turned around and placed in any desired position.

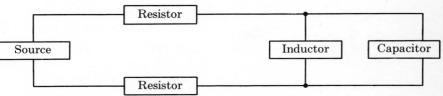

One of the facilities which an electrical engineer must acquire is the ability to recognize the essential nature of a circuit no matter how it is drawn. He must be able to redraw circuits in their simplest form. An example of four equivalent circuits is given in Fig. 1–13.

Figure 1–12. An example of a circuit.

The basic laws which govern the interconnection of electrical elements were first stated by Gustav Kirchhoff in a footnote to a paper written in 1848. Kirchhoff's laws are a consequence of the laws of conservation of energy and conservation of charge. Since conservation of charge postulates that charge is neither created nor destroyed,* the charge which enters a junction point in a network must either leave instantaneously or be stored there. It cannot be stored because the junction is an infinitesimal mathematical point, and the charge possesses a finite mass and size. Hence the charge which arrives at a junction point at any instant must leave immedi-

---

* Atomic disintegrations are excluded from circuit theory.

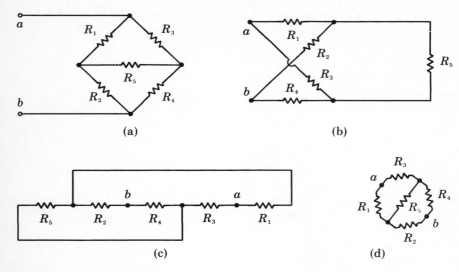

(a)

(b)

(c)

(d)

Figure 1-13. Four equivalent forms of the same circuit.

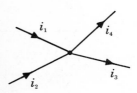

Figure 1-14. An example of Kirchhoff's current law.

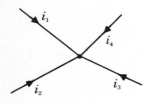

Figure 1-15. Currents entering a junction.

ately. In terms of currents, the total current entering the junction must be equal to the total current leaving the junction. If currents leaving the junction are taken to be positive and currents entering are taken to be negative, the algebraic sum of the currents at the junction will be zero. Thus

$$\sum i = 0. \qquad (1\text{-}16)$$

Equation (1-16) is Kirchhoff's current law. An example of its application to a junction point is given in Fig. 1-14. For this junction Kirchhoff's current law is

$$i_3 + i_4 - i_1 - i_2 = 0 \qquad (1\text{-}17)$$

or, written in terms of currents entering and leaving, it is

$$i_1 + i_2 = i_3 + i_4.$$

The reader should be able to write the equation in either form with no hesitation. Note that the current directions shown in the figure and used in writing the equations are the *assumed* directions. For example, all the reference arrows might point toward the junction, as in Fig. 1-15. The current law equation for this node is

$$i_1 + i_2 + i_3 + i_4 = 0. \qquad (1\text{-}18)$$

Equation (1-18) may seem to be impossible, but not if it is recalled that the directions shown are reference directions only and that the values of some of the currents can be negative, indicating an actual direction away from the node.

The second Kirchhoff's law springs from the law of conservation of energy. In a gravitational field the energy level of a point A with respect to a point B can be found by moving a unit mass from A to B and noting the energy given up in the process. Similarly, in electric circuits the energy level of point A with respect to point B can be obtained by moving a charge from A to B and noting the energy given up in the process. The energy one coulomb gives up as it moves from point A to point B is the same along any path from A to B. (If it were not, we could make a perpetual motion machine by letting the coulombs slide down the path with the large energy difference and then moving them back along the path with the small energy difference.) Since the energy lost by a coulomb in moving from point A to point B is independent of the path, the energy for any round trip must be zero. A voltage drop in the direction of motion of the test charge represents an energy loss, and a voltage rise represents an energy gain. This statement is Kirchhoff's voltage law:

$$\sum e = 0. \tag{1-19}$$

As an example of the Kirchhoff voltage law, consider the circuit of Fig. 1-16. Adding up the voltages around the loop, we obtain

$$e_1 + e_2 - e_4 - e_3 = 0. \tag{1-20}$$

As an alternative we might equate the total voltage drops from A to B by the two paths to obtain

$$e_1 + e_2 = e_3 + e_4.$$

It is essential to be able to write both forms of the equation by inspection of the circuit. As in the case of currents, Kirchhoff's voltage law is written in terms of assumed or reference polarities, and the actual voltages may or may not agree with them.

The idea that voltage is analogous to gravitational elevation suggests the possibility of a reference point analogous to sea level. In electrical networks, this potential is called *ground*. We have previously defined voltages across separate elements only, but by means of Kirchhoff's voltage law we can compute the voltage at any point in a network with respect to the ground or reference voltage. The land surveyor has the same problem. He measures the incremental elevations from one point to the next, and to obtain the elevation above sea level he must add a series of incremental results. Figure 1-17 illustrates the procedure and shows the symbol for the ground point. In terms of the voltages across the elements, the voltages of the junctions A, B, and C with respect to ground are

$$e_C = e_1, \qquad e_B = e_1 + e_2, \qquad e_A = e_1 + e_2 + e_3.$$

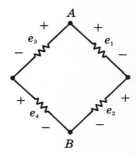

Figure 1-16. An example of Kirchhoff's voltage law.

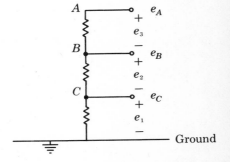

Figure 1-17. Voltages with respect to ground.

Similarly, we can define more general currents by means of Kirchhoff's current law. A particular example of the process is afforded by the circulating currents i_a and i_b in Fig. 1–18. The loop current i_a takes the closed path *abeda*, and the loop current i_b takes the closed path *bcfeb*. Kirchhoff's current law enables us to define these circulating currents in terms of the currents in the elements, according to the following equations:

$$i_1 = -i_a, \qquad i_2 = i_a - i_b, \qquad i_3 = i_b.$$

One final comment about Kirchhoff's laws concerns the notation for the voltages and currents in the separate elements. If the junctions between the elements are assigned symbols, both the currents and the voltages can be expressed in terms of these symbols by means of a double-subscript notation. Thus the current i_1 in Fig. 1–18 could be called i_{ad}, the current i_2 could be called i_{be}, and the current i_3 called i_{cf}. A similar notation could be used for the voltage drops produced by these currents. Thus v_{ad} or e_{ad} is the voltage drop produced by the current from a to d, and v_{be} or e_{be} is the voltage drop produced by the current i_{be}, and v_{cf} or e_{cf} is the voltage drop produced by the current i_{cf}.*

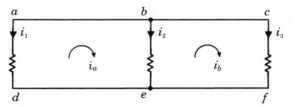

Figure 1–18. Currents flowing around loops.

This chapter has served to introduce the subject of circuit theory. Circuits have been presented as models. The resistance, inductance, and capacitance of the elements have been defined by their volt-ampere relationships. These definitions and Kirchhoff's two laws provide the complete foundation of circuit theory. No additional *ad hoc* laws will be brought in at a later date. The basic rules have been given. We must now learn to play the game!

---

* Some authors use v for voltage drops and e for voltage rises. This is nonsense! It is on a par with using different symbols for the assumed currents entering and leaving a node!

Summary

Model theory

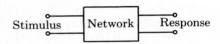

Physical system → Idealized model ↓ ↑ Mathematical equations

Stimulus-response relationships

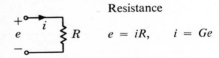

Linearity: response is proportional to stimulus

Response function: relates response and stimulus

Circuit variables

Voltage: e or v,   j/coul

Current: i,   coul/sec

Power: $p = e \cdot i$, j/sec, or watts.

Circuit parameters

Resistance

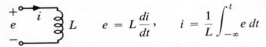

$e = iR$, $i = Ge$

Inductance

$e = L\dfrac{di}{dt},$ $i = \dfrac{1}{L}\displaystyle\int_{-\infty}^{t} e\, dt$

Capacitance

$e = \dfrac{1}{C}\displaystyle\int_{-\infty}^{t} i\, dt,$ $i = C\dfrac{de}{dt}$

Current source

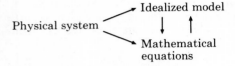

$i = I$

Voltage source

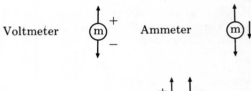

$e = E$

Meters

Voltmeter   Ammeter

Wattmeter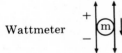

The circuit laws

Current law: $\sum i = 0$

Voltage law: $\sum e = 0$

References

Circuit theory has been introduced in this chapter in terms of model theory and the defined characteristics of the ideal elements. It will prove interesting and instructive to explore some alternative introductions to the subject.

1. E. A. GUILLEMIN, *Introductory Circuit Theory*, John Wiley, New York, 1953. Guillemin introduces the subject through the mathematical theory of topology. The introduction is logical and clear, but it is not for the faint-hearted!

2. MIT EE Staff, *Electric Circuits*, John Wiley, New York, 1943. This text is a classic attempt to introduce circuit theory from the more general field theory. It has never been popular with students because field theory is immeasurably more difficult than circuit theory.

3. KERCHNER and CORCORAN, *Alternating Current Circuits*, 3rd ed., John Wiley, New York, 1951. In this text circuit theory begins with steady-state sine waves and the response of circuits to excitation of this sort.

4. H. H. SKILLING, *Electrical Engineering Circuits*, John Wiley, New York, 1957. Skilling introduces the subject by means of six plausible "experiments." Circuit laws are presented as experimental results.

5. GALBRAITH and SPENCE, *Fundamentals of Electrical Engineering*, The Ronald Press, New York, 1955. The introduction is essentially a review of the physics underlying electrical engineering.

6. SKRODER and HELM, *Circuit Analysis by Laboratory Methods*, Prentice-Hall, New Jersey, 1946. This text is a laboratory manual for circuit theory. The subject is introduced via the laboratory equipment available for building circuits and for testing them.

7. M. B. REED, *Alternating-Current Circuit Theory*, Harper, New York, 1948. A somewhat more advanced and more challenging presentation of the steady-state sinusoid.

Exercises*

SECTION 1–2

1. From the following items, pick 10 that are clearly idealized models and not actual physical entities:

an atom	an electric circuit	a particle
an electron	the economic system	a line
a map	energy	a point
a dollar bill	gasoline	love
a house	oxygen	the equator
a road	a light beam	noise
a circle	a radiowave	fire
the wind	inertia	friction

2. Consider the economy of the United States as a physical system and pair up the stimulus-response relationships below:

Stimulus	*Response*
war	recession
elections	higher wage rates
excess government spending	less graft in government
increased birth rate	inflation
labor-controlled government	higher profit rates
management-controlled government	expanding population
fear and uncertainty	a stock market boom

---

* Answers to Exercises are given at the back of the book. Numerical values are in ohms, henrys, farads, volts, and amperes.

3. Trace the energy conversions in (a) a mechanical phonograph, (b) an electrical phonograph, (c) a hydroelectric power station, (d) a steam-electric power station, (e) a portable gasoline-driven power plant for electricity, (f) a diesel-electric locomotive, (g) a solar battery, (h) a thermostatically controlled electric oven, (i) an automobile lighting system.

4. "Viewed as stimulus-response transactions, purchases in a store are linear operations, but large-scale purchases on the stock market are nonlinear." Explain.

5. Thirty coul/sec of positive charge are passing through a wire in a direction from a to b. (a) What is the current if the assumed reference direction is from a to b? (b) What is the current if the assumed reference direction is from b to a? (c) How would these answers change if the moving coulombs were negative instead of positive?

6. In moving from a to b, a coulomb of charge changes its energy by 10 j. Give the voltage of point a with respect to point b if (a) the charge is positive and the energy is lost, (b) the charge is positive and the energy is gained, (c) the charge is negative and the energy is lost, and (d) the charge is negative and the energy is gained.

7. In a certain two-terminal device a positive current of 10 amp enters at terminal a and leaves from terminal b. What is the power absorbed in the device when (a) the voltage at a is 10 v positive with respect to b? (b) the voltage at b is 10 v positive with respect to a? (c) the voltage at a is -10 v positive with respect to b?

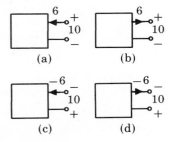

(a)   (b)

(c)   (d)

Figure 1–19

8. Which of the devices of Fig. 1–19 are sources (values are in volts and amperes)?

SECTION 1–3

9. A certain physical resistor is composed of 22 ft of copper wire with a resistance of 1 ohm/ft, in series with 6 in. of carbon rod with a resistance of 2 ohms/in. Find the lumped-parameter resistance value, and show the resistance symbol with the proper value marked on it.

10. A certain physical capacitor is composed of two layers of tinfoil separated by a layer of paper. The capacitance/in^2 is known to be 10×10^{-12} f. Find the capacitance of 10 ft^2 of the combination, and draw the lumped-parameter capacitance symbol with the value marked on it.

11. A certain physical inductor is constructed by winding copper wire with negligible resistance in the form of a solenoidal coil. The inductance increases in proportion to the square of the number of turns. If a 10-turn coil has an inductance of 1×10^{-4} h, find the inductance of a 1000-turn coil, draw the lumped-parameter symbol, and label it.

12. A voltage source of value 6 v is connected in series with a resistance of 2 ohms. Find the current in the circuit and the power absorbed by the resistor.

13. A voltage source of 6 v is connected across a capacitor with a capacitance of 10^{-6} f. Give the energy stored in the capacitor and describe what happens to the energy when the battery is removed.

14. A current of 10 amp is flowing through an inductor of inductance 1 h. What is the energy stored in the inductor, and what happens to the energy if the current source is replaced by a short circuit?

15. How much power is delivered by a 10-v voltage source (a) if it is open-circuited? (b) if a resistance of 1 ohm is placed across it? (c) if it is short-circuited? (d) if it is connected in parallel with a current source of value 1 amp and direction such that the current enters the positive terminal of the voltage source?

16. How much power is delivered by a 10–amp current source (a) if it is open-circuited? (b) if it is short-circuited? (c) if a resistance of 1 ohm is placed in series with it? (d) if a voltage source of 1 v is placed across it so that the current enters at the negative terminal of the voltage source?

SECTION 1-4

17. Redraw the circuit of Fig. 1–20(a) so that it will have the form of part (b).

18. Points *abcd* are junctions in an electric network. The following voltages are known: $V_{ab} = 10$, $V_{bc} = -2$, $V_{ad} = 5$. Find V_{cd}.

19. Points *abcdo* are junctions in an electric network. The following currents are known: $I_{ao} = 4$, $I_{bo} = -3$, $I_{co} = 10$. Find I_{do}.

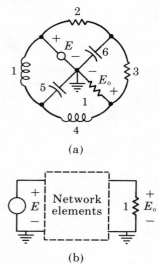

(a)

(b)

Figure 1-20

20. For Fig. 1–21, express the currents in the elements i_{10}, i_{20}, i_{30}, and i_{40} in terms of the mesh currents i_a, i_b, i_c, and i_d.

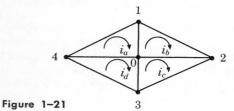

Figure 1-21

21. Points *abcd* are junctions in an electric circuit. Point *a* is the ground or reference point. Point *b* is 6 v above point *a*. Point *c* is 3 v below point *d*, and point *d* is 10 v below *b*. Draw the nodes and find the voltages of *b*, *c*, and *d* relative to ground.

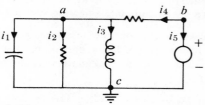

Figure 1-22

22. (a) Write the Kirchhoff current-law equations for the nodes *a*, *b*, and *c* in Fig. 1–22. (b) How are these equations related?

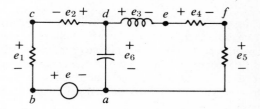

Figure 1-23

23. (a) Write the Kirchhoff voltage-law equations for the paths *abcda*, *adefa*, and *abcdefa* in Fig. 1–23. (b) How are these equations related?

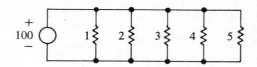

Figure 1-24

24. Find the total current from the voltage source in Fig. 1–24.

Problems

1. Find the voltage across the current source in Fig. 1–25, the power supplied by the source, and the power dissipated in each resistance.

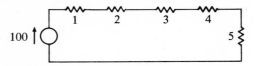

Figure 1–25

2. Find the current from the voltage source in Fig. 1–26, the power supplied by the source and the power absorbed by each resistance.

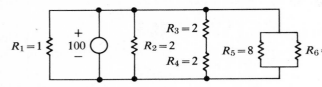

Figure 1–26

3. Compute the power delivered by each of the sources in Fig. 1–27 and the power dissipated in the resistance.

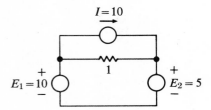

Figure 1–27

4. A meter movement reads full scale with 1 milliamp flowing through it. Its resistance value is 1 ohm. (a) Find the resistance which should be connected in series with it to make it into a voltmeter reading 100 volts full scale to 1% accuracy. (b) Find the resistance which should be connected in parallel with it to make it into an ammeter reading 1 ampere full scale to 1% accuracy.

5. A capacitance of 10^{-6} f is connected to a dc battery of value 1000 v. (a) What is the energy stored, in joules? (b) To what speed would it accelerate a one kg toy automobile if the utilization were 100% efficient?

6. An inductance of 1 h has a current of 1000 amperes flowing in it. (a) What is the energy stored in joules? (b) To what speed would it accelerate a 1 kg projectile if the utilization were 100% efficient? (Low-temperature super conductors would be necessary.)

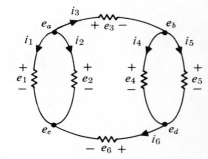

Figure 1–28

7. For the circuit of Fig. 1–28 (a) write all the possible Kirchhoff current-law equations, (b) tell how many of them are independent and not derivable as combinations of the others, (c) write all the possible Kirchhoff voltage-law equations, and (d) tell how many of them are independent.

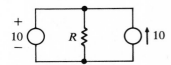

Figure 1–29

8. For the circuit of Fig. 1–29 sketch a curve of the power from the voltage source as a function of the value of the resistance from $R = 0$ to $R = \infty$.

CHAPTER 2

THE *2b* EQUATIONS OF ELECTRICAL NETWORKS

It is idle to expect any great advancement in science from the super-inducing and indrafting of new things upon old. We must begin anew from the very foundations, unless we would revolve forever in a circle with mean and contemptible progress.

Book 1, Novum Organum, FRANCIS BACON, 1620

2–1 Introduction

The problem of *network analysis* is one of finding the currents and voltages in the network elements when the network and the sources are known. Engineers are more often concerned with problems of network *synthesis*, in which the input stimulus and the desired output response are known and a network must be found. Before an engineer can attempt network synthesis, however, he must be very adept at network analysis. Accordingly, we will begin with network analysis.

If a person were infinitely clever, he could solve all of the problems of network analysis by the methods of arithmetic. Most of us, however, find it necessary to resort to algebra. The algebraic procedure is routine. A set of unknown variables is defined, equations are written in terms of these variables, and the equations are solved by the rules of algebra. In electrical circuits the unknown variables are currents and voltages. The laws which are available to write equations for these unknowns are the volt-ampere equations of the elements and Kirchhoff's two laws. All of the methods which we will develop for solving network problems will spring from these foundations.

In the first part of this book we will restrict ourselves to networks containing only resistors and sources. In terms of these networks we will be able to formulate general methods for approaching problems, to derive most of the useful network theorems, and to develop a number of specialized artifices for particular networks. The results which we will obtain will be automatically extended to more general networks in later sections.

2–2 Arithmetic solutions

Two examples of circuits which are simple enough to solve arithmetically are the series circuit and the parallel circuit. A series circuit is one in which the same current flows in all of the elements. A parallel circuit is one in which the same voltage exists across all of the elements.

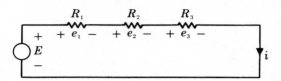

Figure 2–1. A series circuit.

The series circuit. A typical series circuit is shown in Fig. 2–1. Three resistors and a voltage source form a closed path for a single current, which is labeled i in the figure. The current i creates voltage drops of e_1, e_2, and e_3 in the three resistances R_1, R_2, and R_3, given by

$$e_1 = iR_1, \qquad e_2 = iR_2, \qquad e_3 = iR_3.$$

By Kirchhoff's voltage law the voltage rise in the source must balance the sum of the voltage drops in the resistances. Thus,

$$E = iR_1 + iR_2 + iR_3 = i(R_1 + R_2 + R_3), \qquad (2\text{--}1)$$

and the current is

$$i = \frac{E}{R_1 + R_2 + R_3}. \qquad (2\text{--}2)$$

From Eq. (2–2) it is evident that the three resistances have an equivalent total resistance of

$$R_{\text{eq}} = R_1 + R_2 + R_3. \qquad (2\text{--}3)$$

Equation (2–3) can be generalized to the statement that the value of the equivalent resistance of a number of resistances in series is the sum of the values of the individual resistances.

The voltages across the individual elements in Fig. 2–1 have the form

$$e_1 = \frac{R_1}{R_1 + R_2 + R_3} E. \qquad (2\text{--}4)$$

Equation (2–4) expresses the "voltage-divider" principle. The voltage across the resistance R_1 is the same fraction of the total voltage that R_1 is of the total resistance. Stated in another way, the voltage in a series circuit divides in proportion to the resistance. A great many practical devices make use of this effect. For example, the volume control in a radio is a series resistance with a variable wiper arm which can make contact at an arbitrary point along the resistance. It is called a *potentiometer*, or "pot" for short.

The parallel circuit. A typical parallel circuit is shown in Fig. 2–2. Three resistors and a current source form a combination with the same voltage, e, across each one of them. Corresponding to the voltage e across each resistance there must be currents flowing through them of

$$i_1 = e/R_1, \qquad i_2 = e/R_2, \qquad i_3 = e/R_3.$$

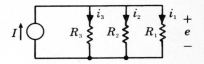

Figure 2–2. A parallel circuit.

By Kirchhoff's current law the current from the source is equal to the sum of the currents in the resistances, or

$$I = \frac{e}{R_1} + \frac{e}{R_2} + \frac{e}{R_3} = e\left(\frac{1}{R_1} + \frac{1}{R_2} + \frac{1}{R_3}\right), \qquad (2\text{--}5)$$

and the voltage is

$$e = I\frac{1}{1/R_1 + 1/R_2 + 1/R_3}. \qquad (2\text{--}6)$$

From Eq. (2–6) it is evident that the effective resistance of the three resistances in parallel is

$$R_{\text{eq}} = \frac{1}{1/R_1 + 1/R_2 + 1/R_3}. \qquad (2\text{--}7)$$

Equation (2–7) can be generalized to the statement that the value of the equivalent resistance of a number of resistances in parallel is equal to the reciprocal of the sum of the reciprocal values of the individual resistances. In terms of conductances which are the reciprocals of the resistances, Eq. (2–7) becomes

$$G_{\text{eq}} = G_1 + G_2 + G_3. \qquad (2\text{--}8)$$

Equation (2–8) looks invitingly simple. The total conductance is simply the sum of the conductances of the branches in parallel. Usually, however, the resistance values are in ohms and the final result is desired in ohms. Under these circumstances Eq. (2–8) represents no net saving, and most people will prefer to use Eq. (2–7) directly.

The case of two resistors in parallel occurs frequently and is worth special consideration. For two resistances,

$$R_{\text{eq}} = \frac{1}{1/R_1 + 1/R_2} = \frac{R_1 R_2}{R_1 + R_2} = \frac{\text{product}}{\text{sum}}. \qquad (2\text{--}9)$$

As an example of Eq. (2–9) we will find the resistance of a 2-ohm and a 6-ohm resistance in parallel. The equivalent resistance is

$$R_{\text{eq}} = \frac{6 \times 2}{6 + 2} = 1.5 \text{ ohms.}$$

The currents in each of the individual elements in Fig. 2–2 have the form

$$i_1 = \frac{1/R_1}{1/R_1 + 1/R_2 + 1/R_3} I. \qquad (2\text{–}10)$$

Equation (2–10) expresses the "current-divider" principle. The current in an element is the same fraction of the total current as the conductance of the element bears to the total conductance.

For the special case of two resistances the "current-divider" formula simplifies to

$$i_1 = \frac{1/R_1}{1/R_1 + 1/R_2} I = \frac{R_2}{R_1 + R_2} I. \qquad (2\text{–}11)$$

Equation (2–11) shows that the current divides as the opposite resistance over the sum of the resistances. Voltage-dividers and current-dividers occur so frequently that Eqs. (2–4) and (2–11) are worth remembering.

Explicitly or implicitly we have used all of the circuit laws in solving the above problems. In the series circuit we made explicit use of the volt-ampere equations and Kirchhoff's voltage law. By making the current identical in each element, we implicitly satisfied Kirchhoff's current law. Similarly in the parallel circuit we used the volt-ampere equations and Kirchhoff's current law explicitly and Kirchhoff's voltage law implicitly in setting the same voltage across each of the elements. In more complicated problems we cannot proceed so haphazardly. We must select our variables carefully and be sure that we write the correct equations to solve for them. In the next section we will consider some definitions which are necessary for this process.

2–3 Topological definitions

In applying the methods of algebra to a network problem we must answer the following questions:
1. How many unknowns are there?
2. Which unknowns should we specify?
3. What equations should we write for them?

Branches and nodes. In order to be precise about these questions we must define the branches, nodes, and independent loops of our networks. A *branch* is an element (resistance) or an element in conjunction with a source of energy. A *node* is a junction point between two branches, and a loop is an independent closed path in the network. Sources are specifically excluded from consideration as branches in the network. The sources are known quantities and we are interested in the branches as an indication of the number of unknowns in the system. From a philosophical point of view it is also desirable to separate the excitation or stimulus for the network from the network itself. In fact a given set of sources can be replaced by many other equivalent sets which will give the same excitation to the network.

Topological graphs. The *topological graph* of a network is obtained by the following process.

1. All of the sources in the network are set equal to zero. Current sources become open circuits; voltage sources become short circuits.

2. The remaining elements are replaced by single lines.
The topological graph which is obtained consists of lines representing the branches in the network and junction points representing the nodes. Elements in series with current sources are removed when the current sources are open-circuited, and elements in parallel with the voltage sources are removed when the voltage sources are short-circuited. These elements represent "dummy" branches whose removal does not affect the remainder of the network, and whose current-voltage solution can be obtained at any time, independently of the remaining algebraic solution. Examples of networks and their topological graphs are shown in Fig. 2–3. In Fig. 2–3(a) all of the resistive elements become branches in the topological graph; in Fig. 2–3(b) those resistive elements which were in parallel with the voltage source or in series with the current source disappear from the topological graph.

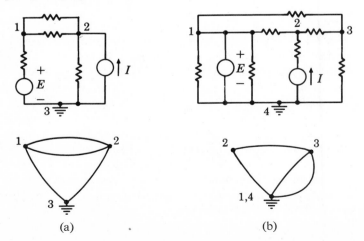

(a)   (b)

Figure 2–3. Networks and their topological graphs.

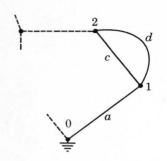

Figure 2–4. The construction of a topological graph.

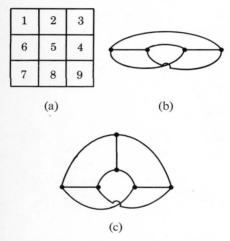

Figure 2–5. Planar and nonplanar graphs.

Loops and meshes. The topological graph which we have developed in the preceding section shows the number of branches and nodes in the network. To set up the algebraic equations of a network one further concept is necessary, that of the independent path or *loop*. We are interested in closed paths for application to Kirchhoff's voltage law, and they must be independent in order that the resulting equations will be independent. By independent we mean that each path and each equation contains some new information which is not in the other equations. There are many possible sets of independent paths and equations. It is necessary to find only one of them since the others can be found by adding and subtracting the elements of the original set.

We will find a particular set of independent paths by constructing the network, branch by branch, as shown in Fig. 2–4. We start with the reference node 0. The first branch, *a*, which is added contributes one node, 1, and no loops. The second branch, *c*, which is added contributes a second node, 2, but no loops. The third branch, *d*, connects nodes 2 and 1. It adds no new nodes but it does produce a closed path, or loop, which consists of branches *c* and *d*.

Each time we add a branch to the network we obtain either a new node or a new closed path. The closed path goes through the new branch and some route through the remainder of the network. It is independent because it contains the just-added branch. We have thus shown that, apart from the reference node, the number of branches must be equal to the number of nodes plus the number of loops. This result is the basic theorem of topology:

$$b = n + l - 1 \tag{2–12}$$

or

$$l = b - n + 1,$$

where b = number of branches, n = number of nodes, and l = number of independent paths or loops. Since b and n are obvious from the topological graph, Eq. (2–12) is most useful in determining the number of independent paths, l. For a certain class of networks, called planar networks, the number of loops is also obvious by inspection. A *planar* network is one which can be drawn flat on a sheet of paper without requiring any lines to leave the plane of the paper and cross over the other lines. Examples of planar and nonplanar networks are shown in Fig. 2–5. The graphs (a) and (b) are planar, and (c) is nonplanar. The mere presence of a crossed wire as in (b) is not indicative of a nonplanar graph. It must be impossible to draw the network without it.

For a planar graph the *meshes* are a suitable set of independent paths or loops. If the graph is viewed as a fishnet, the meshes are the cords surrounding the holes in the net. To prove that the meshes are independent loops they should be added a row at a time as indicated by the numbering in Fig. 2–5(a). Taken in this order each mesh satisfies the requirements for an independent loop.

As an example of the use of the topological formula we will find the number of branches, loops (here meshes), and nodes for the graphs of Fig. 2–3. For either graph, we see that $b = 4$, $n = 3$, and $l = b - n + 1 = 2$, as may be verified by counting the meshes.

2–4 The 2*b* equations

When we have reduced a network to a topological graph containing only branches and nodes, we are in a position to pick the algebraic unknowns and to write equations from which they can be found by means of the volt-ampere equations of the branches and Kirchhoff's two laws.

The selection of variables. A branch in a topological graph represents a resistance or a resistance in conjunction with source elements. If we pick the branch currents and the branch voltages as our variables, we can include the sources by virtue of their effects on the volt-ampere equations of the branches. Since there are b branches in a network we will have b unknown currents and b unknown voltages or a total of $2b$ algebraic unknowns. In summary,

$$\text{Number of unknowns} = 2b.$$

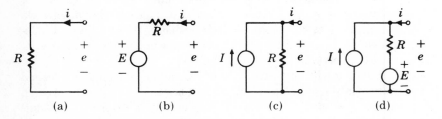

(a)   (b)   (c)   (d)

Figure 2–6. Volt-ampere equations of branches.

The volt-ampere equations. Each branch in a topological graph contains a separate and distinct resistance. Each volt-ampere equation for a branch therefore contains new information and is independent of the other equations. Typical branches are shown in Fig. 2–6. The simplest branch is a single resistance as in Fig. 2–6(a). The volt-ampere equation for this branch is

$$e = iR. \qquad (2\text{–}13)$$

The addition of a voltage source as in Fig. 2–6(b) results in the volt-ampere equation:

$$e = E + iR. \tag{2–14}$$

A current source in the branch as in Fig. 2–6(c) produces the equation

$$e = IR + iR. \tag{2–15}$$

Finally a combination of a voltage source and a current source, as in Fig. 2–6(d), results in the equation

$$e = E + IR + iR. \tag{2–16}$$

Since we have restricted ourselves to branches containing a single resistance, the volt-ampere equation cannot be any more complicated than Eq. (2–16).

A voltage source without a series resistance is a nonphysical device and it poses a problem for our topology. One procedure is to add a small series resistance which is later allowed to become zero in the solution. An alternative procedure is to use the source transformation discussed at the end of this section. A current source with no parallel resistance is likewise a nonphysical device and it again poses topological problems. In this case a large parallel resistance can be added which is later allowed to approach infinity, or alternatively the source transformation discussed at the end of this section can be used. In summary,

Number of independent volt-ampere equations $= b$.

The $\sum i$ equations. The Kirchhoff current law can be written for any node or for any collection of nodes (a supernode) in a network. Not all of these equations are independent. We can find an independent set by constructing the current-law equations while we construct the network.

Beginning with the reference node we add a branch and a second node. Only one independent current-law equation can be written for these two nodes because only one current is involved. As additional branches are added some will create new nodes and some will not. Each branch which creates a new node provides the opportunity for writing a new current-law equation at that node, which is independent because it involves a new current. Each branch which bridges existing nodes alters the current-law equations already written at these nodes, but provides no opportunity for writing new equations. Thus the Kirchhoff current-law equations written at each node except one constitute an independent set and, in summary

Number of independent current-law equations $= n - 1$.

The $\sum e$ equations. The Kirchhoff voltage-law equations can be written around any closed path in a network, including open-circuits through nonexistent branches. Not all of these equations are independent. We will find an independent set by utilizing the topology which was developed in the preceding section.

A set of independent loops, or meshes in a planar network, was characterized by the fact that each path of the set contained information not present in the other paths. Thus if the current-law equations are written around a set of loops or meshes, a set of independent equations will be obtained. In summary,

Number of independent voltage-law equations = l.

The 2b equations. The total number of unknown currents and voltages in a problem is $2b$. The number of independent volt-ampere equations which can be written is b. The number of independent current-law equations is $n - 1$. The number of independent voltage-law equations is l. Thus the total number of independent equations is

$$b + n - 1 + l. \qquad (2\text{--}17)$$

By the basic theorem of topology (Eq. 2–12), $b = n - 1 + l$. Hence the total number of equations is $2b$. We have thus been able to find $2b$ independent equations for our $2b$ unknown variables, and the unknowns can be found by the simple rules of algebra.

Example of the 2b equations. In this section we shall consider the $2b$ method for a network as shown in Fig. 2–7(a). The topological graph is shown in Fig. 2–7(b). In it there are three branches, two nodes, and two meshes. The number of unknown variables is thus six, and the equations to be written for them include three volt-ampere equations, one $\sum i$ equation, and two $\sum e$ equations.

The variables ($2b$ of them). The six variables are the three branch currents i_1, i_2, and i_3, and the three branch voltages e_1, e_2, and e_3. The current directions are assumed at random, but the voltage polarities are taken to agree with them.

The v-a equations (b, or 3, of them):

$$e_1 = 2i_1 + 10, \qquad e_2 = 3i_2, \qquad e_3 = 6i_3.$$

The $\sum i$ laws ($n - 1$, or 1, of them):

$$i_1 + i_2 + i_3 = 0.$$

The $\sum e$ laws (l, or 2, of them):

$$e_1 = e_2, \qquad e_2 = e_3.$$

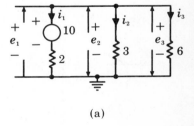

(a)

(b)

Figure 2–7. An example solved by the $2b$ method.

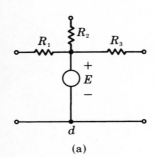

(a)

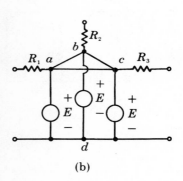

(b)

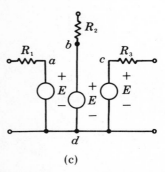

(c)

Figure 2–8. A transformation for resistanceless voltage sources.

Solution. The above six equations are independent and can be used to solve for the six unknowns, as follows:

From the $\sum i$ law:

$$i_1 + i_2 + i_3 = 0.$$

From the v-a equations:

$$\frac{e_1 - 10}{2} + \frac{e_2}{3} + \frac{e_3}{6} = 0.$$

From the $\sum e$ laws:

$$\frac{e_1}{2} + \frac{e_1}{3} + \frac{e_1}{6} = 5 \quad \text{and} \quad e_1 = 5.$$

The other values can be obtained from this one by the use of the original equations:

$$e_1 = e_2 = e_3 = 5,$$

$$i_1 = \frac{e_1 - 10}{2} = \frac{-5}{2}, \quad i_2 = \frac{5}{3}, \quad i_3 = \frac{5}{6}.$$

Real voltage sources and real current sources will always have resistances associated with them and can be handled by the method described above. Sometimes, however, the resistance in series with a voltage source is so small that we wish to neglect it in comparison with the other resistances in the circuit, and sometimes the resistance in parallel with a current source is so large that we wish to remove it from the circuit in comparison with the other resistances in the circuit. These resistanceless sources pose minor topological problems which can be solved by the use of the source transformations. The function of the source is to provide a stimulus for the network. Any combinations of sources which provide identical stimuli to the network are equivalent as far as the network is concerned.

Voltage source with no series resistance. A voltage source with no series resistance can be replaced by a set of voltage sources associated with other resistances in the circuit. Consider the case shown in Fig. 2–8. The voltage source shown in Fig. 2–8(a) has no series resistance. We can, however, split it up into three identical sources in parallel, as shown in Fig. 2–8(b). Now let us remove the three connections joining the terminals of the sources. The voltages at the points *a*, *b*, and *c* do not change and are in fact identical. The connections between them therefore carry no current and have no significance to the circuit. It makes no difference whether they are present or not. Hence the circuit of Fig. 2–8(c) is equivalent to that of Fig. 2–8(a) as far as the excitation of the network is concerned.

The net effect is to replace a single resistanceless voltage source by three voltage sources associated with resistances. The node has been pushed through the voltage source. It coalesces with the ground node and the voltage source appears in each of the branches which originally radiated from the node.

Current source with no parallel resistance. A current source with no parallel resistance can be replaced by a set of current sources associated with other resistances in the circuit. Consider the case shown in Fig. 2–9. The current source in Fig. 2–9(a) appears directly across the nodes *a-b* and has no parallel resistance. As far as the network is concerned the function of the current source is to pump *I* amperes out of node *a* and *I* amperes into node *b*. Any other combination of sources which accomplishes this net result is equivalent. Such a combination is shown in Fig. 2–9(b). The first source pumps the current from *a* to *c*. The second source immediately pumps it from *c* to *d*, and the third source takes it from *d* to *b*. The net current deposited at *c* and *d* is zero and the net result of the three sources is to remove the current *I* from node *a* and to deposit it at node *b*. Hence the circuit of Fig. 2–9(b) is equivalent to that of Fig. 2–9(a) as far as the excitation of the network is concerned.

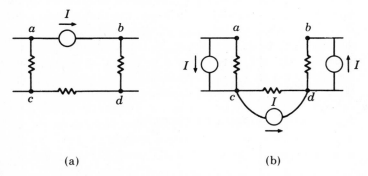

(a)   (b)

Figure 2–9. A current source with no parallel resistance.

The effect of the transformation of Fig. 2–9 is to replace a single resistanceless current source by three current sources associated with resistances. The current sources form a chain which can loop around any closed path in the network and is only constrained to begin and to end at the same nodes as the original source.

Summary

Series circuit

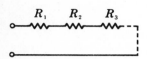

$$R = R_1 + R_2 + R_3$$

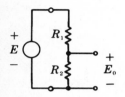

$$E_0 = \frac{R_2}{R_1 + R_2} E$$

Parallel circuit

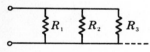

$$R = \frac{1}{1/R_1 + 1/R_2 + 1/R_3 + \cdots}$$

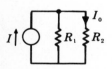

$$I_0 = \frac{R_1}{R_1 + R_2} I$$

Topology

No. of branches $= b$ (sources dead)
No. of nodes $= n$
No. of independent nodes $= n - 1$
No. of independent loops $= l$
Basic equation $b = n + l - 1$

The 2b equations

No. of unknowns $= 2b$ (b currents and b voltages)
No. of volt-ampere equations $= b$
No. of independent i laws $= n - 1$
No. of independent e laws $= l$
Total number of equations $= b + n - 1 + l$
$\qquad = 2b$

Branch equations

$$e = iR$$

$$e = iR + E$$

(dead source = short circuit)

$$e = iR + IR$$

(dead source = open circuit)

$$e = iR + E + IR$$

Source transformation

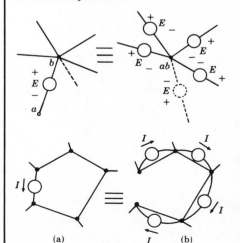

(a)   (b)

References

In this book a clear distinction has been made between those problems which are solved by arithmetic and those problems which are solved by algebra. The arithmetic methods of solving circuit problems are covered in almost all elementary circuit-theory books. The algebraic methods of solving circuit problems were known to Kirchhoff in 1847, but are covered adequately in very few elementary circuit-theory books. References for network algebra and network topology are listed below.

1. G. KIRCHHOFF, "Über die Auflösung der Gleichungen auf welche man bei der Untersuchung der linearen Vertheilung galvanischer Ströme geführt wird," *Ann. Phys. u. Chem.*, **2**, 72 (1847). Kirchhoff applied mathematical topology to the solution of network problems in 1847. Modern writers usually just rediscover his results.

2. G. KRON, *Tensor Analysis of Networks*, John Wiley, New York, 1939. Kron was the first of the modern writers to recognize the importance of topology in network theory. He presents the 2*b* method as the basic or primitive method for networks. The tensor notation which he uses has prevented a wider understanding of his work.

3. P. LE CORBEILLER, *Matrix Analysis of Electric Networks*, John Wiley, New York, 1950. Le Corbeiller translates Kron's work into more usual electrical notation. The level is a little above most undergraduates.

4. E. A. GUILLEMIN, *Introductory Cirtuit Theory*, John Wiley, New York, 1953. Chapters 1 and 2 of Guillemin's text present topology in very much the same notation as that of Kron. The level is such that good sophomore students can read the material.

5. GARDNER and BARNES, *Transients in Linear Systems*, John Wiley, New York, 1942. This standard graduate-level text presents a clear introduction to circuit topology. It is singled out because *it treats sources as separate branches* and modifies the topological formulas accordingly.

6. J. L. SYNGE, "The Fundamental Theorem of Electrical Networks," *Quarterly of Applied Math*, Vol. 9, pp. 113–127 (1951). The basic theorem of topology is presented clearly by a master mathematician.

Exercises

SECTION 2–2

1. Two resistors, R_1 and R_2, are connected in series. Give an equivalent single resistor when R_1 and R_2 have the following values:

   (a) $R_1 = R_2 = 1$

   (b) $R_1 = R_2 = 10^6$

   (c) $R_1 = 1, \quad R_2 = 0$

   (d) $R_1 = 1, \quad R_2 = \infty$

   (e) $R_1 = 3, \quad R_2 = 6$

2. By using series-parallel combinations, reduce the branch in Fig. 2–10 to a single resistance at terminals a–b.

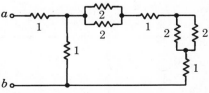

Figure 2–10

3. Two resistors, R_1 and R_2, are connected in parallel. Give an equivalent single resistor when R_1 and R_2 have the following values:

   (a) $R_1 = R_2 = 1$

   (b) $R_1 = R_2 = 10^6$

   (c) $R_1 = 1, \quad R_2 = 0$

   (d) $R_1 = 1, \quad R_2 = \infty$

   (e) $R_1 = 3, \quad R_2 = 6$

4. Find an expression for the resistance of three resistors in parallel in the form of a single quotient. Give the equivalent parallel resistance when R_1, R_2, and R_3 have the following values:

   (a) $R_1 = R_2 = R_3 = 3$

   (b) $R_1 = R_2 = R_3 = 1$

   (c) $R_1 = R_2 = 2, \quad R_3 = 1$

   (d) $R_1 = 3, \quad R_2 = 6, \quad R_3 = 2$

   (e) $R_1 = 1, \quad R_2 = 2, \quad R_3 = 3$

5. Three resistors, $R_1 = 10$, $R_2 = 5$, and $R_3 = 5$ ohms, are connected in series across a 100-v source. What is the voltage across R_3?

6. Three resistors, $R_1 = 10$, $R_2 = 10$, and $R_3 = 5$ ohms, are connected in parallel across a 10-amp source. What is the current through the 5-ohm resistor?

7. Without writing any algebraic equations, find the voltage e_0 in the circuit of Fig. 2–11.

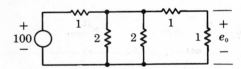

Figure 2–11

8. Without writing any algebraic equations, find the current i_0 in the circuit of Fig. 2–12.

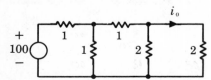

Figure 2–12

SECTION 2–3

9. For the circuit of Fig. 2–13, give the number of branches, the number of nodes, the number of loops, the number of current equations, the number of voltage equations, and the number of volt-ampere equations.

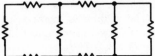

Figure 2–13

10. For the circuit of Fig. 2–14, give the number of branches, loops, nodes, current equations, voltage equations, and volt-ampere equations.

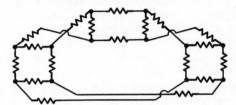

Figure 2–14

11. For the circuit of Fig. 2–15, give the number of branches, loops, nodes, current equations, voltage equations, and volt-ampere equations.

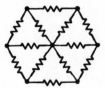

Figure 2–15

12. The circuit in Fig. 2–16 has two parts joined at the single node g, but otherwise separate. Find b, n, and l for this network, and show that the basic formula of topology holds. How many times is the node g counted?

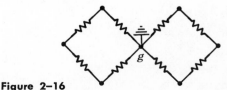

Figure 2–16

13. Which of the four networks of Fig. 2–17 are planar? Redraw those that are planar in a form in which no wires are crossed.

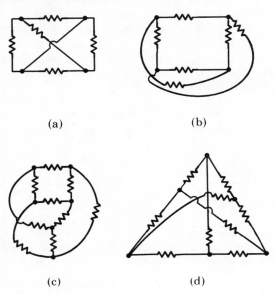

(a)   (b)

(c)   (d)

Figure 2–17

14. Make topological graphs for the circuits of Fig. 2–18 and give b, n, and l.

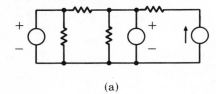

(a)

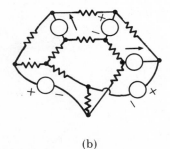

(b)

Figure 2–18

15. Make a topological graph of the circuit of Fig. 2–19 and give b, n, and l.

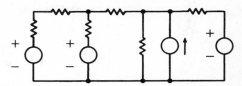

Figure 2–19

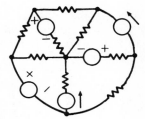

Figure 2–20

16. Make a topological graph of the circuit of Fig. 2–20 and give b, n, and l.

SECTION 2–4

17. For the network of Fig. 2–21, find the number of branches, nodes, and loops. Write the $2b$ current equations, voltage equations, and volt-ampere equations, and solve for all the unknown voltages and currents.

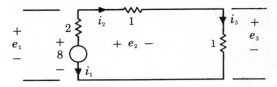

Figure 2–21

18. By the $2b$ method, find all the currents and all the voltages in the network of Fig. 2–22.

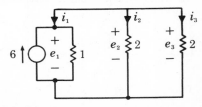

Figure 2–22

19. Solve for the currents i_1 and i_2 and the voltages e_1 and e_2 in the network of Fig. 2–23.

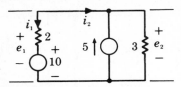

Figure 2–23

20. Without changing the topology of the network (i.e., without combining resistances) reduce the excitation to a single source in the network of Fig. 2–24.

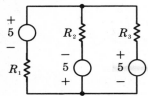

Figure 2–24

21. Without combining any of the resistance branches, reduce the excitation in the circuit of Fig. 2–25 to a single source.

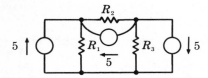

Figure 2–25

22. Make a source transformation which associates the current source with each of a pair of the resistances in the circuit of Fig. 2–26. Use the 2*b* method

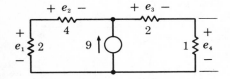

Figure 2–26

to solve the resultant network for the voltages across each of the resistances. Also find the voltage across the current source in the original circuit.

23. Make a source transformation which associates the voltage source in the circuit of Fig. 2–27 with two of the resistors. Use the 2*b* method on the resultant circuit to solve for the current in each of the resistances. Also find the current through the source in the original network.

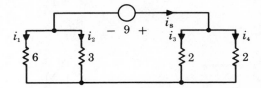

Figure 2–27

24. Without combining any of the resistance branches, reduce the networks of Fig. 2–28 to forms with only one sourse.

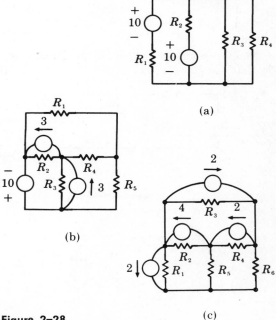

Figure 2–28

Problems

1. Reduce the combination of resistances in Fig. 2–29 to a single equivalent value at terminals a–b.

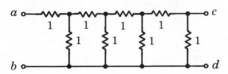

Figure 2–29

2. Reduce the combination of resistances in Fig. 2–29 to a single resistance at terminals c–d.

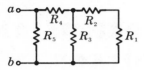

Figure 2–30

3. Find the input resistance of the circuit of Fig. 2–30 at terminals a–b.

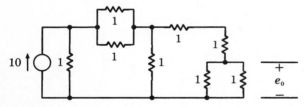

Figure 2–31

4. By inspection, find the voltage e_0 in the circuit of Fig. 2–31.

5. Find e_0 in the circuit of Fig. 2–32.

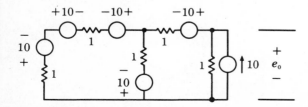

Figure 2–32

6. Make a topological graph for the circuit of Fig. 2–33 and give the values of b, n, and l. Some of the resistances and all of the sources can be considered to be dummy branches. How many dummy branches are there, and how many dummy meshes and dummy nodes are created by these branches? Show that the basic law of topology is applicable to the totality of branches, meshes, and nodes, including the dummy ones.

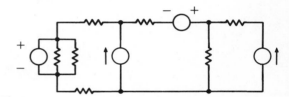

Figure 2–33

7. How many topologically independent branches, loops and nodes exist in the circuit of Fig. 2–34? How many dummy branches, loops, and nodes? Verify the basic formula of topology for the totality of branches, meshes, and nodes, including the dummy ones. Find the current in each resistance.

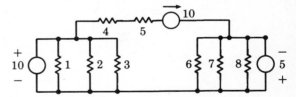

Figure 2–34

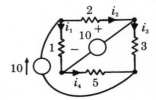

Figure 2–35

8. After making the appropriate source transformations, solve the circuit of Fig. 2–35 for all the currents and voltages by the 2b method.

CHAPTER 3

MESH CURRENTS AND NODE VOLTAGES

Brain succeeds better than brawn.

OVID, METAMORPHOSES 111–54

3–1 Introduction

For many centuries it has been recognized that an intellectual approach to a problem is superior to a brute-force approach. The $2b$ method falls in the class of brute-force approaches. It can be used to solve any network problem, but it is laborious because of the great number of equations involved. We can improve on the $2b$ method in two ways. The first is by means of an *efficient notation*. Anyone who has tried to multiply Roman numerals will appreciate the value of an efficient notation! The second is by means of an *orderly procedure*. As a result of an efficient choice of variables and an orderly procedure for writing down the equations, we can reduce to a minimum the number of equations that are written explicitly. The two methods which meet these requirements are called the *mesh-current method* and the *node-voltage method*.

3–2 Mesh currents

The $2b$ equations are basic to any formulation of the algebraic equations for a network. All of the $2b$ equations must be satisfied but not all of them must be stated explicitly. It is possible, for example, to use the currents as variables and to satisfy the volt-ampere equations by inspection. The number of equations explicitly stated is then reduced to b. If, in addition, we combine the branch currents into a new set of variables which automatically satisfy the Kirchhoff current law at each of the $n - 1$ independent nodes in the network. we need to state only $b - n + 1 = l$ of the original $2b$ equations,

An obvious possibility for the unknowns is a set of l circulating currents which traverse the independent loops.* These currents close on themselves and automatically satisfy Kirchhoff's current law, since they enter and leave each node in their paths. Furthermore, since they circulate around independent paths they must be themselves independent. From the above arguments we can conclude that the l circulating currents which flow around the contours of a set of independent loops are a suitable set of variables to use in a network problem. The l Kirchhoff voltage-law equations provide the means for solving for them. If the graph is planar, the most obvious independent paths are the meshes and the currents are the mesh currents. Most readers will be familiar with the resolution of forces and velocities into components. The mesh currents are a similar resolution. They do not represent actual physical currents in a network, but only their mathematical components.

The following is a summary of the mesh-current method for solving a circuit problem:

1. Sets of clockwise mesh currents are assigned as the unknowns. This selection automatically satisfies Kirchhoff's current laws.

2. Kirchhoff's voltage-law equations are written for each mesh in terms of the current variables and they incorporate the volt-ampere equations.

3. The mesh currents are found by solving these equations. The branch currents can be found from the mesh currents, and the branch voltages from the branch currents.

As a first example of the mesh-current method we will solve the circuit of Fig. 3–1. There is a single mesh in this circuit and we therefore assume a single mesh current flowing around it in a clockwise direction. It is the only current in each branch and the branch currents are equal to the mesh current. The application of Kirchhoff's voltage law around the mesh gives

$$i(R_1 + R_2 + R_3) = E. \qquad (3\text{–}1)$$

The left side of Eq. (3–1) represents the voltage drop produced in the three resistors by the mesh current i, and the right side represents the voltage source which tends to make current flow in the assumed clockwise direction. A solution of Eq. (3–1) is

$$i = \frac{E}{R_1 + R_2 + R_3}. \qquad (3\text{–}2)$$

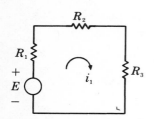

Figure 3–1. A single-mesh circuit.

---

* An infinite number of other possibilities also exists, but very little use has ever been made of them in network theory. Any combination of branch currents could be variable. The only restrictions are that the variables used should be independent and equal in number to the equations available for their solution.

The branch currents are equal to i, and the branch voltages can be obtained by multiplying i by the appropriate value of resistance.

Mesh currents are normally assumed to flow in a clockwise direction around the meshes as shown in Figs. 3–1 and 3–2. The actual current in a branch is equal to the mesh current if the branch is an outside one, and is equal to the difference of two mesh currents if the branch is an internal one between two meshes. Thus if we have solved for the mesh current variables we can find the branch currents, and knowing the branch currents it is a simple matter to find the branch voltages.

The circuit shown in Fig. 3–2 has two meshes and requires two mesh currents for its solution. If they are taken to be i_1 and i_2 in the clockwise direction, the current in the center branch is $i_1 - i_2$ in the downward direction. A voltage-law equation must be written around each of the meshes, as follows:

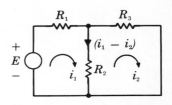

Figure 3–2. A two-mesh circuit.

$$\text{Mesh 1: } i_1R_1 + (i_1 - i_2)R_2 = E. \qquad (3\text{–}3)$$

$$\text{Mesh 2: } i_2R_3 - R_2(i_1 - i_2) = 0. \qquad (3\text{–}4)$$

If we collect the coefficients of i_1 and i_2 in Eqs. (3–3) and (3–4), we obtain

$$i_1(R_1 + R_2) - i_2(R_2) = E, \qquad (3\text{–}5)$$

$$-i_1(R_2) + i_2(R_2 + R_3) = 0. \qquad (3\text{–}6)$$

The first term in Eq. (3–5) is the voltage drop produced in mesh 1 by the mesh current i_1, and the second term is the voltage drop produced in mesh 1 by the current in mesh 2. This latter term is negative relative to the first one because i_2 flows through R_2 in a direction opposite to that of i_1. The term on the right side of the equation is the net source voltage which tends to make current flow in the assumed clockwise direction.

Equation (3–6) represents the application of the voltage law to mesh 2. The first term is the voltage drop produced in mesh 2 by mesh current i_1. The second term is the voltage drop produced in mesh 2 by its own mesh current i_2. Usually this second term is taken to be positive, in which case the first term is negative. There are no sources in this mesh and therefore the right side of the equation is zero.

It is important to learn to write the mesh equations directly in the form of Eqs. (3–5) and (3–6). The symmetry is useful and will help in avoiding minor errors. Note that all the terms produced by a current in its own mesh are positive, while all the terms produced by a current in any other mesh are negative. Furthermore, the mutual terms are similar, since the branch between two meshes is common to both meshes.

The mesh-current method can be generalized to the case of an arbitrary number of meshes, k. Clockwise currents are assumed in each mesh and the voltage-law equation is written around each mesh in turn. The resulting equations will have the form

$$
\begin{aligned}
i_1(r_{11}) - i_2(r_{12}) - \cdots - i_k(r_{1k}) &= E_1, \\
-i_1(r_{12}) + i_2(r_{22}) - \cdots - i_k(r_{2k}) &= E_2, \\
\vdots \\
-i_1(r_{1k}) - i_2(r_{2k}) - \cdots + i_k(r_{kk}) &= E_k,
\end{aligned}
\tag{3–7}
$$

where i_1 is the mesh current in mesh 1, r_{11} is the sum of the resistances through which mesh current 1 flows, r_{12} is the resistance common to meshes 1 and 2, E_1 is the net source voltage tending to produce clockwise current in mesh 1, and so on.

The network is characterized by the left side of these equations, the sources by the right side. The convention regarding mesh currents is so well established that we can describe the network by the array of coefficients alone, as shown in the following equation:

$$
\begin{bmatrix}
r_{11} & -r_{12} & \cdots & -r_{1k} \\
-r_{12} & r_{22} & & -r_{2k} \\
-r_{1k} & -r_{2k} & \cdots & r_{kk}
\end{bmatrix}.
\tag{3–8}
$$

Such an array is called a resistance parameter matrix.

Numerical example. As a numerical example we consider the circuit of Fig. 3–2 with $R_1 = 1$, $R_2 = 2$, and $R_3 = 3$ ohms, and $E = 10$ volts. The numerical mesh equations are

$$
i_1(3) - i_2(2) = 10,
$$
$$
-i_1(2) + i_2(5) = 0,
$$

from which

$$
i_1 = \frac{\begin{vmatrix} 10 & -2 \\ 0 & 5 \end{vmatrix}}{\begin{vmatrix} 3 & -2 \\ -2 & 5 \end{vmatrix}} = \tfrac{50}{11} \quad \text{and} \quad i_2 = \frac{\begin{vmatrix} 3 & 10 \\ -2 & 0 \end{vmatrix}}{\begin{vmatrix} 3 & -2 \\ -2 & 5 \end{vmatrix}} = \tfrac{20}{11}.
$$

The branch currents and the branch voltages can be found from the mesh currents. The current in R_2 is

$$
i_1 - i_2 = \tfrac{30}{11},
$$

and the voltages across the resistors are

$$e_{R_1} = \tfrac{50}{11},$$

$$e_{R_2} = \tfrac{30}{11} \times 2 = \tfrac{60}{11},$$

$$e_{R_3} = \tfrac{20}{11} \times 3 = \tfrac{60}{11}.$$

Dummy mesh currents. The mesh equations are written for the sum of voltages around a closed path. A voltage source can therefore be easily included in the equations. A current source, on the other hand, requires the use of a dummy mesh current or one of the source transformations discussed in Chapter 4.

The concept of a dummy mesh current comes from topology. The topological meshes in a network are those which are present when all the sources are "dead," that is, when the current sources are replaced by open circuits and the voltage sources by short circuits. Mesh currents are defined around these topological meshes. *Dummy mesh currents* are defined around the apparent meshes created by the presence of current sources in the network. No voltage-law equation can be written for a dummy mesh current. Instead it must be defined in terms of the current source which created it. The defining equation is called a *constraint* equation. The following is a summary of the dummy mesh-current method:

1. Mesh currents are defined around all the apparent meshes in a circuit without regard for whether or not true topological meshes exist.

2. Voltage-law equations are written around each topological mesh.

3. A constraint equation is written for each of the dummy meshes created by each current source.

An example of the use of a dummy mesh current to solve a circuit containing a current source is shown in Fig. 3-3. The mesh current i_1 is assumed in the genuine topological mesh and a dummy mesh current i_d is assumed around the dummy mesh created by the current source. The dummy current i_d is treated as an ordinary mesh current so far as the equation for the i_1 mesh is concerned, but no equation is written around the dummy mesh. Instead, it is merely observed that the source I constrains the dummy mesh current i_d to be equal to I. The two equations are

$$i_1(R_1 + R_2) - i_d(R_1) = 0$$

and

$$i_d = I, \tag{3-9}$$

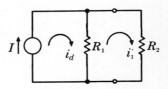

Figure 3-3. An example of a dummy mesh.

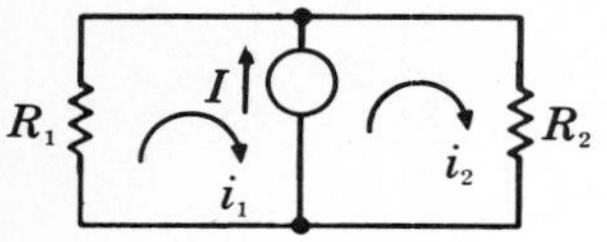

Figure 3–4. A dummy mesh produced by an internal source.

from which

$$i_1 = \frac{R_1}{R_1 + R_2} I.$$

The dummy-variable method is perfectly general. A somewhat more complicated example is shown in Fig. 3–4. There are two apparent meshes, and currents are defined around them. The topological mesh is the path containing the resistors R_1 and R_2, and it does not agree with either of the mesh currents which have been defined. Two equations can be written for them, however. The first is a voltage-law equation around the topological mesh:

$$i_1 R_1 + i_2 R_2 = 0. \qquad (3\text{--}10)$$

The second is a constraint equation. The mesh current i_1 flows downward through the source, and the mesh current i_2 flows upward through the source. Hence

$$i_1 - i_2 = -I. \qquad (3\text{--}11)$$

A simultaneous solution of Eqs. (3–10) and (3–11) gives the two currents i_1 and i_2 as

$$i_1 = \frac{-R_2}{R_1 + R_2} I \quad \text{and} \quad i_2 = \frac{R_1}{R_1 + R_2} I.$$

The two examples which have been solved by the dummy-variable method show that the procedure is easier if the current source occurs in an outside branch of the network. Often a circuit can be redrawn to achieve this form.

3–3 The node-voltage method

The voltage variables which have been used in the previous chapters have been branch voltages. A branch voltage is analogous to the elevation of one point on a map with respect to another point. An alternative method of specifying elevations is with respect to a reference level, usually sea level. A similar alternative exists in electrical networks. We can describe the voltage level of each node with respect to some datum, or reference point, which is usually called the "ground." Node-to-datum voltages automatically satisfy Kirchhoff's voltage law around any path. Hence we do not have to write the voltage-law equations explicitly. If we consider the volt-ampere equations to be trivial we are left with only

$$b - l = n - 1 \qquad (3\text{--}12)$$

equations. Since we must have one variable for each equation, we need $n - 1$ variables. The voltages of the $n - 1$ nodes with respect to the ground node are a suitable set. There are $n - 1$ of them and they are independent, since the nodes are independent.*

As an example of the way in which the node-to-datum voltages automatically satisfy Kirchhoff's voltage laws consider the circuit of Fig. 3–5.

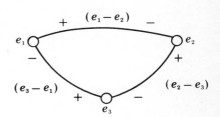

The node-to-datum voltages are e_1, e_2, and e_3. The branch voltages are differences of node voltages, $e_1 - e_2$, $e_2 - e_3$, and $e_3 - e_1$, with polarities as shown. The sum of the voltages around the loop is

$$e_1 - e_2 + e_2 - e_3 + e_3 - e_1 = 0. \qquad (3\text{–}13)$$

Figure 3–5. Node-to-datum voltages and the voltage law.

Equation (3–13) is identically equal to zero for all values of e_1, e_2, and e_3, and therefore Kirchhoff's voltage law is always satisfied.

The following is a procedure for using the node-to-datum (hereafter called just node) voltages:

1. A datum node is selected and node voltages with respect to this datum are assigned as unknowns. The Kirchhoff voltage laws are automatically satisfied by these variables.

2. A Kirchhoff current-law equation is written at each of these nodes. The volt-ampere equations are included by inspection and the equations are written in terms of the node voltages.

3. The equations are solved for the node voltages and the branch currents, and branch voltages are found from the node voltages.

As a first example of the method we consider the circuit of Fig. 3–6. The lower node will be assumed as ground or datum, and the upper node will be assigned the unknown value e_a. The current-law equation at the upper node yields

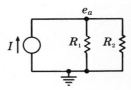

Figure 3–6. A one-node-voltage problem.

$$e_a \left(\frac{1}{R_1} + \frac{1}{R_2} \right) = I \qquad (3\text{–}14)$$

or

$$e_a(G_1 + G_2) = I, \qquad (3\text{–}15)$$

where

$$G_1 = \frac{1}{R_1} \quad \text{and} \quad G_2 = \frac{1}{R_2}.$$

The left side of Eq. (3–14) represents the currents flowing away from the node voltage e_a, and the right side represents the current source flowing into the node and tending to make the node positive.

A second example of the node-voltage method will be the solution of the circuit shown in Fig. 3–7. In this circuit there are two

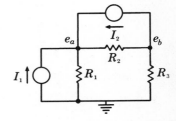

Figure 3–7. A two-node-voltage problem.

---

* Other sets of voltages between supernodes can be used, but they are less common than the node-to-datum set.

unknown nodes e_a and e_b, in addition to the ground node. The current-law equations are

$$e_a \frac{1}{R_1} + (e_a - e_b)\frac{1}{R_2} - I_1 - I_2 = 0 \qquad (3\text{–}16)$$

and

$$(e_b - e_a)\frac{1}{R_2} + e_b\frac{1}{R_3} + I_2 = 0. \qquad (3\text{–}17)$$

Equation (3–16) represents the sum of the currents flowing away from the node voltage e_a. The first term is the current through R_1 and the second is the current through R_2. The remaining terms are the source currents. Equation (3–17) represents the currents flowing away from node e_b. The first term is the current through R_2, the second term is the current through R_3, and the third term is the source current. (Note that the voltage across R_2 is either $e_a - e_b$, or $e_b - e_a$, depending on which polarity is assumed for the reference voltage across the branch.) It is usually more convenient to rewrite Eqs. (3–16) and (3–17) in the form

$$e_a \left(\frac{1}{R_1} + \frac{1}{R_2}\right) - e_b\frac{1}{R_2} = I_1 + I_2 \qquad (3\text{–}18)$$

and

$$-e_a\frac{1}{R_2} + e_b\left(\frac{1}{R_2} + \frac{1}{R_3}\right) = -I_2. \qquad (3\text{–}19)$$

An alternative interpretation of Eqs. (3–18) and (3–19) is very useful. The first term in Eq. (3–18) represents the sum of the currents flowing away from the node voltage e_a when all the other node voltages are equal to zero or connected to the ground point. The coefficient which multiplies e_a is thus the sum of the conductances which radiate from the node. In fact, if a circle is drawn around the node each resistor which it intersects will be included in the coefficient. The second term of Eq. (3–18) is the current which flows away from the node voltage e_a when e_b is given a positive value and when e_a is grounded or zero. It is a negative term because the current obviously flows into the node and not away from it. The coefficient of e_b is the mutual conductance which joins the node e_a to the node e_b. The terms on the right side of the equation are the source currents which enter the node and tend to give the voltage its assumed positive value.

Equation (3–19) can be interpreted similarly. The first term is the current which the voltage e_a would produce at node b. The second term is the total current which would flow from e_b if it were given a positive value and the other nodes were all grounded. The term on the right side is the net source current tending to make e_b

positive. Since the source current is directed away from the node
it has a negative sign in this equation.

The symmetry of Eqs. (3–18) and (3–19) is useful. All of the elements on the principal diagonal, from the upper left to the lower
right, are positive. These elements are "self" elements, having to
do with the effect of a voltage at its own node. All of the terms off
the principal diagonal are negative, and the coefficients are equal
in pairs, since the conductance between node a and node b is the
same as the conductance between node b and node a. The student
should learn to write the equations directly in the form of Eqs. (3–18)
and (3–19). They are easier to use than the other equations and the
symmetry provides an automatic check on minor algebraic errors.

The symmetry is even more obvious with respect to the array of
the coefficients in the equations. This array is called a *conductance
parameter matrix* because the elements have the dimensions of conductance. For Eqs. (3–20) and (3–21) the matrix is

$$\begin{bmatrix} \dfrac{1}{R_1} + \dfrac{1}{R_2} & -\dfrac{1}{R_2} \\ -\dfrac{1}{R_2} & \dfrac{1}{R_2} + \dfrac{1}{R_3} \end{bmatrix}. \tag{3–20}$$

In terms of conductances the matrix is written as

$$\begin{bmatrix} G_1 + G_2 & -G_2 \\ -G_2 & G_2 + G_3 \end{bmatrix}. \tag{3–21}$$

The node-voltage method can be generalized to the case of k
independent nodes. The node voltages are all assumed to be positive with respect to the datum and the current-law equations at
each node in turn are written:

$$\begin{aligned}
e_1(g_{11}) - e_2(g_{12}) - \cdots - e_k(g_{1k}) &= I_1, \\
-e_1(g_{12}) + e_2(g_{22}) - \cdots - e_k(g_{2k}) &= I_2, \\
\vdots \qquad\qquad\qquad & \\
-e_1(g_{1k}) - e_2(g_{2k}) - \cdots + e_k(g_{kk}) &= I_k,
\end{aligned} \tag{3–22}$$

where e_1 is the node voltage at node 1, g_{11} is the total conductance
radiating from node 1, g_{12} is the conductance between nodes 1 and
2, I_1 is the net source current tending to make a positive voltage
at node 1, and so on.

Numerical example. The complete solution of a problem by the
node-voltage method will be illustrated by means of a numerical
example. Let us consider the circuit of Fig. 3–7 with $I_1 = 2$ amp,

$I_2 = 1$ amp, $R_1 = 1$ ohm, $R_2 = 2$ ohms, and $R_3 = 3$ ohms. The node-voltage equations are

$$e_a(1 + \tfrac{1}{2}) - e_b(\tfrac{1}{2}) = 1 + 2 = 3,$$

$$-e_a(\tfrac{1}{2}) + e_b(\tfrac{1}{2} + \tfrac{1}{3}) = -1,$$

from which

$$e_a = \frac{\begin{vmatrix} 3 & -\tfrac{1}{2} \\ -1 & \tfrac{5}{6} \end{vmatrix}}{\begin{vmatrix} \tfrac{3}{2} & -\tfrac{1}{2} \\ -\tfrac{1}{2} & \tfrac{5}{6} \end{vmatrix}} = 2 \quad \text{and} \quad e_b = \frac{\begin{vmatrix} \tfrac{3}{2} & 3 \\ -\tfrac{1}{2} & -1 \end{vmatrix}}{\begin{vmatrix} \tfrac{3}{2} & -\tfrac{1}{2} \\ -\tfrac{1}{2} & \tfrac{5}{6} \end{vmatrix}} = 0.$$

The voltage across R_2 is $e_a - e_b = 2$, and the currents in the three resistors are

$$i_{R_1} = \frac{e_a}{R_1} = 2 \text{ amp}, \qquad i_{R_2} = \frac{e_a - e_b}{R_2} = 1 \text{ amp},$$

$$i_{R_3} = \frac{e_a}{R_3} = 0 \text{ amp}.$$

Dummy node variables. Node-voltage equations are written for the sum of the currents leaving nodes. Current sources can therefore be included directly. Voltage sources, however, require the use of dummy node-voltage variables or one of the source transformations discussed in Chapter 4. Dummy node voltages are based on topological considerations. Each voltage source can be considered to introduce a dummy node into the circuit. Each dummy node can be included in the equations by means of a dummy node voltage. The current-law equations are written only at genuine topological nodes, and the dummy node voltage is defined by a voltage constraint equation involving the voltage source. The following is a summary of the dummy node-voltage method:

1. Node voltages are defined at each node in the network, including the dummy nodes created by voltage sources.

2. Current-law equations are written at each genuine topological node or supernode. (Topologically, the two terminals of each voltage source are shorted together. They belong to the same supernode.)

3. A constraint equation is written for each of the dummy nodes created by a voltage source.

An example of the use of a dummy node voltage to solve a problem containing a voltage source is shown in Fig. 3–8. The node voltage e_2 is assumed at the genuine topological node and the dummy node voltage e_d at the dummy node created by the voltage source.

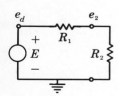

Figure 3–8. An example of a dummy node.

The constraint equation is simply

$$e_d = E. \qquad (3\text{–}23)$$

The node equation at the topological node e_2 is written as though e_d were a true node voltage. It is

$$e_2 \left(\frac{1}{R_1} + \frac{1}{R_2} \right) - e_d \frac{1}{R_1} = 0. \qquad (3\text{–}24)$$

A combination of Eqs. (3–27) and (3–28) gives the value of e_2 as

$$e_2 = E_1 \frac{R_2}{R_1 + R_2}. \qquad (3\text{–}25)$$

When the voltage source is connected to ground, as in this example, the dummy variable is defined directly by the source. When the voltage source is not connected to ground, the method can still be applied, but the constraint equation is more complicated. As an example, consider the circuit of Fig. 3–9. Topologically, it has just one unknown node and a ground node. One of the apparent nodes is a dummy. It doesn't matter which of the nodes is taken to be the unknown and which the dummy. For the arrangement shown the dummy voltage is defined by the constraint equation

$$e_d = e_a + E. \qquad (3\text{–}26)$$

The current-law equation must be written at a genuine topological node; here it is a combination of e_a and e_d obtained by collapsing the voltage source to zero. Effectively e_a and e_d form a supernode, as shown in Fig. 3–9. The Kirchhoff current-law equation for this supernode is obtained by equating to zero the sum of the currents leaving it:

$$\frac{e_a}{R_1} + \frac{e_d}{R_2} = 0. \qquad (3\text{–}27)$$

From Eqs. (3–26) and (3–27) we obtain

$$e_a = - \frac{R_1}{R_1 + R_2} E$$

and

$$e_d = \frac{R_2}{R_1 + R_2} E.$$

It is more difficult to write the dummy node equations when the voltage source is not connected to ground. Whenever possible it is desirable to shift the ground point to make the analysis easier.

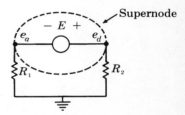

Figure 3–9. A dummy node produced by a floating source.

3–4 Theorems

Duality. In this section we shall explore the similarity between the general mesh equations (Eqs. 3–7) and the general node equations (Eqs. 3–22). This similarity is based on an important network principle called *duality.* Two networks are said to be dual when the mesh equations for one are numerically equal to the node equations for the other.

The dual of a given network can be found as follows:

1. A set of mesh equations with numerical coefficients is written for the original network.

2. The variables are changed from current to voltage.

3. The resulting node equations are interpreted as the dual network.

The first two steps are straightforward. The third step is really network synthesis, and we must show that it is always possible to find the dual network. First of all, let us consider the mutual elements between two meshes in the original network. In the transformed equations these terms will occur in the position of mutual conductances between the corresponding pairs of node voltages. They may be interpreted as physical resistances between the nodes with values which are numerically equal in mhos to the original resistance values in ohms. Each resistance which appears only in a self-resistance term in the mesh equations will transform to a conductance which appears only in the self-conductance term in the dual equations. Such an element can be interpreted as a conductance to ground in the dual network. Voltage sources in the mesh equations transform to current sources in the node equations, with values which are numerically the same. Current sources in the mesh equations result in dummy mesh equations which transform to dummy node equations in the dual set. The dummy node equations describe voltage sources which are numerically equal to the current sources in the original network.*

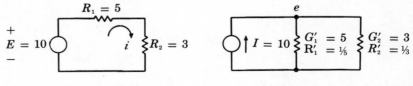

Figure 3–10. A circuit and its dual.   (a) Original circuit   (b) Dual circuit

---

* Only planar networks have duals. Nonplanar networks have three or more loop currents passing through a single resistance. The dual would require a single resistance between three or more nodes.

As an example of duality consider the circuit of Fig. 3–10(a). The mesh equation for this circuit is

$$i(R_1 + R_2) = E \tag{3–28}$$

or, numerically,

$$i(5 + 3) = 10. \tag{3–29}$$

The duality transformation changes Eq. (3–33) to

$$e(5 + 3) = 10. \tag{3–30}$$

Equation (3–34) can be interpreted as the node-voltage equation for two parallel resistances driven by a current source, for which the following equation holds:

$$e(G'_1 + G'_2) = I. \tag{3–31}$$

The values of the elements in the dual circuit are

$$G'_1 = 5 \quad \text{or} \quad R'_1 = \tfrac{1}{5} \text{ ohm,}$$

$$G'_2 = 3 \quad \text{or} \quad R'_2 = \tfrac{1}{3} \text{ ohm,}$$

and

$$I = 10 \text{ amp.}$$

The dual circuit is shown in Fig. 3–10(b).

The technique we have just discussed can always be used to find the dual of a planar network. We will now examine a geometrical adaptation of this method which arrives at the final dual network without the necessity of writing down any of the equations. Each mesh current in the original network transforms to a node voltage in the dual network. We can therefore locate the correct nodes by by placing a dot in the center of each mesh. The process is valid for both real and dummy meshes. Each element that occurs between two meshes must appear in dual form between the corresponding nodes in the dual circuit. These elements can be located geometrically by drawing lines between the two nodes in such a way that they cut each element that exists between the corresponding meshes. Each line is then replaced by the dual of the element it cuts.

Only the elements which occur in the mutual branches between meshes will be accounted for in the above construction. The remaining elements are on the outside of the original network. In the dual network they represent elements which go to ground from the nodes. It is apparent that the geometrical equivalent of the ground node is a ring around the outside of the diagram. Each line that cuts an element between a node and this ground ring can be replaced by the dual of the element.

The conventional positive direction for mesh currents is clockwise, and the conventional polarity for the node voltages is positive with respect to ground. *Thus a voltage or a current source which tends to produce a clockwise current around a mesh in the original circuit should be replaced in the dual circuit by the dual source element with a polarity which tends to make the node at the center of the mesh positive.*

As an example of the geometrical process, two duals are obtained geometrically in Fig. 3–11. In part (a) a node is assumed in the center of the mesh and a ground node completely encircling the figure is drawn. Lines from the node to the circle cut the two resistances and the source. Each line is replaced by the dual of the element it cuts. The original voltage source tended to produce clockwise current in the mesh and therefore the current source in the dual circuit must enter the node and tend to make it positive.

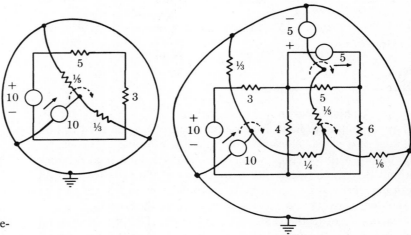

Figure 3–11. The geometrical determination of dual circuits.

(a) Example 1   (b) Example 2

In Fig. 3–11(b) two real nodes are installed in the real meshes and a dummy node in the dummy mesh. The lines joining the nodes are replaced by the duals of the elements which they cut. The ground node encircles the diagram and has connections to each of the three nodes. The voltage source in mesh 1 of the original circuit tends to produce clockwise current, and hence the current source in the dual network must enter the corresponding node. The current source in the original network flows in the clockwise direction in the dummy node, and hence the corresponding dummy voltage must be positive with respect to ground.

TABLE 3–1

Original network		Dual network
current i	transforms to	voltage e
voltage e	transforms to	current i
source current I	transforms to	source voltage E
source voltage E	transforms to	source current I
resistance R	transforms to	conductance G
inductance L	transforms to	capacitance C
capacitance C	transforms to	inductance L
series branches	transform to	parallel branches
parallel branches	transform to	series branches
open circuits	transform to	short circuits
short circuits	transform to	open circuits
mesh currents	transform to	node voltages
node voltages	transform to	mesh currents

The geometrical method of obtaining the dual circuit is surprisingly easy after a little practice, and it discloses many general properties of dual circuits. For example, it is apparent that the dual network is unique and that two successive applications of the duality transformation bring us back to the original network. Some of the other consequences of duality are listed in Table 3–1.

Linearity and superposition. Mesh and node equations are useful for solving specific network problems. They also provide a method for discussing networks in a generalized way, and for deriving theoretical relationships. Of these the most important and far reaching are the theorems of *linearity* and *superposition.* Linearity states that the response at any point in a network is proportional to the stimulus which is causing it. Superposition is an extension of the linearity principle to the case of multiple excitation. When the superposition principle applies, the output response from a number of sources acting simultaneously is simply the sum of the responses which would be produced by each of the sources acting alone with all of the other sources dead. The superposition theorem includes the linearity theorem as a special case since increasing the value of a stimulus is equivalent to adding a second stimulus to it.

Proof. To prove the linearity and superposition principles we will assume the general set of mesh equations:

$$
\begin{aligned}
i_1(r_{11}) - i_2(r_{12}) - \cdots - i_k(r_{1k}) &= E_1, \\
-i_1(r_{12}) + i_2(r_{22}) - \cdots \qquad\qquad &= E_2, \\
\vdots \qquad\qquad\qquad\qquad & \\
-i_1(r_{1k}) - i_2(r_{2k}) - \cdots \quad i_k(r_{kk}) &= E_k.
\end{aligned}
\tag{3-32}
$$

Only voltage sources appear in Eqs. (3–32). Current sources introduce dummy-mesh currents. The elimination of these by means of the constraint equations modifies the right-hand side of Eqs. (3–32) but does not change the general form.

The solution for a response current is of the form

$$
i_1 = \frac{\begin{vmatrix} E_1 & -r_{12} & \cdots & -r_{1k} \\ E_2 & r_{22} & & \\ \vdots & & & \\ E_k & -r_{2k} & \cdots & -r_{kk} \end{vmatrix}}{\begin{vmatrix} r_{11} & -r_{12} & \cdots & -r_{1k} \\ -r_{12} & r_{22} & \cdots & \\ \vdots & & & \\ -r_{1k} & -r_{2k} & \cdots & r_{kk} \end{vmatrix}} \tag{3–33}
$$

or

$$
i = \frac{E_1}{\Delta} \begin{vmatrix} r_{22} \cdots r_{2k} \\ \vdots \\ -r_{2k} \cdots r_{kk} \end{vmatrix} + \frac{(-E_2)}{\Delta} \begin{vmatrix} -r_{12} & \cdots & -r_{1k} \\ -r_{23} & & \\ \vdots & & \\ -r_{2k} & \cdots & r_{kk} \end{vmatrix} + \cdots , \tag{3–34}
$$

where Δ is the denominator determinant. Equation (3–34) is obtained by a Laplace expansion of the numerator determinant of Eq. (3–33). Each term in Eq. (3–34) is written as if only the source involved in that term were acting and all the other sources were zero. The total response is the sum of the responses which would be produced by each of the sources acting separately, with the other sources equal to zero. Equation (3–34) is thus a verification of the superposition theorem.

The linearity theorem is proved by noting that the response produced by any one of the sources acting alone is directly proportional to the value of that source in Eq. (3–34).

In applications of superposition it is important to know exactly what we mean by the statement that the response for any one source is computed with the "other sources dead." *A dead voltage source is a zero voltage constraint between two points or, in other words, a short circuit. A dead current source means that there is zero current flowing between two points or, in other words, an open circuit.*

As an example of the use of the superposition theorem we will compute the output voltage in the circuit of Fig. 3–12(a). We can consider this voltage to be composed of two parts, e_1 and e_2, contributed by the voltage source and the current source respectively.

The component e_1 is computed from the circuit of Fig. 3–12(b). It is

$$e_1 = \tfrac{1}{2} \times 10 = 5 \text{ volts.}$$

The component e_2 is computed from the circuit of Fig. 3–12(c). It is

$$e_2 = 10 \times \tfrac{1}{2} = 5 \text{ volts.}$$

The total output voltage e is the sum of these two components:

$$e = e_1 + e_2 = 10 \text{ volts.}$$

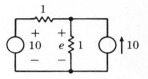

(a) Original circuit

Superposition is particularly useful when the components produced by the separate sources can be obtained by inspection, as in the problem just solved. If each response must be obtained by mesh or node equations it is better to apply them directly to the original circuit.

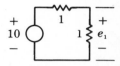

(b) Voltage-source component

A direct application of the principle of linearity is *normalization*. Since the output response in a network is directly proportional to the value of the source, it is convenient to use source values of 1 volt and 1 amp, and to scale up the value of the response to agree with any other source value. The concept of normalization can be extended to the resistance values as well. The resulting circuit is a "linear model" of the original problem. The normalization can be carried out in two ways. If the voltages are left alone and all the resistances are multiplied by a constant, all of the currents will be divided by the same constant. This result can be verified in Eq. (3–34), but it is intuitively obvious from Ohm's law. Alternatively, the currents can be left unchanged, and then, if the resistances are multiplied by a constant, the voltages will be multiplied by the same constant. In many problems both the source and resistance values are scaled and a single normalization constant is used to convert the normalized solution to the solution for the original problem.

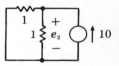

(c) Current-source component

Figure 3–12. A circuit solved by superposition.

A change in units can accomplish much the same results as normalization and is essentially equivalent to it. Common unit multipliers used in electrical work are the following:

> M, Mega: multiplies the size of the unit by 10^6,
>
> K, Kilo: multiplies the size of the unit by 10^3,
>
> m, milli: multiplies the size of the unit by 10^{-3},
>
> μ, micro: multiplies the size of the unit by 10^{-6}.

As an example, 1 megohm (written 1 M) is 10^6 ohms, and 1 microvolt (written 1 μ-volt) is 10^{-6} of 1 volt. Certain combinations of units are self-consistent. For example, a useful set in electronics is volts, kilohms, and milliamps.

We have considered some special applications of linearity and superposition. The real importance of the theorems, however, lies in the flexibility which they lend to linear circuit analysis. The most general problem which need be considered is one with a single source and a single response. Multiple sources can be handled by superposition. The single "stimulus-response" relationship thus becomes the central theme of linear circuit theory, and the remainder of the book will be devoted to it.

Summary

Mesh currents

$$i_1 r_{11} - i_2 r_{12} - \cdots - i_k r_{1k} = E_1,$$

$$-i_1 r_{12} + i_2 r_{22} - \cdots - i_k r_{2k} = E_2,$$

$$\vdots$$

$$-i_1 r_{1k} - i_2 r_{2k} - \cdots + i_k r_{kk} = E_k,$$

where

r_{11} = total resistance around mesh 1,

r_{12} = resistance between mesh 1 and mesh 2,

E_1 = net source voltage producing clockwise current in mesh 1,

and so on.

Dummy mesh currents

Dummy mesh

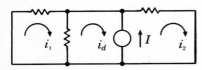

Constraint equation

$$i_2 - i_d = I$$

Node voltages

$$e_1 g_{11} - e_2 g_{12} - \cdots - e_k g_{1k} = I_1,$$

$$-e_1 g_{12} + e_2 g_{22} - \cdots - e_k g_{2k} = I_2,$$

$$\vdots$$

$$-e_1 g_{1k} - e_2 g_{2k} - \cdots + e_k g_{kk} = I_k,$$

where

g_{11} = total conductance radiating from node 1,

g_{12} = conductance between node 1 and node 2,

I_1 = net source current tending to make the voltage at node 1 positive,

and so on.

Dummy node voltages

Dummy node

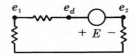

Constraint equation

$$e_d = e_2 + E$$

Duality

Duality Transformation

current i	transforms to	voltage e
voltage e	transforms to	current i
resistance R	transforms to	conductance G
inductance L	transforms to	capacitance C
capacitance C	transforms to	inductance L
series	transforms to	parallel
parallel	transforms to	series
open circuit	transforms to	short circuit
mesh current	transforms to	node voltage
node voltage	transforms to	mesh current

Linearity. In a linear network the response is directly proportional to the stimulus.

For voltage source:

$$E_0 = K_1 E_s \quad \text{or} \quad I_0 = K_2 E_s,$$

where

E_s = the source stimulus,

E_0 = output voltage response,

I_0 = output current response,

K_1 = a dimensionless constant,

K_2 = a constant with dimensions of conductance.

For current source:

$$E_0 = K_3 I_s \quad \text{or} \quad I_0 = K_4 I_s,$$

where

I_s = the source stimulus,

E_0 = output voltage response,

I_0 = output current response,

K_3 = a constant with the dimensions of resistance,

K_4 = a dimensionless constant.

Superposition. In a linear network the response for two or more sources acting simultaneously is the sum of the responses for each source acting alone with the other voltage sources short circuits and the other current sources open circuits.

$$E_0 = K_1 I_1 + K_2 E_1 + \cdots,$$
$$I_0 = K_3 I_1 + K_4 E_1 + \cdots,$$

where

E_0 = the output voltage response,

I_0 = the output current response,

I_1 = a current source stimulus,

E_1 = a voltage source stimulus,

K_1 = a constant with dimensions of resistance,

K_2 = a dimensionless constant,

K_3 = a dimensionless constant,

K_4 = a constant with dimensions of conductance.

Scaling of units

M, Mega: multiplies size of unit by 10^6

K, Kilo: multiplies size of unit by 10^3

m, milli: multiplies size of unit by 10^{-3}

μ, micro: multiplies size of unit by 10^{-6}

References

Mesh currents are traditional in electrical engineering texts. Node voltages, promoted by Professor Guillemin of M.I.T., are now found in most modern texts. The treatment of dummy variables given here is original, although occasional references to special cases will be found in the literature. Additional references on these basic methods are the following.

1. E. A. GUILLEMIN, *Introductory Circuit Theory*, John Wiley, New York, 1953. Mesh and node methods are presented in the framework of topology and are spread through the first three chapters. Duality is also presented as a general topological concept.

2. M. B. REED, *Alternating-Current Circuit Theory*, Harper, New York, 1956. A more advanced treatment relying on matrix theory. One of the few books which gives the transformations to be used with resistanceless sources.

3. SESHU and BALBANIAN, *Linear Network Analysis*, John Wiley, New York, 1959. A graduate-level treatment which follows Reed's approach. An example is given which involves a dummy variable.

4. H. H. SKILLING, *Electrical Engineering Circuits*, John Wiley, New York, 1957. Mesh and node equations are presented in terms of steady-state impedances.

5. MIT EE Staff, *Electric Circuits*, John Wiley, New York, 1943. This text contains one of the earliest discussions of node equations. It is very straightforward. Source transformations are used to obtain voltage sources in mesh analysis, and current sources in node analysis.

Exercises

SECTION 3-2

1. Set up the mesh equations for the circuit of Fig. 3–13 and use them to find the voltage drop from point a to point b.

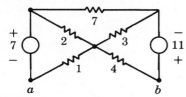

Figure 3–13

2. Write the mesh equations for the circuit of Fig. 3–14. Solve for the mesh currents.

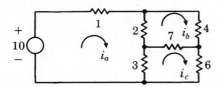

Figure 3–14

3. Find the voltage e_0 in the circuit of Fig. 3–15 by means of mesh equations.

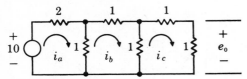

Figure 3–15

4. The following equations are known to be mesh equations:

$$6i_a - 3i_b - i_c = 6,$$

$$-3i_a + 5i_b - i_c = -6,$$

$$-i_a - i_b + 4i_c = 0.$$

Reconstruct the network from which they came, knowing that there is only one source present.

5. Write and solve the equations for the mesh currents in the circuit of Fig. 3–16.

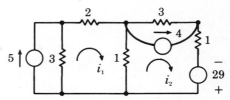

Figure 3–16

6. The circuit of Fig. 3–17 involves two resistance-less sources. Solve the problem by means of dummy mesh currents. Find i_1, i_2, and i_3.

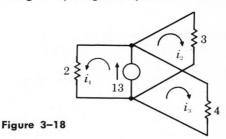

Figure 3–17

7. Solve for the currents i_1, i_2, and i_3 in the circuit of Fig. 3–18, using dummy mesh currents.

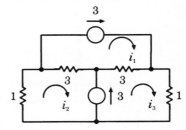

Figure 3–18

8. If a current source occurs in an outside loop the dummy mesh method is particularly simple. In the circuit of Fig. 3–19 this effect can be accom-

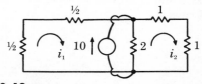

Figure 3–19

plished by bridging the current source in the third dimension. A dummy mesh current can be assumed in the dummy mesh, which is at right angles to the plane of the paper. Find i_1 and i_2, using this technique.

SECTION 3–3

9. Write and solve the node-voltage equations for the circuit of Fig. 3–20.

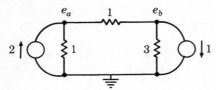

Figure 3–20

10. Write the node equations for the circuit of Fig. 3–21 and solve for the node voltages.

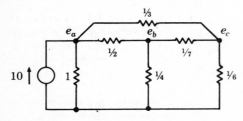

Figure 3–21

11. Find the voltage across the source in Fig. 3–22 by writing and solving the node-voltage equations.

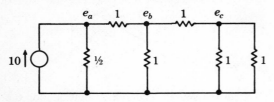

Figure 3–22

12. The following equations are known to be node-voltage equations:

$$3e_a - e_b - e_c = 5,$$
$$- e_a + 4e_b - 2e_c = 3,$$
$$- e_a - 2e_b + 5e_c = -8.$$

Reconstruct the network from which they came, using a minimum number of sources.

13. Solve for e_a and e_b in the circuit of Fig. 3–23, using a dummy node voltage.

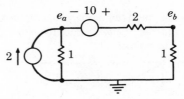

Figure 3–23

14. Solve for the voltages e_a, e_b, and e_c in the circuit of Fig. 3–24, using the dummy voltage technique and writing an equation at the supernode containing e_a and e_c.

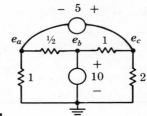

Figure 3–24

15. Solve for the node voltages e_a, e_b, and e_c in the circuit of Fig. 3–25, using the dummy voltage method.

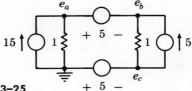

Figure 3–25

16. Find the voltages e_a, e_b, and e_c in the circuit of Fig. 3–26 by means of node-voltage equations and a constraint equation for the dummy variable.

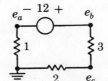

Figure 3–26

SECTION 3–4

17. (a) Write the mesh equations for the circuit of Fig. 3–27. Transform these equations into the equations of the dual circuit. Construct the dual circuit (be sure the values are in ohms, volts, amperes). (b) Obtain the dual of the circuit in (a) by the geometrical method.

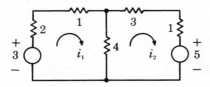

Figure 3–27

18. (a) Write the mesh equations and the constraint equations for the dummy variables in the circuit of Fig. 3–28. Transform these equations to the dual form. Construct the dual circuit. (b) Obtain the dual of the circuit in (a) by the geometrical method.

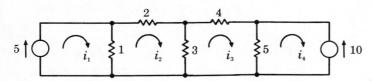

Figure 3–28

19. Find the dual of the network of Fig. 3–29 and then obtain the dual of the dual network.

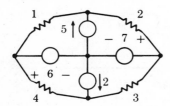

Figure 3–29

20. (a) For the circuit of Fig. 3–30 write the three topological mesh equations and the constraint equation for the current source. Transform these equations to dual form and construct the dual network from the equations. (b) Obtain the dual by the geometrical method.

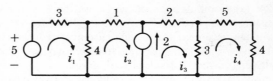

Figure 3–30

21. (a) By means of superposition, find the current in the resistor in the circuit of Fig. 3–31. (b) With both sources acting, give the power from the voltage source, the power from the current source, and the power used in the resistor. (c) Formulate and solve the dual-circuit problem.

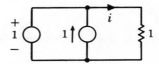

Figure 3–31

22. Find the current i through the 1-ohm resistor in the circuit of Fig. 3–32 by means of the superposition theorem.

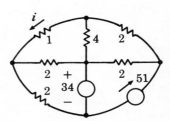

Figure 3–32

23. (a) Find the value of the current in the 3-ohm resistance in the circuit of Fig. 3–33. (b) What does this current become when the input voltage is raised to 100 v? (c) What does this current become if the input voltage is raised to 100 v and the resistance values are simultaneously increased by 10^6?

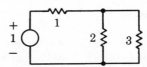

Figure 3–33

24. (a) Compute the voltage across the 3-ohm resistor in the circuit of Fig. 3–34. (b) What does this voltage become if the driving current is reduced to 1 ma? (c) What does this voltage become if the driving current is reduced to 1 ma and simultaneously the resistance values are increased by a factor of 10^6?

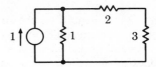

Figure 3–34

Problems

1. Find the currents i_1, i_2, i_3, and i_4 in the circuit of Fig. 3–35, using dummy mesh currents.

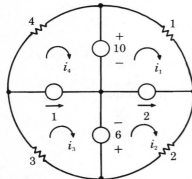

Figure 3–35

2. Solve for the voltages e_a, e_b, e_c, and e_d in the circuit of Fig. 3–36.

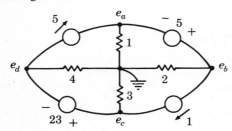

Figure 3–36

3. (a) A linear passive circuit has two sets of terminal-pairs. When 10-v sources are applied to both of them the input currents are each 1 amp.

When one of the voltages is dropped to 5 v the current from the other source drops to zero. What value of voltage at the source with zero current would cause the current to drop to zero if the voltage at the other terminal were left at 10 v? (b) Two current sources I_1 and I_2 are applied to a network and a voltage e is read at a third terminal-pair. When $I_1 = 1$ and $I_2 = 0$, the voltage e is 1 v. When $I_1 = 0$ and $I_2 = 1$ the voltage e is -2 v. What is the voltage e when $I_1 = -1$ amp and $I_2 = 2$ amp?

4. It is possible that the superposition method will result in an answer which is the difference between two large quantities. If so, computational care must be used in order to obtain an answer which is not grossly in error. As an example, find the current i in the circuit of Fig. 3–37 by means of superposition.

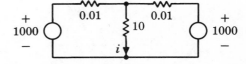

Figure 3–37

5. The dual network has been obtained by writing the mesh equations, transforming them to the node equations of the dual network, and synthesizing the network from these equations. Show that the same result would be obtained if the node equations were written and transformed to the mesh equations of the dual network and the network synthesized from them.

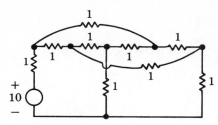

Figure 3–38

6. The network in Fig. 3–38 is nonplanar. Pick a set of loops, write the loop equations and solve them.

7. Given the two equations

$$ai_1 - bi_2 = f \quad \text{and} \quad -ci_1 + di_2 = g,$$

where a, b, c, d, f, and g are positive numbers, show that the determinant $ad - bc = 0$ is a necessary but not sufficient condition for the equations to represent the mesh equations of a network with positive resistances. What are the necessary conditions? What are the special conditions when $ad - bc = 0$? Derive the networks.

8. Show that the use of a dummy variable is equivalent to a source transformation in a network and derive the transformation.

Consider the four cases:

(a) a current source in parallel with a resistance,

(b) a voltage source in series with a resistance,

(c) a resistanceless current source,

(d) a resistanceless voltage source.

CHAPTER 4

ONE-TERMINAL-PAIR RESISTIVE NETWORKS

I sometimes think that never blows so red
The Rose, as where some buried Caesar bled;
That every Hyacinthe the Garden wears
Dropt in her lap from some once lovely head.

RUBÁIYÁT OF OMAR KHAYYÁM

4–1 Introduction

In this chapter we shall begin to investigate the special properties of linear circuits. Almost no area of applied mathematics has been developed to the level of sophistication of this one, and we can properly join old Omar the tentmaker in appreciating the sufferings of those who prepared the way for us! As a consequence of linearity and superposition in a network we need consider only a single excitation function at a time. Two cases arise, however, depending on where the response is measured. In a *one-terminal-pair network* the stimulus and the response occur at the same pair of terminals. One of them is a current and the other a voltage. In a *two-terminal-pair network* the stimulus is applied at one pair of terminals and the response is measured at another.

In this chapter we shall consider one-terminal-pair networks. They take the form of branches, which may be simple or compound and which are described mathematically, or characterized, by the equivalent resistance of the branch.

When a one-terminal-pair network contains sources as well as resistances, it can still be reduced to an equivalent simple branch which now contains a source as well as a resistance. If the branch is taken to be a voltage source in series with a resistance we have *Thévenin's theorem*, and if it is taken as a current source in parallel with a resistance we have *Norton's theorem*. Occasionally it is desirable to substitute a voltage source for a known value of voltage at some point in a circuit, or a current source for a known value of current. The equivalence seems obvious, but it is dignified by the name *substitution theorem*.

4–2 Equivalent resistive branch

The equivalent resistances of series and parallel elements, which we obtained in Chapter 2, are special cases of the general concept of equivalent resistance. Any resistive network with one pair of terminals can be replaced by a single resistance which draws the same current as the original network when it is excited by the same voltage.

Series-parallel circuits. By successive applications of the rules for combining resistors in series and in parallel it is possible to reduce many complicated branches to single resistors.* As an example we will find the equivalent resistance for the network of Fig. 4–1. The network is reduced from the right-hand side. The first step is to combine the two resistors in series. The equivalent resistance is

$$R_1 = 1 + 1 = 2 \text{ ohms.}$$

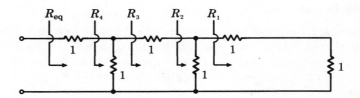

Figure 4–1. A series-parallel circuit.

The next step is to combine R_1 with the first shunt resistance, with which it is now in parallel. This combination is given by

$$R_2 = \frac{R_1 \times 1}{R_1 + 1} = \tfrac{2}{3} \text{ ohm.}$$

The resultant R_2 is now in series with the second series resistance and can be added to it to give

$$R_3 = 1 + R_2 = \tfrac{5}{3} \text{ ohms.}$$

The resistance R_3 is then in parallel with a 1-ohm resistance and can be combined with it to give a new resultant,

$$R_4 = \frac{R_3 \times 1}{R_3 + 1} = \tfrac{5}{8} \text{ ohm.}$$

Finally, the resistance R_4 can be added to the remaining series resistance to give the input resistance R_{eq}:

$$R_{\text{eq}} = 1 + R_4 = \tfrac{13}{8} \text{ ohms.}$$

The combination of resistors in series and in parallel is easy and will often save a good deal of work.

---

* To reduce a general branch it is necessary to use the Y–Δ transformation as well as the formulas for series and parallel resistors.

The Y–Δ transformation. The Y–Δ transformation is more general then the series-parallel formula because it relates to the behavior of a three-terminal network instead of a two-terminal network. A Y-network is composed of three resistances connected to a common point, as shown in Fig. 4–2(a). A Δ-network consists of three resistances connected in a triangular form, as shown in Fig. 4–2(b). When we are concerned only with the effect upon some external network we can find values of the resistances which make a Y-network and a Δ-network equivalent.

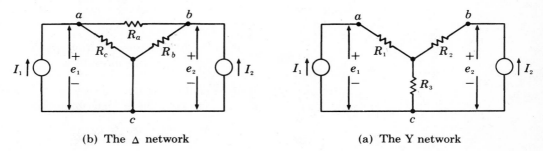

(b) The Δ network   (a) The Y network

We will establish the equivalence of the Y and the Δ by driving the terminal-pairs with current sources and requiring that the voltages be the same in the Y and the Δ. The two equivalent networks with their excitations are shown in Fig. 4–2. The responses can be written down by inspection for each network by means of the superposition theorem. For the Y-network the voltages are

Figure 4–2. The Y–Δ transformation.

$$e_1 = (R_1 + R_3)I_1 + \quad R_3 I_2,$$
$$e_2 = \quad R_3 \quad I_1 + (R_2 + R_3)I_2, \tag{4–1}$$

and for the Δ-network they are

$$e_1 = \frac{R_c(R_a + R_b)}{R_a + R_b + R_c} I_1 + \frac{R_c R_b}{R_a + R_b + R_c} I_2,$$
$$e_2 = \frac{R_c R_b}{R_a + R_b + R_c} I_1 + \frac{R_b(R_a + R_c)}{R_a + R_b + R_c} I_2. \tag{4–2}$$

The coefficients in Eqs. (4–1) and (4–2) must be identical, and thus

$$R_1 + R_3 = \frac{R_c(R_a + R_b)}{R_a + R_b + R_c},$$
$$R_3 = \frac{R_b R_c}{R_a + R_b + R_c}, \tag{4–3}$$
$$R_2 + R_3 = \frac{R_b(R_a + R_c)}{R_a + R_b + R_c}.$$

From Eq. (4–3) we can obtain

$$R_1 = \frac{R_a R_c}{R_a + R_b + R_c},$$

$$R_2 = \frac{R_a R_b}{R_a + R_b + R_c}, \qquad (4\text{–}4)$$

$$R_3 = \frac{R_b R_c}{R_a + R_b + R_c}.$$

Inspection of Fig. 4–2 makes it apparent that a general expression for the Y-resistance is

$$\text{Y-resistance} = \frac{\text{Product of adjacent } \Delta\text{-resistances}}{\text{Sum of } \Delta\text{-resistances}}. \qquad (4\text{–}5)$$

Alternatively, Eq. (4–3) could have been solved for the Δ-resistors and the following equations would have been obtained:

$$R_a = \frac{R_1 R_2 + R_2 R_3 + R_3 R_1}{R_3},$$

$$R_b = \frac{R_1 R_2 + R_2 R_3 + R_3 R_1}{R_1}, \qquad (4\text{–}6)$$

$$R_c = \frac{R_1 R_2 + R_2 R_3 + R_3 R_1}{R_2}.$$

Again an inspection of Fig. 4–2 reveals that the Δ-resistances are given by

Δ-resistance

$$= \frac{\text{Sum of the products of the Y-resistances taken in pairs}}{\text{The opposite Y-resistance}}. \qquad (4\text{–}7)$$

It is also possible to convert Eq. (4–6) to conductances, and obtain

$$G_a = \frac{G_1 G_2}{G_1 + G_2 + G_3},$$

$$G_b = \frac{G_2 G_3}{G_1 + G_2 + G_3}, \qquad (4\text{–}8)$$

$$G_c = \frac{G_3 G_1}{G_1 + G_2 + G_3}.$$

Equation (4–8) is in the form

$$\Delta\text{-conductance} = \frac{\text{Product of adjacent Y-conductances}}{\text{Sum of Y-conductances}}. \qquad (4\text{–}9)$$

Equations (4–7) and (4–9) are equivalent and the choice between them is dictated by personal preference. Some people like to work in ohms, and some people like the similarity of Eqs. (4–5) and (4–9).

When all the resistances in the Y are equal, the equivalent Δ-resistances are also equal, and are equal to three times the Y-resistances. Similarly, if the Δ-resistances are equal the Y-resistances, which are equivalent, are also equal, and are equal to one-third of the Δ-resistances. This symmetrical transformation, shown in Fig. 4–3, is a useful one to remember as a check on one's memory of the general transformation.

As an example of the reduction of a complex branch to a single resistance by means of the Y–Δ transformation and the series-parallel formulas, we consider the circuit of Fig. 4–4(a). The first step in the reduction procedure is a Y–Δ transformation of the section of the network enclosed by *bde*. The resultant circuit is shown in Fig. 4–4(b). The node *c* has been removed and the circuit has a series-parallel form. The node *d* can be removed by combining resistances in parallel and then in series. The circuit then appears as in Fig. 4–4(c), and the input resistance can be found by inspection to be

$$R_{ae} = \tfrac{24}{11} \text{ ohms,}$$

as in the previous examples.

A combination of Y–Δ or Δ–Y transformations and the series-parallel formulas can be used to reduce any resistance network to a single equivalent resistance. This method is very easy when the Y–Δ transformation is symmetrical, as in this example. When the Y–Δ transformations are unsymmetrical this method is seldom any less work than the mesh- and node-equation methods.

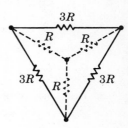

Figure 4–3. The symmetrical Y–Δ transformation.

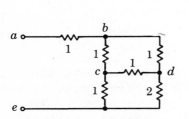

(a) Original circuit

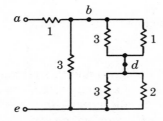

(b) Circuit after Y–Δ transformation

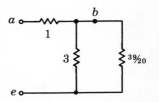

(c) Circuit after series- parallel transformation

Figure 4–4. Equivalent resistance by Y–Δ transformation.

General method. In the laboratory the equivalent resistance of a device is obtained by applying a current source and measuring the resulting voltage or by applying a voltage source and measuring the resulting current. (Actually both the current and the voltage are measured. A measured value is equivalent to a source.) The same procedure can be used analytically.

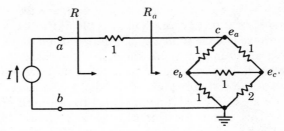

Figure 4–5. Resistance computation.

As an example we will find the resistance of the circuit in Fig. 4–5 at the terminal pair a–b. The resistance in series with the current source is trivial, and so we will find the resistance R_a between the terminals c and b. There are three nodes in the circuit, whose equations are

$$e_a(2) - e_b(1) - e_c(1) = I,$$

$$-e_a(1) + e_b(3) - e_c(1) = 0, \qquad (4\text{–}10)$$

$$-e_a(1) - e_b(1) + e_c(\tfrac{5}{2}) = 0.$$

The voltage is

$$
e_a = \frac{\begin{vmatrix} I & -1 & -1 \\ 0 & 3 & -1 \\ 0 & -1 & \tfrac{5}{2} \end{vmatrix}}{\begin{vmatrix} 2 & -1 & -1 \\ -1 & 3 & -1 \\ -1 & -1 & \tfrac{5}{2} \end{vmatrix}} = \tfrac{13}{11}I,
$$

and the resistance is

$$R_a = \frac{e_a}{I} = \tfrac{13}{11} \text{ ohms.}$$

The input resistance is

$$R = 1 + R_a = \tfrac{24}{11} \text{ ohms.}$$

In order to find the resistance at a terminal pair either a current source or a voltage source can be applied. The mesh-current method and/or the node-voltage method are both available to solve the network problem, and the choice between them should be based on which method requires the fewer equations.

4–3 Equivalent source branches

In the preceding section we have shown that a complex branch containing only resistances can be reduced to a single equivalent resistance. In this section we will show that a complex branch containing resistances and sources can be reduced to a single resistance plus a single source. There are two separate theorems. In Thévenin's theorem the equivalent elements are a voltage source in series with a resistance, and in Norton's theorem a current source in parallel with a resistance.

Thévenin's and Norton's theorems. A general statement of Thévenin's theorem is the following:

> *Any linear two-terminal network branch with sources can be replaced by an equivalent voltage source in series with an equivalent passive branch. The voltage source is the voltage measured at the terminals when nothing is connected to the external circuit, and the passive branch is the "dead" network, in which all of the sources have been reduced to zero. In a resistive network the "dead" network is a single equivalent resistance.*

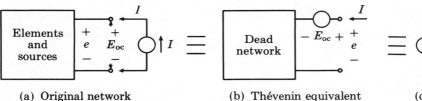

(a) Original network   (b) Thévenin equivalent network   (c) Thévenin equivalent for a resistive network

Figure 4–6. Thévenin's theorem.

Thévenin's theorem is the volt-ampere relationship of a general network branch containing sources. Consider the general branch shown in Fig. 4–6(a). The volt-ampere relationship can be obtained by exciting the circuit with a current source and measuring the resultant voltage. By the superposition theorem this voltage is composed of two parts:

$$e = \left(\begin{matrix}\text{voltage from external}\\\text{current source}\end{matrix}\right) + \left(\begin{matrix}\text{voltage from sources}\\\text{within the network}\end{matrix}\right). \quad (4\text{--}11)$$

The voltage produced by the external current source is measured with the sources inside the network placed equal to zero. It is the voltage which the current I would produce in the "dead" network. The voltage from the sources within the network is obtained with the external current source "dead." It is the voltage which exists across the terminals when they are open. We have thus interpreted Eq. (4–11) in the form of Fig. 4–6(b). The voltage e produced at the terminals of the network is the sum of two components, one of which is the voltage which the current would produce in the "dead" network and the other of which is the open-circuit voltage across the terminals. For a network of sources and resistances the "dead" network reduces to a single equivalent resistance and the Thévenin equivalent circuit takes the form shown in Fig. 4–6(c).

Norton's theorem is the dual of Thévenin's theorem. It can be stated as follows:

> *Any linear two-terminal network branch with sources can be replaced by an equivalent current source in parallel with an equivalent passive branch. The current source is the current which would flow from the terminals if they were short-circuited, and the passive branch is the "dead" network, with all of the sources reduced to zero. In a resistive network the "dead" network is a single equivalent resistance.*

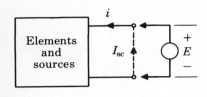

(a) Original network

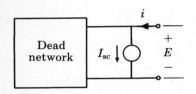

(b) Norton equivalent circuit

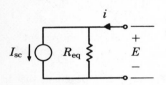

(c) Norton circuit for a resistive network

Figure 4–7. Norton's theorem.

To prove Norton's theorem we obtain the volt-ampere relationship of the general branch when it is excited by a voltage source, as shown in Fig. 4–7(a). By the principle of superposition the current i which flows from the source is the sum of two components:

$$i = \begin{pmatrix} \text{current from the external} \\ \text{voltage source} \end{pmatrix} + \begin{pmatrix} \text{current from sources} \\ \text{within the network} \end{pmatrix}.$$

$$(4\text{–}12)$$

The current produced by the external voltage source is measured with all of the sources within the network placed equal to zero. It is the current which the voltage source E would produce in the "dead" network. The current from sources within the network is obtained with the external voltage source "dead," and a "dead" voltage source is a short-circuit across the terminals. We can thus interpret Eq. (4–12) in the form of Fig. 4–7(b). The input current i is the sum of two components, one of which is the current produced in the dead network by the voltage E, and the other of which is the short-circuit current available at the terminals. If the network is resistive, the "dead" network can be replaced by a single equivalent resistance, and the Norton equivalent circuit takes the form shown in Fig. 4–7(c).

The source polarity for Thévenin's and Norton's theorems is usually best obtained by inspection. The equivalent circuit must produce current flow *in the external circuit* in the same direction as in the original problem.

We have proved Thévenin's and Norton's theorems using the concept of superposition and therefore requiring the network to be linear. The theorems can be extended to single-valued nonlinear circuits as well and are among the most general and most useful theorems in all of science.

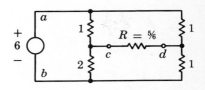

(a) Voltage source   (b) Norton equivalent   (c) Current source   (d) Thévenin equivalent

Figure 4–8. Source transformations by Thévenin's and Norton's theorems.

Applications of Thévenin's and Norton's theorems. Thévenin's and Norton's theorems provide the most direct way of making current-source to voltage-source transformations. Consider the circuit of Fig. 4–8(a). The short-circuit current produced by the voltage source is

$$I_{sc} = \frac{E}{R},$$

and the resistance at the terminals with the voltage source dead is simply

$$R_{eq} = R.$$

The Norton equivalent circuit is thus a current source of value E/R in parallel with the resistance R, as shown in Fig. 4–8(b). Similarly, Thévenin's theorem can be applied to the current source in parallel with a resistance, as shown in Fig. 4–8(c). The open-circuit voltage is

$$E_{oc} = IR,$$

and the resistance at the terminals with the current source open is

$$R_{eq} = R.$$

The Thévenin equivalent circuit is thus a voltage source of value IR in series with a resistance R, as shown in Fig. 4–8(d).

Thévenin's and Norton's theorems are more general, however, than the current-source to voltage-source transformations. As an example we will use Thévenin's theorem to find the current in the resistance R in Fig. 4–9(a). The procedure will be to find a Thévenin equivalent circuit at the terminals c–d and then to apply the resistance R to this circuit. The open-circuit voltage can be found from the circuit of Fig. 4–9(b). The node voltages are

$$e_c = \tfrac{2}{3} \times 6 = 4 \text{ volts} \quad \text{and} \quad e_d = \tfrac{1}{2} \times 6 = 3 \text{ volts}.$$

The open-circuit voltage across the terminals c–d is

$$e_c - e_d = 1 \text{ volt}.$$

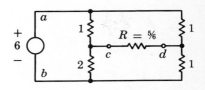

(a) Original circuit

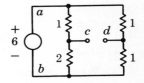

(b) Open circuit at c-d

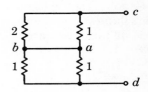

(c) Resistance at c-d

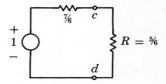

(d) Equivalent Thévenin circuit

Figure 4–9. The complete solution of a problem by Thévenin's theorem.

The resistance at the terminals c–d can be found from the circuit of Fig. 4–9(c). It is

$$R_{eq} = \frac{2 \times 1}{2 + 1} + \frac{1 \times 1}{1 + 1} = \tfrac{7}{6} \text{ ohms.}$$

The Thévenin equivalent circuit is shown in Fig. 4–9(d) to the left of the terminals c–d, and the resistance $R = \tfrac{5}{6}$ ohm is applied to the right of these terminals. Since the Thévenin equivalent circuit accurately represents the circuit so far as its effect at the terminals c–d is concerned, the current in the $\tfrac{5}{6}$-ohm resistance will be the same in Fig. 4–9(a) and (d). It is

$$i = \frac{1}{(\tfrac{7}{6}) + (\tfrac{5}{6})} = \tfrac{1}{2} \text{ amp.}$$

Other methods of solution involve a great deal more work.

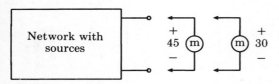

(a) Voltage measured with finite resistance voltmeters

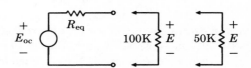

(b) Equivalent circuit of network and meters

Figure 4–10. The application of Thévenin's theorem to the measurement of voltage with finite-resistance meters.

Another application of Thévenin's and Norton's theorems is to the measurement problem in electrical circuits. When we insert physical voltmeters and ammeters into the circuit, we disturb the circuit, and the readings we obtain are not those which existed previously. By taking two sets of readings on different scales, we can compute the correct values by means of Thévenin's and Norton's theorems. Consider the example shown in Fig. 4–10(a). The voltage across the terminals is measured with two nonideal voltmeters. The first meter has a resistance of 100,000 ohms and gives a reading of 45 volts. The second meter has a resistance of 50,000 ohms and gives a reading of 30 volts. (The meters are calibrated to read correctly the voltage across their terminals regardless of how it is obtained.)

The Thévenin equivalent circuit for the device is shown in Fig. 4–10(b). The problem is to find the open-circuit voltage which existed before the meters were placed across the terminals. From the first meter reading,

$$E = \frac{100,000}{100,000 + R} \times E_{oc} = 45 \text{ volts,} \qquad (4\text{–}13)$$

and from the second,

$$E = \frac{50,000}{50,000 + R} \times E_{oc} = 30 \text{ volts.} \qquad (4\text{–}14)$$

A simultaneous solution of Eqs. (4–13) and (4–14) gives the required value:

$$E_{oc} = 90 \text{ volts.}$$

A similar application of Norton's theorem can be made to the case of a nonideal ammeter. Other applications of Thévenin's and Norton's theorems will be given later.

4–4 More general equivalences

We observed previously that a perfect voltage source can be obtained in the laboratory by measuring the voltage and adjusting it to the desired value. A similar remark holds for a perfect current course. These statements are examples of more general equivalences, involving the substitution of sources for network elements and the recognition of symmetry in the network which facilitates the substitution process.

The substitution theorem. A statement of the substitution theorem is the following:

A known voltage in a circuit can be replaced by an ideal voltage source, and a known current can be replaced by an ideal current source.

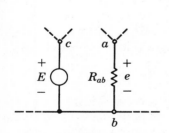

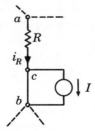

(a) Voltage source substitution   (b) Current source substitution   **Figure 4–11.** The substitution theorem.

In order to prove this theorem we will consider a resistance R_{ab} connected between points a and b in a network, as shown in Fig. 4–11(a). A voltage source is connected to point b. If the voltage rise from b to c is the same as the rise from b to a, the points c and a will be at the same potential. They can be shorted together. The resistance R_{ab} is then in parallel with a voltage source and can be removed, so far as the rest of the circuit is concerned. The net result is the replacement of the resistance by a voltage source with the same value of voltage across it.

A similar argument holds for the current source in Fig. 4–11(b). Suppose that a current i_R is flowing in the resistance from point a to point b. A current source can be inserted in parallel with the short-circuit between points c and b without changing anything. If the current source I is the same as the current i_R, there will be no current in the connection between b and c, and it can be removed. The resistance R is then in series with the current source and it can be removed so far as the rest of the circuit is concerned. The net result is that the resistance R has been replaced by an ideal current source with the same value of current through it.

The substitution theorem is surprisingly useful in many circuit applications. As an example of the sort of reasoning which it fosters we will solve the circuit problem of Fig. 4–12(a) for the output voltage E_3.

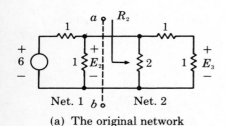

(a) The original network

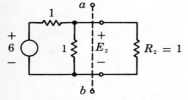

(b) Computation of voltage E_2 for the substitution theorem

Figure 4–12. A solution by the substitution theorem.

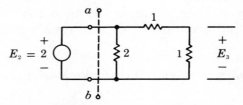

(c) A solution by the substitution theorem

The part of the network to the right of the line a–b is replaced by an equivalent resistance R_2, as shown in Fig. 4–12(b). The voltage across it is computed to be 2 volts. By the substitution theorem this voltage can be replaced by a voltage source, as shown in Fig. 4–12(c), and from this circuit the desired output voltage is obtained as

$$E_3 = 1 \text{ volt.}$$

The importance of the reasoning process used here cannot be overestimated. It leads directly to the partitioning of complicated circuits into smaller sub-sections which can be solved by inspection. Most vacuum-tube and transistor circuits, for example, are solved in this fashion.

Symmetry. When a network possesses inherent symmetry it is often possible to deduce certain currents or voltages by inspection and to apply the substitution theorem. Zero current and zero voltage are particularly interesting since a zero-current source is an open circuit and a zero-voltage source is a short circuit. Four of the possibilities are:

1. *A branch with no voltage across it.* Such a branch can be replaced by a short circuit without altering the rest of the network.

2. *A branch with no current in it.* Such a branch can be removed without altering the rest of the network.

3. *Two nodes at the same potential.* A short circuit can be placed between these nodes without altering the rest of the circuit.

4. *Two adjacent mesh currents which are clockwise and equal.* The branch between the two meshes can be opened up because it has no current in it.

The balanced bridge shown in Fig. 4–13 is an example of a symmetrical circuit. We will find the input resistance making use of each of the four possibilities listed above.

Method 1. Branch voltage. The branch R has no voltage across it and can therefore be replaced by a short circuit. This conclusion is easiest to reach by noting that if R is removed from the circuit the voltages at points a and b are equal. If R is replaced by a short circuit the resistance between c and d is

$$R_{cd} = \frac{2 \times 1}{2 + 1} + \frac{2 \times 1}{2 + 1} = \tfrac{4}{3} \text{ ohms.}$$

Method 2. Branch current. The currents i_1 and i_2 are equal and hence the current through the branch R is zero and the branch can be removed. To see that $i_1 = i_2$, we reverse the source. Because of the symmetry, the current i_{da} which then flows must have the same magnitude as the original current i_1. Thus

$$(i_{da})_{\text{source reversed}} = (i_1)_{\text{original source}}.$$

Changing the source to its original polarity would reverse i_{da} and give

$$(i_{da})_{\text{original source}} = -(i_1)_{\text{original source}}.$$

However, by definition i_{da} is the negative of i_2 and hence

$$i_2 = i_1.$$

If R is replaced by an open circuit the resistance between c and d is

$$R_{cd} = \frac{2 \times 4}{2 + 4} = \tfrac{4}{3} \text{ ohms.}$$

Method 3. Node voltage. The node voltages e_a and e_b are equal and hence a short circuit can be placed between them. To prove that e_a and e_b are equal, we must first show that $i_1 = i_2$, as in the previous section. Then, since the resistances are equal, $e_a = E/2$.

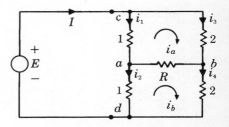

Figure 4–13. A symmetrical bridge circuit.

Similarly, $i_3 = i_4$, and since the resistances are again equal, $e_b = E/2$, which is the same value as e_a.

Method 4. Mesh current. The mesh currents are equal and hence the current in R is zero and it may be replaced by an open circuit. To show that the mesh currents i_a and i_b are equal, we need only write the mesh equations:

$$i_a(4) - i_b(1) = I, \qquad -i_a(1) + i_b(4) = I.$$

The two equations are perfectly symmetrical and hence the two currents must be equal. (Symmetrical equations are a sufficient, but not a necessary, condition for the equality of the variables.)

Summary

Equivalent resistive branches

(a) Series

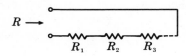

$$R = R_1 + R_2 + R_3 + \cdots$$

(b) Parallel

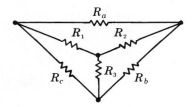

$$R = \frac{1}{1/R_1 + 1/R_2 + 1/R_3} \cdots$$

(c) Y–Δ

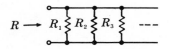

$$R_1 = \frac{R_a R_c}{R_a + R_b + R_c}$$

$$R_2 = \frac{R_a R_b}{R_a + R_b + R_c}$$

$$R_3 = \frac{R_b R_c}{R_a + R_b + R_c}$$

$$R_a = \frac{R_1 R_2 + R_2 R_3 + R_3 R_1}{R_3}$$

$$R_b = \frac{R_1 R_2 + R_2 R_3 + R_3 R_1}{R_1}$$

$$R_c = \frac{R_1 R_2 + R_2 R_3 + R_3 R_1}{R_2}$$

(d) General

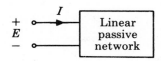

(1) Apply E and compute I
(2) Apply I and compute E

$$R = \frac{E}{I}$$

Equivalent source branches

Thévenin's theorem

"A two-terminal network with sources can be replaced by the open-circuit voltage in series with the input resistance of the dead network."

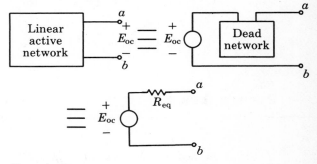

Norton's theorem

"A two-terminal network with sources can be replaced by the short-circuit current in parallel with the input resistance of the dead network."

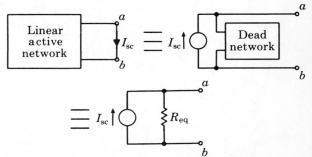

Source transformations

(a)

(b)

General equivalences

The substitution theorem

"A *known* voltage can be replaced by a voltage source, and a *known* current by a current source."

Symmetry

(a) Replace branches with no voltage by short circuits.

(b) Replace branches with no current by open circuits.

(c) Nodes at the same voltage can be shorted.

(d) Meshes with the same mesh currents can be opened.

References

Most elementary textbooks on circuit theory discuss equivalent two-terminal networks. The treatment of symmetry here is original. References for special topics are listed below.

1. M. B. REED, *Alternating-Current Circuit Theory*, Harper, New York, 1948. Reed gives a particularly complete discussion of the theorems of electric circuits, including several which we have not included. All of the proofs are by matrices and determinants and in steady-state ac notation.

2. E. A. GUILLEMIN, *Introductory Circuit Theory*, John Wiley, New York, 1953. Guillemin gives a very general discussion of Y–Δ transformations in terms of mesh and node equations. There is no formal discussion of the substitution theorem, but it is used in a number of examples. Some discussion of symmetry is given.

3. H. H. SKILLING, *Electrical Engineering Circuits*, John Wiley, New York, 1957. Skilling discusses most of the theorems given by Reed and the proofs are more elementary.

4. MIT EE Staff, *Electric Circuits*, John Wiley, New York, 1943. In this standard text it is noted that Helmholtz really discovered Thévenin's theorem! Norton's theorem is not explicitly stated.

5. W. B. BOAST, *Principles of Electric and Magnetic Circuits*, Harper, New York, 1950. Boast gives a particularly good discussion of Y–Δ transformations and is one of the few authors to include the general star-to-mesh transformation.

Exercises

SECTION 4-2

1. Find the input resistance of the network in Fig. 4–14 by applying series-parallel formulas.

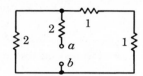

Figure 4-14

2. Find the equivalent resistance of the network of Fig. 4–14 at the terminals *a–b* by (a) applying a voltage source and writing mesh equations, (b) using a current source as the excitation and writing mesh equations to solve for the unknowns, (c) applying a current source and writing node equations to solve for the unknowns, (d) applying a voltage source and writing node equations to find the unknowns.

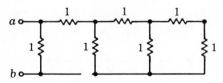

Figure 4-15

3. Find the resistance of the network in Fig. 4–15 considered as a branch between points *a* and *b*.

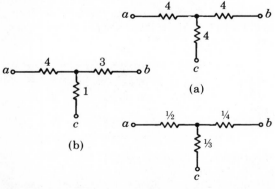

(a)

(b)

(c)

Figure 4-16

4. Change the networks of Fig. 4–16 from Y to Δ, and change the networks of Fig. 4–17 from Δ to Y.

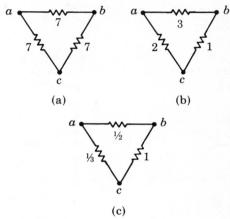

(a)   (b)

(c)

Figure 4-17

5. Reduce the network of Fig. 4–18 to a three-resistance Y between the points *a*, *b*, and *c*.

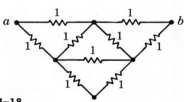

Figure 4-18

6. Reduce the network of Fig. 4–19 to a single resistance by means of series-parallel and Y–Δ transformations.

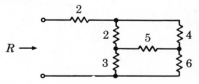

Figure 4-19

7. Find the input resistance of the circuit of Fig. 4–20 by using several Δ–Y transformations.

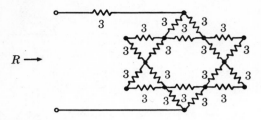

Figure 4–20

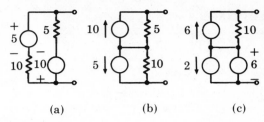

Figure 4–23

8. Find the input resistance of the circuit of Fig. 4–21 by means of series-parallel and Y–Δ transformations which reduce the network to a single resistance.

11. Convert the branches in Fig. 4–24 to single current sources in parallel with single resistors.

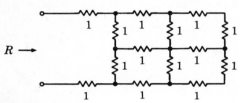

Figure 4–21

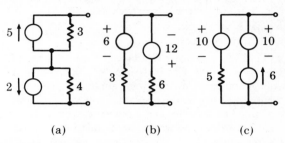

(a)   (b)   (c)

Figure 4–24

SECTION 4–3

9. Write the volt-ampere equations of the source branches in Fig. 4–22.

12. Find both the Thévenin and Norton equivalent circuits for the network of Fig. 4–25 at the terminals a–b.

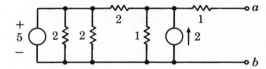

Figure 4–25

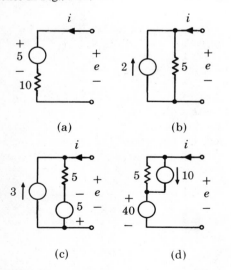

(a)   (b)

(c)   (d)

Figure 4–22

13. Give the Thévenin and the Norton equivalent circuits which hold for the terminal pair a–b in the circuit of Fig. 4–26.

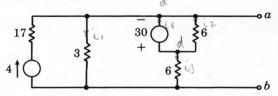

Figure 4–26

10. Convert the branches in Fig. 4–23 to single voltage sources in series with single resistors.

14. Directly from the circuit of Fig. 4–27 compute the open-circuit voltage, the short-circuit current,

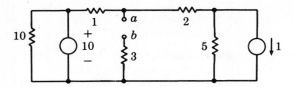

Figure 4-27

and the equivalent resistance at the terminal pair
a–b. From these give the Thévenin and Norton
equivalent circuits.

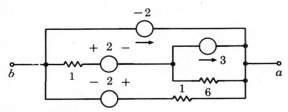

Figure 4-28

15. Obtain the Thévenin equivalent circuit at the
terminals a–b in the network of Fig. 4–28 by (a) a
direct computation of the open-circuit voltage and
the equivalent resistance, (b) a reduction of the network to a single branch by means of series-parallel
formulas and voltage-to-current source transformations.

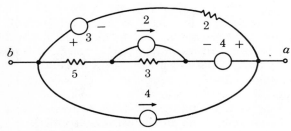

Figure 4-29

16. Obtain the Norton equivalent circuit at the
terminals a–b in the network of Fig. 4–29 by (a) a
direct computation of the short-circuit current and
the equivalent resistance, (b) a reduction of the network to a single branch by means of series-parallel
and current-to-voltage source transformations.

SECTION 4-4

17. (a) Solve for the input resistance of network B
in Fig. 4–30. (b) Find the voltage E_2 when network

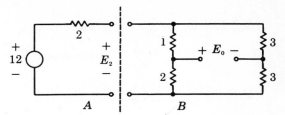

Figure 4-30

B is connected to network A. (c) Find the voltage
E_0 by means of the substitution theorem.

18. In Fig. 4–31, (a) find the input resistance of network B, (b) find the voltage E_2 when network B is
connected to network A, (c) find the current I_0 by
means of the substitution theorem.

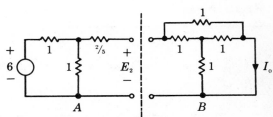

Figure 4-31

19. In Fig. 4–32, find the voltage e_a by finding the
equivalent resistances of the two sections of the network, and then solve for the voltage e_0 by means of
the substitution theorem.

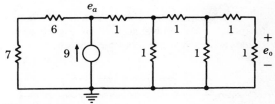

Figure 4-32

20. Find the resistance of the circuit of Fig. 4–33.

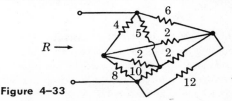

Figure 4-33

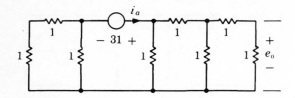

Figure 4–34

21. In Fig. 4–34, find the current i_a by finding the equivalent resistances of the two sections of the net- work, and then solve for the voltage e_0 by means of the substitution theorem.

22. A cube is constructed by soldering together twelve 1-ohm resistors to represent the twelve edges. Find the resistance between any two adjacent corners.

23. For the cube of Exercise 22, find the resistance between any pair of diagonally opposite corners.

24. For the cube of Exercise 22, find the resistance between any two diagonally opposite corners of any one face of the cube.

Problems

1. Find the input resistance of the network of Fig. 4–35.

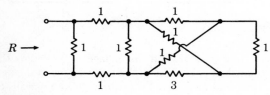

Figure 4–35

2. Use the series-parallel and Y–Δ transformations to reduce the "double ladder" of Fig. 4–36 to a single resistance at the input terminals.

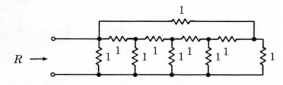

Figure 4–36

3. Find the input resistance of the circuit of Fig. 4–37 by assuming a voltage of 1 v across the right-hand resistance and working backward to the input ter- minals. Verify your answer by solving the same problem as a symmetrical network.

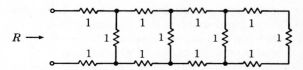

Figure 4–37

4. In the laboratory, certain measurements are made on the "black box" of Fig. 4–38. The resistance at the input terminals is found to be 5 ohms. The re- sistance at the output terminals is found to be 10 ohms. (In both cases the other terminals are left open-circuited.) When a voltage source of 5 v is applied to E_1, the output voltage E_2 reads 1 v. If a 6-v source with an internal resistance of 1 ohm were applied to the input terminals, what output voltage E_2 would be obtained?

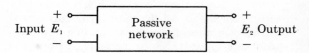

Figure 4–38

5. When a network is symmetrical but the excita- tion is not, it is usually possible to resolve the excitation into symmetrical and antisymmetrical

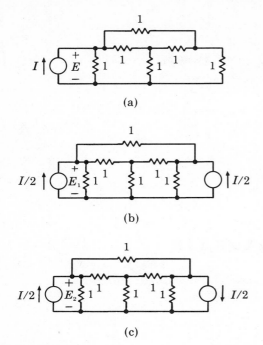

(a)

(b)

(c)

Figure 4–39

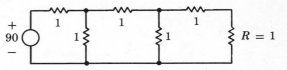

Figure 4–40

7. In the circuit of Fig. 4–41 a resistance of 1 ohm is added in parallel with the output resistance R. Use the substitution theorem to find the corresponding change in the source current.

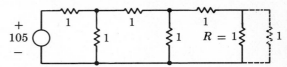

Figure 4–41

8. (a) An ammeter with resistance R_m is used to measure the current in a circuit. The resistance looking back into the network at the terminals of the ammeter is R. Use the substitution theorem to show that the correct current reading (i.e., the reading of a zero-resistance ammeter) is given by

$$I \text{ (correct)} = I \text{ (meter)} (1 + R_m/R).$$

(b) A voltmeter with resistance R_m is used to measure the voltage in a circuit. The resistance looking back into the network at the terminals of the voltmeter is R. Use the substitution theorem to show that the correct voltage reading (i.e., the reading of an infinite-resistance voltmeter) is given by

$$E \text{ (correct)} = E \text{ (meter)} (1 + R/R_m).$$

components. The network of Fig. 4–39(a) is an example. Show that the voltage E in Fig. 4–39(a) is the sum of the voltage E_1 in Fig. 4–39(b) and E_2 in Fig. 4–39(c). By finding the voltages E_1 and E_2, obtain the input resistance to the original circuit.

6. In the circuit of Fig. 4–40 the resistance R is changed from 1 ohm to 2 ohms. Use the substitution theorem to find the change in source current caused by this change in resistance.

CHAPTER **5**

TWO-TERMINAL-PAIR NETWORKS

Love of an idea is love of God. Understanding is love.

FRANK LLOYD WRIGHT

5–1 Introduction

In this chapter we will examine the two-terminal-pair network. Linearity and superposition make it the most general linear network.

The complete description of a two-terminal-pair network involves more than one stimulus-response relationship. If we apply a stimulus at one of the terminal pairs we produce a response at that terminal pair and the second one. Excitation of the second terminal pair involves two more relationships. Apparently a total of four stimulus-response relationships are involved. For most networks two of the four are identical, however, by the *reciprocity theorem.*

When the network is resistive the stimulus-response relationships are simply equivalent resistances, and therefore a two-terminal-pair resistive network can be reduced to three equivalent resistances. The Ohm's law relationships between the voltages and currents at the two terminal pairs also involve three constants. Three elements are sufficient if the input and output terminals have a common ground, or if the network can be reduced to such a form. Six elements are required for the general network in which the input and output terminals must be separated. The three-element cases are called three-terminal or unbalanced networks and the six-element cases are called four-terminal or balanced networks. Fortunately, most practical networks are unbalanced, or can be treated as if they were.

5–2 The reciprocity theorem

The reciprocity theorem concerns the stimulus-response relationships of the two-terminal-pair network shown in Fig. 5–1. Let us suppose that we have excited the network with a voltage source at E_1 and a voltage source at E_2. We can then write a set of mesh

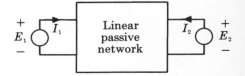

Figure 5–1. Two-terminal-pair network for which reciprocity holds.

equations to describe the system as follows:

$$i_1 r_{11} - i_2 r_{12} - i_3 r_{13} - \ \cdots \ -i_n r_{1n} = E_1,$$

$$-i_1 r_{12} + i_2 r_{22} - i_3 r_{23} - \ \cdots \ -i_n r_{2n} = E_2,$$

$$-i_1 r_{13} - i_2 r_{23} + i_3 r_{33} - \ \cdots \ -i_n r_{3n} = 0, \qquad (5\text{–}1)$$

$$\vdots$$

$$-i_1 r_{1n} - i_2 r_{2n} - r_3 r_{3n} - \ \cdots \ +i_n r_{nn} = 0.$$

The only two sources are E_1 and E_2. First of all, we will let $E_2 = 0$ and compute the current i_2, which then flows in the short circuit. It is

$$i_2 = \frac{-E_1}{\Delta} \begin{vmatrix} -r_{12} & -r_{23} & \cdots & -r_{2n} \\ -r_{13} & r_{33} & \cdots & -r_{3n} \\ \vdots & & & \vdots \\ -r_{1n} & -r_{3n} & \cdots & r_{nn} \end{vmatrix}, \qquad (5\text{–}2)$$

where Δ is the determinant of the coefficients on the left side of the equation. Now we will let $E_1 = 0$ and compute the current i_1, which flows in it in response to the voltage E_2:

$$i_1 = \frac{-E_2}{\Delta} \begin{vmatrix} -r_{12} & -r_{13} & \cdots & -r_{1n} \\ -r_{23} & r_{33} & \cdots & -r_{3n} \\ \vdots & & & \vdots \\ -r_{2n} & -r_{3n} & \cdots & r_{nn} \end{vmatrix}. \qquad (5\text{–}3)$$

The determinants of Eqs. (5–2) and (5–3) are the same except for an interchange of the first row and first column. It is easy to verify from the Laplace expansion for a determinant that this interchange does not change the value of the determinant, and hence that the two determinants are equal. A necessary condition for this equality, of course, is the symmetry of the original determinant of the coefficients. The element between mesh 1 and mesh 2 must look the same when viewed from either mesh. All resistances, of course, meet this requirement, but not all network elements do. Those that do are called *bilateral* elements and those that do not are called unilateral elements.* When the two determinants are equal we have shown that the current produced at i_2 per volt at E_1 is the same as the current produced at i_1 per volt at E_2. An alternative statement of the reciprocity theorem is:

> *An ideal voltage source and an ideal ammeter in any two branches of a passive network which is linear and bilateral can be interchanged without changing the numbers read on either of them.*

———————

* Many nonlinear elements are not bilateral, but the only linear element which is not bilateral is the gyrator.

An analogous argument can be carried out with current sources as the excitation for the network and voltages as the responses, and the following conclusion can be reached:

A current source and a voltmeter across any two node-pairs in a passive network which is linear and bilateral can be interchanged without changing the numbers read on either of them.

These two statements constitute the *reciprocity theorem*. It is easy to remember, since the elements which are interchanged must have the same internal impedance. The voltage source and the ammeter have zero resistance. The current source and the voltmeter have infinite resistance.

Reciprocity in terms of r-parameters. Let us return to our central problem of an equivalent circuit for the general two-terminal-pair network, as shown in Fig. 5–2. If we consider the two currents as the excitations and the two voltages as the responses, we can write by means of the superposition theorem

$$E_1 = r_{11}I_1 + r_{12}I_2,$$
$$E_2 = r_{21}I_1 + r_{22}I_2, \qquad (5\text{–}4)$$

where the *r*-parameters are constants of proportionality [in general not the same as those in Eq. (5–1)] obtained by computing the response due to a unit value of each source, with the other source dead. Thus

$$r_{11} = \frac{E_1}{I_1} \qquad \text{with} \qquad I_2 = 0,$$

$$r_{12} = \frac{E_1}{I_2} \qquad \text{with} \qquad I_1 = 0,$$

$$r_{21} = \frac{E_2}{I_1} \qquad \text{with} \qquad I_2 = 0, \qquad (5\text{–}5)$$

$$r_{22} = \frac{E_2}{I_2} \qquad \text{with} \qquad I_1 = 0.$$

Since a zero-current source is simply an open circuit, the resistance r_{11} is the input resistance of the network with the output open-circuited. The resistance r_{22} is the output resistance of the network with the input open-circuited. The constant r_{12} is the voltage E_1 produced at the open-circuited input terminals per ampere of output current I_2, and the constant r_{21} is the voltage E_2 produced at the open-circuited output terminals per ampere of input current I_1. By the reciprocity theorem these two constants are equal, or

$$r_{12} = r_{21}, \qquad (5\text{–}6)$$

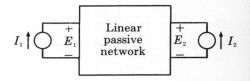

Figure 5–2. Two-terminal-pair network with current excitation.

and we can write the volt-ampere relationships (or Ohm's law equations) for the two-terminal-pair network as

$$E_1 = r_{11}I_1 + r_{12}I_2,$$

$$E_2 = r_{12}I_1 + r_{22}I_2. \qquad (5\text{–}7)$$

Usually the r's are obtained from Eq. (5–5) by direct calculation. Then Eq. (5–7) represents a complete algebraic characterization of the device, so far as its effect on the rest of the circuit is concerned.* As written, it describes the voltages produced by currents into the two terminal pairs. Just as Ohm's law is valid for both types of excitation, however, so is Eq. (5–7). If the voltages are the input excitations, the currents can be obtained by solving the equations. The three constants r_{11}, r_{12}, and r_{22} completely describe the network behavior for any type of excitation.

When the network is resistive, Eq. (5–7) represents a three-resistance network, as shown in Fig. 5–3. From the equations, we find that the mutual resistance R_3 between the two meshes in the network is equal to r_{12}:

$$R_3 = r_{12}. \qquad (5\text{–}8)$$

The total self-resistance in mesh 1 is r_{11}, and therefore

$$R_1 = r_{11} - r_{12}. \qquad (5\text{–}9)$$

Similarly,

$$R_2 = r_{22} - r_{12}. \qquad (5\text{–}10)$$

The equivalent T-circuit is perfectly general in a mathematical sense. However, in a physical sense it is not, since any of the resistances given by Eqs. (5–8), (5–9), and (5–10) can turn out to be negative. A negative value of R_3 results if the output voltage is opposite in polarity from the input voltage, and a negative value of R_1 or R_2 occurs when r_{12} is larger than r_{11} or r_{22}. We need not be disturbed by the negative r's, since we do not have to build the circuit.† For purposes of computation these r's are just as good as positive ones; they mean only that the T-equivalent circuit is not the most general form for a two-terminal-pair passive network. Later we will show that the lattice is.

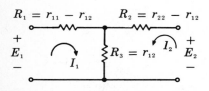

Figure 5–3. Two-terminal-pair equivalent T-circuit.

---

* Provided that the input and the output terminals have a common ground or can be treated as if they did.

† Negative resistances are not physically realizable in passive circuits; they represent sources of energy and hence require "active" circuits.

Reciprocity in terms of the g-parameters. If the voltages are the excitations in Fig. 5–2 and the currents are the responses, by means of the superposition theorem we can write

$$I_1 = g_{11}E_1 + g_{12}E_2,$$
$$I_2 = g_{21}E_1 + g_{22}E_2, \qquad (5\text{–}11)$$

where the g-parameters are coefficients of proportionality between the individual sources and the individual responses, given by

$$g_{11} = \frac{I_1}{E_1} \quad \text{with} \quad E_2 = 0,$$

$$g_{12} = \frac{I_1}{E_2} \quad \text{with} \quad E_1 = 0,$$

$$\qquad\qquad\qquad\qquad\qquad\qquad\qquad (5\text{–}12)$$

$$g_{21} = \frac{I_2}{E_1} \quad \text{with} \quad E_2 = 0,$$

$$g_{22} = \frac{I_2}{E_2} \quad \text{with} \quad E_1 = 0.$$

The constant g_{11} is the input admittance of the network with a short circuit on the output terminal pair. It should be observed particularly that g_{11} is not the reciprocal of r_{11} of Eq. (5–5), since the output terminals are open-circuited for the measurement of r_{11}. Similarly, g_{22} is the admittance at the output terminal pair. The constant g_{12} is current produced at the input per volt applied to the output, and the constant g_{21} is the current produced at the output per volt at the input. These two quantities are equal by the reciprocity theorem:

$$g_{12} = g_{21}. \qquad (5\text{–}13)$$

As a result of Eq. (5–13), the general Ohm's law relationships of Eq. (5–11) can be simplified to

$$I_1 = g_{11}E_1 + g_{12}E_2,$$
$$I_2 = g_{12}E_1 + g_{22}E_2. \qquad (5\text{–}14)$$

Equation (5–14) represents an alternate form of the volt-ampere equations of a two-terminal-pair network given in Eq. (5–7). It is equally valid and equally general. Although we derived it by assuming the voltages as excitations, it is true if the currents are the excitations. The equivalent π-circuit of Fig. 5–4 represents Eq. (5–14). From the equation, the mutual conductance is g_{12}, and hence the resistance R_b between the two nodes is $-1/g_{12}$, or

$$R_b = \frac{-1}{g_{12}}. \qquad (5\text{–}15)$$

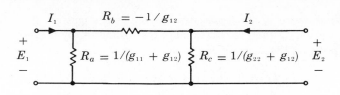

Figure 5–4. Two-terminal-pair equivalent π-circuit.

The negative sign occurs because of the direction assumed for I_2. The total conductance at node 1 is g_{11}. The mutual conductance is $-g_{12}$. The conductance to ground at node 1 is therefore $g_{11} + g_{12}$, and thus

$$R_a = \frac{1}{g_{11} + g_{12}}. \tag{5–16}$$

Similarly, the total conductance at node 2 is g_{22} and the net conductance to ground is $g_{22} + g_{12}$. Thus

$$R_c = \frac{1}{g_{22} + g_{12}}. \tag{5–17}$$

The π-circuit is no more general than the T-circuit. Any of the resistances given by Eqs. (5–15), (5–16), and (5–17) can turn out to be negative.

The T-circuit of Fig. 5–3 and the π-circuit of Fig. 5–4 are general forms of the Y- and Δ-circuits, and they are related by the Y–Δ transformation.

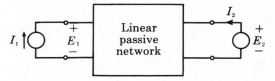

Figure 5–5. The hybrid parameters.

Reciprocity in terms of h-parameters. The r-parameters have the dimensions of resistance and the g-parameters have the dimensions of conductance. Many other sets of parameters are possible among which the h- or hybrid parameters are perhaps the most useful. To define the hybrid parameters the network is excited by means of a current source at the input and a voltage source at the output, as shown in Fig. 5–5, and the responses are the input voltage and the output current.

By means of the superposition theorem we can write

$$\begin{aligned} E_1 &= h_{11}I_1 + h_{12}E_2, \\ I_2 &= h_{21}I_1 + h_{22}E_2, \end{aligned} \tag{5–18}$$

where we find that

$$h_{11} = \frac{E_1}{I_1} \quad \text{with} \quad E_2 = 0,$$

$$h_{12} = \frac{E_1}{E_2} \quad \text{with} \quad I_1 = 0,$$

$$\text{(5–19)}$$

$$h_{21} = \frac{I_2}{I_1} \quad \text{with} \quad E_2 = 0,$$

$$h_{22} = \frac{I_2}{E_2} \quad \text{with} \quad I_1 = 0.$$

The parameter h_{11} is the input resistance with a short circuit on the output terminal. The parameter h_{12} is the reverse voltage gain obtained by applying a voltage at the output and computing the resultant open-circuit voltage at the input. The parameter h_{21} is the forward current gain obtained by applying a current at the input and computing the resultant short-circuit current at the output. The parameter h_{22} is the output admittance with an open circuit at the input. By means of the reciprocity theorem it is a simple matter to show that $h_{21} = -h_{12}$.

The equivalent circuit for the h-parameters of Eq. (5–27) is shown in Fig. 5–6. The equations for this circuit are identical with Eqs. (5–18). The resistive elements are shown in ohms and the voltage and current ratios appear as sources.

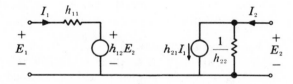

Figure 5–6. Equivalent circuit for h-parameters.

There are obvious relationships between the h-parameters and the r- and g-parameters, which can be found by manipulating the h-parameter equations into the form of the r-parameter equations or the g-parameter equations. Usually a single set of parameters is used for a given problem, however, and these relationships are academic.

Example. The h-parameters will be found for the circuit of Fig. 5–7(a). The short-circuit input resistance is

$$h_{11} = 1 + \tfrac{1}{2} = \tfrac{3}{2} \text{ ohms.}$$

The open-circuit reverse voltage gain is

$$h_{12} = \tfrac{1}{2}.$$

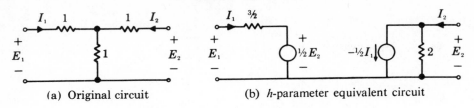

Figure 5-7. An example of h-parameters.

The short-circuit forward current gain is

$$h_{21} = -\tfrac{1}{2}.$$

The open-circuit output admittance is

$$h_{22} = \tfrac{1}{2}\,\text{mho}.$$

The h-parameter equivalent circuit is shown in Fig. 5–7(b). It is not an accident that $h_{21} = -h_{12}$ but rather a consequence of reciprocity.

5–3 Equivalent circuits for three-terminal networks

Many two-terminal-pair networks have a common ground between the input and the output, as shown in Fig. 5–8. These networks have in reality only three terminals. They constitute an important sub-class, for which the r-, g-, or h-parameters provide a complete description.

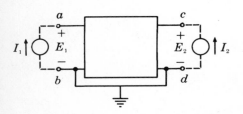

Figure 5-8. Three-terminal network.

Equivalent T-networks. Example 1. A two-terminal-pair network which can be reduced to three equivalent resistances is shown in Fig. 5–9(a). The r-parameters will be obtained and from them the equivalent T. The constant r_{11} is the input resistance of the network with the output terminals open-circuited. It can be obtained by applying an input of 1 amp and measuring the input voltage which it produces. Here

$$r_{11} = \frac{E_1}{I_1} = \tfrac{5}{3}\,\text{ohms.}$$

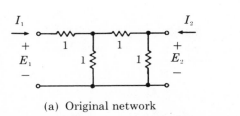

(a) Original network

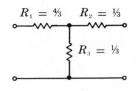

(b) Equivalent network

Figure 5-9. Network conversion by r-parameters.

The constant r_{12} is obtained by applying an input current of 1 amp and computing the output voltage with the second pair of terminals open-circuited. By the reciprocity theorem, the transfer resistances in both directions are the same. Here

$$r_{12} = \frac{E_2}{I_1} = \tfrac{1}{3} \text{ ohm.}$$

The constant r_{22} is the input resistance at the second terminal pair of the network with an open circuit at the first terminal pair:

$$r_{22} = \frac{E_2}{I_2} = \tfrac{2}{3} \text{ ohm.}$$

The equivalent T-network can be synthesized directly from Eqs. (5–8), (5–9), and (5–10). The result is shown in Fig. 5–9(b). The resistance values are given by

$$R_1 = r_{11} - r_{12} = \tfrac{5}{3} - \tfrac{1}{3} = \tfrac{4}{3} \text{ ohm,}$$

$$R_2 = r_{22} - r_{12} = \tfrac{2}{3} - \tfrac{1}{3} = \tfrac{1}{3} \text{ ohm,}$$

$$R_3 = r_{12} = \tfrac{1}{3} \text{ ohm.}$$

Example 2. A second example of reduction to a T-circuit is shown in Fig. 5–10(a). For ease in computation the lattice form of Fig. 5–10(a) is redrawn as a bridge in Fig. 5–10(b). In this circuit each branch has a resistance of 4 ohms and the input resistance with an open circuit at the output is therefore

$$r_{11} = 2 \text{ ohms.}$$

The output resistance with an open circuit at the input is the parallel

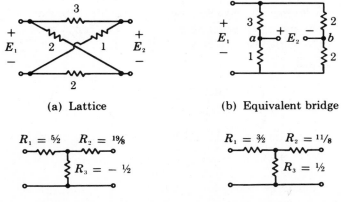

(a) Lattice   (b) Equivalent bridge

(c) Equivalent T   (d) Modified T

Figure 5–10. The conversion of a lattice to a T.

combination of 5 and 3 ohms, or

$$r_{22} = \tfrac{15}{8} \text{ ohms.}$$

To obtain the transfer resistance a current of 1 amp is applied at the input. It divides equally between the two paths, and the voltage at a is therefore $\tfrac{1}{2}$ volt and at b is 1 volt. The output voltage is $-\tfrac{1}{2}$ volt and

$$r_{12} = \frac{E_2}{I_1} = -\tfrac{1}{2} \text{ ohm.}$$

The equivalent circuit is shown in Fig. 5–10(c). The resistance values are

$$R_1 = r_{11} - r_{12} = 2 + \tfrac{1}{2} = \tfrac{5}{2} \text{ ohms,}$$

$$R_2 = r_{22} - r_{12} = \tfrac{15}{8} + \tfrac{1}{2} = \tfrac{19}{8} \text{ ohms,}$$

$$R_3 = r_{12} = -\tfrac{1}{2} \text{ ohm.}$$

The circuit of Fig. 5–10(c) is a mathematical equivalent of the original circuit. The negative sign in the mutual element is a consequence of the polarity chosen for the output. If the assumed direction of E_2 is reversed, the sign of r_{12} is reversed but the other parameters stay the same. Then

$$R_1 = r_{11} - r_{12} = 2 - \tfrac{1}{2} = \tfrac{3}{2} \text{ ohms,}$$

$$R_2 = r_{22} - r_{12} = \tfrac{15}{8} - \tfrac{1}{2} = \tfrac{11}{8} \text{ ohms,}$$

$$R_3 = r_{12} = \tfrac{1}{2} \text{ ohm.}$$

The new equivalent circuit is shown in Fig. 5–10(d). The only difference between the circuits of Fig. 5–10(c) and (d) is the polarity of the output voltage in response to a positive stimulus at the input. Bridge, or lattice, structures have this flexibility in the polarity of the output voltage because they are four-terminal networks. A T-circuit is a three-terminal network, and can achieve this generality only by the use of a negative resistance.

Figure 5–11. Network conversion by g-parameters.

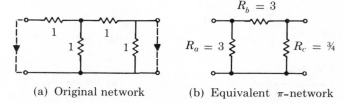

(a) Original network   (b) Equivalent π–network

Equivalent π-networks. The network of Fig. 5–11(a) is to be reduced to an equivalent π-circuit. The constant g_{11} is the input conductance of the network with a short circuit at the output terminal pair. It can be obtained by applying a voltage of 1 volt at the input and computing the resulting input current. Here,

$$g_{11} = \frac{I_1}{E_1} = \tfrac{2}{3} \text{ mho.}$$

The constant g_{12} is the current in the short circuit at terminal pair 2 when 1 volt is applied to terminal pair 1. It is called the short-circuit transfer conductance, and is, of course, the same for both network directions, by the reciprocity theorem. Here,

$$g_{12} = \frac{I_2}{E_1} = -\tfrac{1}{3} \text{ mho.}$$

The negative sign is a consequence of the assumed polarity of the current I_2 which is into the network at the output terminal pair. For three-terminal networks the current I_2 which flows in response to a positive value of 1 volt at the input will always be negative, and hence g_{12} will always be negative. For four-terminal networks it can have either polarity. The constant g_{22} is similar to g_{11}. It is the output short-circuit conductance of the network. It can be computed by applying 1 volt to the output terminal pair and a short circuit to the input terminal pair and finding the current which flows from the source by reducing the network to a single equivalent resistance or conductance. Here,

$$g_{22} = \tfrac{5}{3} \text{ mhos.}$$

The node equations for the equivalent network are thus

$$\tfrac{2}{3}E_1 - \tfrac{1}{3}E_2 = I_1,$$
$$-\tfrac{1}{3}E_1 + \tfrac{5}{3}E_2 = I_2.$$

The network synthesized from these equations is shown in Fig. 5–11(b). The resistance values are

$$R_a = \frac{1}{g_{11} + g_{12}} = \frac{1}{\tfrac{2}{3} - \tfrac{1}{3}} = 3 \text{ ohms,}$$

$$R_b = \frac{-1}{g_{12}} = \frac{-1}{-\tfrac{1}{3}} = 3 \text{ ohms,}$$

$$R_c = \frac{1}{g_{22} + g_{12}} = \frac{1}{\tfrac{5}{3} - \tfrac{1}{3}} = \tfrac{3}{4} \text{ ohm.}$$

The networks of Figs. 5–11(b) and 5–9 are two equivalent forms for the same network. They are, of course, related by the Y–Δ trans-

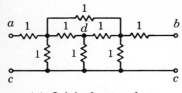

(a) Original network

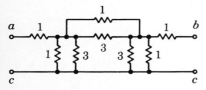

(b) Effect of Y–Δ transformation

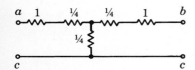

(c) Effect of Δ–Y transformation

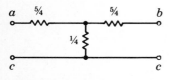

(d) Final Y or T network

Figure 5–12. The reduction of a three-terminal network to three resistances.

formation, and we could have obtained the π from the T in this fashion. In some problems the g-parameters are simpler than the r-parameters, and it is convenient to be able to use either of them.

The direct reduction of three-terminal networks. A three-terminal network can be reduced to a T or a π by means of series-parallel and Y–Δ transformations. Sometimes this method is easier than a direct computation of the r-, g-, or h-parameters.

Example. An example of direct reduction is shown in Fig. 5–12. The original network is shown in Fig. 5–12(a). In the first step, the node d is removed by a Y–Δ transformation resulting in the network of Fig. 5–12(b). The parallel resistances are then combined to give three $\frac{3}{4}$-ohm equivalents, and a Y–Δ transformation is applied to these to give the network of Fig. 5–12(c). Finally the series resistances are combined to give the T-network of Fig. 5–12(d).

5–4 Equivalent circuits for four-terminal networks

A four-terminal network is shown in Fig. 5–13. The input and output terminal pairs are completely separate and do not have a common ground point. As far as the relationship between the input and the output terminals are concerned the four-terminal network can be treated in the same fashion as a three-terminal network. If there are to be external connections between the input and output terminals, however, the third terminal pair, marked $E_3 I_3$, must be considered. Assuming the currents to be excitations and the voltages to be responses, we can write, by superposition,

$$E_1 = r_{11}I_1 + r_{12}I_2 + r_{13}I_3,$$
$$E_2 = r_{21}I_1 + r_{22}I_2 + r_{23}I_3, \qquad (5\text{–}20)$$
$$E_3 = r_{31}I_1 + r_{32}I_2 + r_{33}I_3,$$

where the r's are constants with the dimensions of resistance.

By the reciprocity theorem $r_{12} = r_{21}$, $r_{13} = r_{31}$, and $r_{23} = r_{32}$. The remaining six r-parameters describe the general four-terminal

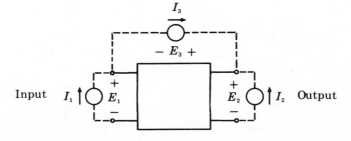

Figure 5–13. A four-terminal network.

network, and correspondingly a general four-terminal network can
be reduced to six resistances.

The symmetrical lattice. The symmetrical lattice shown in Fig.
5–14(a) is the most common four-terminal network. It has only
four of the six possible resistances. The other two would be across
the input and output terminal pairs. Furthermore the resistances
are equal in pairs, and thus there are only two independent parameters in a symmetrical lattice. When there are no external connections between the input and the output terminals the lattice can
be replaced by an equivalent three-terminal T- or π-network. The
constants of the T- and the π-network are most readily obtained
by redrawing the lattice in the form of the bridge circuit of Fig.
5–14(b).

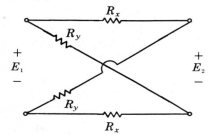
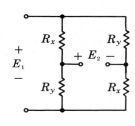

(a) A symmetrical lattice   (b) The equivalent bridge form   **Figure 5–14.** The symmetrical lattice.

The equivalent T-circuit. The r-parameters can be obtained by
inspection from the bridge circuit of Fig. 5–14(b). They are

$$r_{11} = r_{22} = \tfrac{1}{2}(R_x + R_y),$$

$$r_{12} = \tfrac{1}{2}(R_y - R_x). \tag{5-21}$$

An equivalent T-circuit can be obtained directly from the r-param-
eters. The circuit is shown in Fig. 5–15(a). The resistance values
are

$$R_1 = R_2 = r_{11} - r_{12} = R_x,$$

$$R_3 = r_{12} = \tfrac{1}{2}(R_y - R_x). \tag{5-22}$$

If R_x is greater than R_y the output voltage in Fig. 5–14(b) is nega-

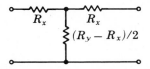
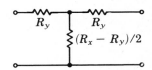

(a) T circuit for positive output $(R_y > R_x)$ (b) T circuit for negative output $(R_x > R_y)$

Figure 5–15. The T-circuit equivalents for the symmetrical lattice.

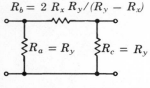

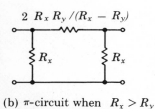

(a) π-circuit when $R_y > R_x$

(b) π-circuit when $R_x > R_y$

Figure 5–16. The equivalent circuits for the symmetrical lattice.

tive. The corresponding effect can be achieved in the T-circuit of Fig. 5–15(a) only by means of a negative shunt resistance. The lattice is more general than the T, since it has the option of either polarity of output voltage. If the polarity of the output voltage is not important, the alternative equivalent circuit of Fig. 5–15(b) can be used. The negative resistance is removed at the expense of changing the polarity of the output voltage.

The equivalent π-circuit. The g-parameters for the lattice circuit can be obtained from Fig. 5–14(b). They are

$$g_{11} = g_{22} = \frac{R_x + R_y}{2R_xR_y} = \tfrac{1}{2}(G_x + G_y),$$

$$g_{12} = \frac{R_x - R_y}{2R_xR_y} = \tfrac{1}{2}(G_y - G_x). \tag{5-23}$$

The equivalent π-circuit is determined directly from the g-values in Eq. (5–23). The circuit is shown in Fig. 5–16(a). The values are

$$R_a = R_c = \frac{1}{g_{11} + g_{12}} = R_y,$$

$$R_b = \frac{-1}{g_{12}} = \frac{2R_xR_y}{R_y - R_x}. \tag{5-24}$$

An alternative form of the circuit, obtained by reversing the polarity of the output voltage from the lattice, is shown in Fig. 5–16(b). As with the T-circuit, a negative resistance can be removed at the expense of reversing the polarity of the output voltage.

Lattices from unbalanced circuits. Symmetrical unbalanced circuits such as T's and π's can be converted into balanced lattice forms which will have the same input-output relationships. A T-circuit is shown in Fig. 5–17(a). The r-parameters for this circuit are

$$r_{11} = R_1 + R_2 = r_{22},$$

$$r_{12} = R_2. \tag{5-25}$$

The lattice arms can be obtained in terms of the r-parameters by means of Eqs. (5–21):

$$R_x = r_{11} - r_{12} = R_1,$$

$$R_y = r_{11} + r_{12} = R_1 + 2R_2. \tag{5-26}$$

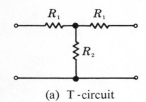

(a) T-circuit

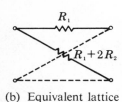

(b) Equivalent lattice

Figure 5–17. Lattice equivalent of a T-circuit.

The equivalent lattice is shown in Fig. 5–17(b). By convention the lower arms are shown by broken lines.

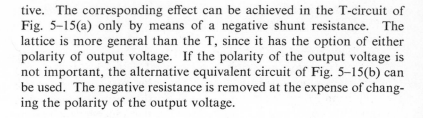

A symmetrical π-circuit and its equivalent lattice are shown in Fig. 5–18. The g-parameters are

$$g_{11} = \frac{1}{R_1} + \frac{1}{R_2} = g_{22},$$

$$g_{12} = \frac{1}{R_2}. \tag{5-27}$$

The lattice arms are obtained from Eqs. (5–23) as

$$G_x = g_{11} + g_{12} = \frac{1}{R_2} + \frac{2}{R_2} = \frac{2R_1 + R_2}{R_1 R_2},$$

$$G_y = g_{11} - g_{12} = \frac{1}{R_1}. \tag{5-28}$$

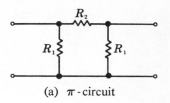

(a) π-circuit

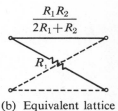

(b) Equivalent lattice

Figure 5–18. Lattice equivalent of a π-circuit.

The direct reduction of four-terminal networks. The direct reduction of three-terminal networks was accomplished by means of Y–Δ transformations. Four-terminal networks require an extended Y–Δ transformation called a star-mesh transformation. A general star, such as the one shown in Fig. 5–19(a), can be reduced to a general mesh which eliminates the node E_0, as shown in Fig. 5–19(b). The general mesh has a resistance between each pair of its nodes. In terms of the node voltages, the currents in the star are

$$i_1 = G_1(E_1 - E_0),$$
$$i_2 = G_2(E_2 - E_0),$$
$$i_3 = G_3(E_3 - E_0), \tag{5-29}$$
$$\vdots$$
$$i_n = G_n(E_n - E_0),$$

from which

$$i_1 + i_2 + \cdots + i_n = -(G_1 + G_2 + G_n + \cdots + G_n)E_0$$
$$+ G_1E_1 + G_2E_2 + G_3E_3 + \cdots + G_nE_n.$$

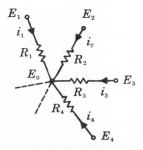

(a) General star

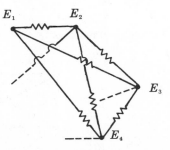

(b) General mesh

Figure 5–19. The general star-mesh transformation.

By Kirchhoff's law, the sum of the currents is equal to zero, and hence

$$E_0 = \frac{G_1}{\sum G} E_1 + \frac{G_2}{\sum G} E_2 + \cdots + \frac{G_n}{\sum G} E_n. \qquad (5\text{–}30)$$

From Eqs. (5–29) and (5–30) the current i_1 can be expressed in terms of the mesh node voltages:

$$i_1 = G_1 E_1 - G_1 E_0$$

$$= G_1 E_1 - \frac{G_1^2}{\sum G} E_1 - \frac{G_1 G_2}{\sum G} E_2 - \frac{G_1 G_3}{\sum G} E_3 - \cdots - \frac{G_1 G_n}{\sum G} E_n$$

$$= \frac{G_1 G_2}{\sum G} (E_1 - E_2) + \frac{G_1 G_2}{\sum G} (E_1 - E_2) + \cdots$$

$$+ \frac{G_1 G_n}{\sum G} (E_1 - E_n). \qquad (5\text{–}31)$$

Equation (5–31) represents a resistance between node E_1 and each of the other nodes, whose value is given by

$$G \text{ (mesh)} = \frac{\text{Product of adjacent } G\text{'s (star)}}{\text{Sum of the } G\text{'s (star)}}. \qquad (5\text{–}32)$$

The formula in Eq. (5–32) can be extended to the other nodes of the system by symmetry. It is identical in form to the Y–Δ formula given in Eq. (4–9). Observe, however, that there is no corresponding Δ–Y equation in the general case. The reason is obvious. If the general

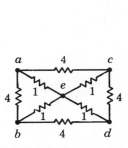

(a) Original network

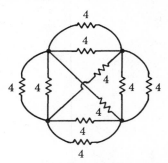

(b) Effect of star-mesh transformation

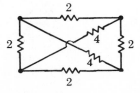

(c) Final equivalent

Figure 5–20. The reduction of a four-terminal network to six resistances.

star has n resistances, the equivalent mesh of Eq. (5–32) will have $n(n - 1)/2$ resistances.   Thus, four Y-resistances become six Δ-resistances.   The mesh-star transformation cannot exist, because six independent resistances cannot be compressed into four.

Example.   An example of the reduction of a four-terminal network is shown in Fig. 5–20(a).   The general star-mesh transformation is applied to remove the node e.   This result cannot be accomplished by Y–Δ transformations without removing one of the nodes a, b, c, d at the same time.   The four resistances emanating from e are replaced by six that join the four nodes a, b, c, and d in pairs.   Because of the symmetry the resistances are equal and are given by

$$G \text{ (mesh)} = \frac{\text{Product of adjacent } G\text{'s (star)}}{\text{Sum of the } G\text{'s (star)}} = \frac{1 \times 1}{4},$$

or

$$R \text{ (mesh)} = 4 \text{ ohms.}$$

The transformed network is shown in Fig. 5–20(b), and a six-resistance equivalent in Fig. 5–20(c).   Other four-terminal networks can be reduced in a similar fashion.   In general, the resulting network will contain six resistances, although in special cases it may contain fewer.

Summary

Reciprocity theorem. A current source and a voltmeter, or a voltage source and an ammeter can be interchanged in a circuit without any change in the readings.

The r-parameters

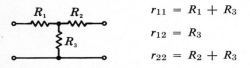

$$E_1 = r_{11}I_1 + r_{12}I_2$$
$$E_2 = r_{21}I_1 + r_{22}I_2$$

$$r_{11} = \frac{E_1}{I_1}\bigg|\, I_2 = 0 \qquad r_{22} = \frac{E_2}{I_2}\bigg|\, I_1 = 0$$

$$r_{12} = \frac{E_1}{I_2}\bigg|\, I_1 = 0 \qquad r_{21} = \frac{E_2}{I_1}\bigg|\, I_2 = 0$$

$$r_{12} = r_{21} \text{ (reciprocity)}$$

The T-circuit

$$r_{11} = R_1 + R_3$$
$$r_{12} = R_3$$
$$r_{22} = R_2 + R_3$$

The g-parameters

$$I_1 = g_{11}E_1 + g_{12}E_2$$
$$I_2 = g_{21}E_1 + g_{22}E_2$$

$$g_{11} = \frac{I_1}{E_1}\bigg|\, E_2 = 0 \qquad g_{22} = \frac{I_2}{E_2}\bigg|\, E_1 = 0$$

$$g_{12} = \frac{I_1}{E_2}\bigg|\, E_1 = 0 \qquad g_{21} = \frac{I_2}{E_1}\bigg|\, E_2 = 0$$

$$g_{12} = g_{21} \text{ (reciprocity)}$$

The π-circuit

$$g_{11} = \frac{1}{R_a} + \frac{1}{R_b}$$

$$g_{12} = \frac{1}{R_b} \qquad g_{22} = \frac{1}{R_c} + \frac{1}{R_b}$$

Relationship of r- and g-parameters

$$g_{11} = \frac{r_{22}}{r_{11}r_{22} - r_{12}^2} \qquad g_{22} = \frac{r_{11}}{r_{11}r_{22} - r_{12}^2}$$

$$g_{12} = \frac{-r_{12}}{r_{11}r_{22} - r_{12}^2}$$

$$r_{11} = \frac{g_{22}}{g_{11}g_{22} - g_{12}^2} \qquad r_{22} = \frac{g_{11}}{g_{11}g_{22} - g_{12}^2}$$

$$r_{12} = \frac{-g_{12}}{g_{11}g_{22} - g_{12}^2}$$

The h-parameters

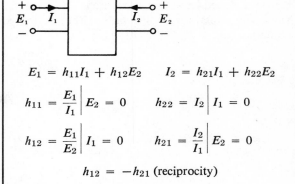

$$E_1 = h_{11}I_1 + h_{12}E_2 \qquad I_2 = h_{21}I_1 + h_{22}E_2$$

$$h_{11} = \frac{E_1}{I_1}\bigg|\, E_2 = 0 \qquad h_{22} = I_2\bigg|\, I_1 = 0$$

$$h_{12} = \frac{E_1}{E_2}\bigg|\, I_1 = 0 \qquad h_{21} = \frac{I_2}{I_1}\bigg|\, E_2 = 0$$

$$h_{12} = -h_{21} \text{ (reciprocity)}$$

The h-circuit

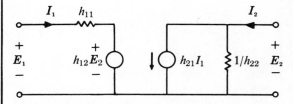

Symmetrical lattice

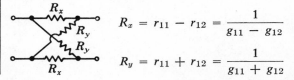

$$R_x = r_{11} - r_{12} = \frac{1}{g_{11} - g_{12}}$$

$$R_y = r_{11} + r_{12} = \frac{1}{g_{11} + g_{12}}$$

Lattice T-equivalence

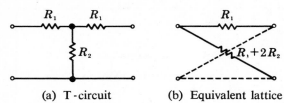

(a) T-circuit   (b) Equivalent lattice

Lattice π-equivalence

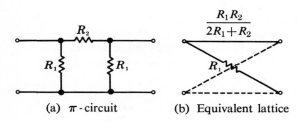

(a) π-circuit   (b) Equivalent lattice

Star-mesh transformation

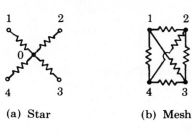

(a) Star   (b) Mesh

$$G \text{ (mesh)} = \frac{\text{Product of adjacent } G\text{'s}}{\text{Sum of } G\text{'s (star)}}$$

References

The subject of two-terminal-pair networks is very well covered in the literature. In addition to the *r*-, *g*-, and *h*-parameters, there are the general-circuit or *ABCD* parameters, the iterative parameters, the image parameters, and the scattering parameters. Many of them are developed for particular applications, such as lossless filters, transmission lines, or waveguides, and are best discussed in connection with these applications. Specific references for further reading are listed below.

1. E. A. GUILLEMIN, *Communications Networks*, Vol. 2, John Wiley, New York, 1935. This text is the standard reference in English on two-terminal-pair networks. The only set of parameters not covered in detail is the scattering set. Chapter 4 gives the equations relating most of the sets of parameters.

2. M. B. REED, *Electric Network Synthesis*, Prentice-Hall, New Jersey, 1955. In this text Reed gives a complete account of the image-parameter method of filter theory. It is, of course, a specialized work for the designer of filters.

3. SESHU and BALBANIAN, *Linear Network Analysis*, John Wiley, New York, 1959. This text gives one of the few general discussions of the scattering parameters. They are confined usually to texts on microwave circuits and to original literature, such as the *IRE-PCGT*, Vol. 3, June 1956.

4. W. B. BOAST, *Principles of Electric and Magnetic Circuits*, Harper, New York, 1950. Boast gives an interesting method for checking the accuracy of a complex network reduction by applying arbitrary voltages as tests at selected points in the network and its equivalent reduction.

5. A. C. BARTLETT, *The Theory of Artificial Lines and Filters*, John Wiley, New York, 1930. Bartlett's bisection theorem for lattice equivalents is stated here.

Exercises

SECTION 5–2

1. When the voltage E is 10 v, the current i is 1 amp in the circuit of Fig. 5–21. If a voltage of 100 v is applied to the terminals c–d, and a short circuit is placed across terminals a–b, what current will flow in the short circuit?

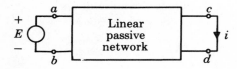

Figure 5–21

2. When the current I is 10 amp in the circuit of Fig. 5–22 a voltage of -2 v appears across the terminals c–d. If a current of 20 amp is applied at terminals c–d and if the current source at terminals a–b is removed, what voltage will appear at terminals a–b? Give the polarity of the voltage, assuming that the current enters at c and that terminal a is positive for the voltage measurement.

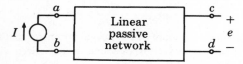

Figure 5–22

3. Verify the reciprocity theorem for the circuit of Fig. 5–23 by computing the current which is flowing in the ammeter m, and then interchanging the voltage source and the ammeter and recomputing the current in the ammeter.

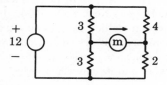

Figure 5–23

4. Verify the reciprocity theorem for the circuit of Fig. 5–24 by computing the voltage that would be

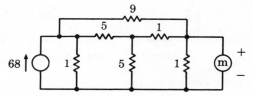

Figure 5–24

measured by the voltmeter m, and then interchanging the current source and the voltmeter and recomputing the voltage read by the voltmeter.

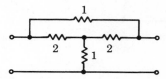

Figure 5–25

5. (a) Find the r-parameters for the circuit of Fig. 5–25 and from them derive an equivalent three-resistance T-circuit. (b) Find the g-parameters for the network of Fig. 5–25, and from them derive the equivalent π-network. (c) Find the h-parameters for the network of Fig. 5–25 and from them derive the equivalent h-network.

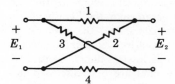

Figure 5–26

6. (a) Find the r-parameters for the network of Fig. 5–26 and give an equivalent three-resistance T. What happens to the r-parameters and to the T-network if the polarity of the output voltage E_2 is assumed in the opposite direction? (b) Find the g-parameters for the network of Fig. 5–26 and give the equivalent π-network.

7. Prove that $h_{12} = -h_{21}$ as a consequence of the reciprocity theorem.

8. Express the *h*-parameters in terms of *r*-parameters and *g*-parameters. Draw the equivalent T- and π-networks.

SECTION 5–3

9. Find the *r*-parameters and the equivalent T-network for the network of Fig. 5–27.

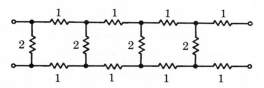

Figure 5–27

10. Find the *g*-parameters and the equivalent π-network for the one shown in Fig. 5–27.

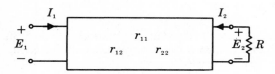

Figure 5–28

11. The two-terminal-pair network of Fig. 5–28 is defined by the *r*-parameters, r_{11}, r_{12}, r_{22}. The load resistance *R* is connected to the output terminals. Show that the ratios E_1/I_1 and E_2/I_1 with the load connected are

$$R_1 = r_{11} - \frac{r_{12}^2}{r_{22} + R} = \frac{E_1}{I_1}$$

and

$$R_{12} = \frac{r_{12}R}{r_{22} + R} = \frac{E_2}{I_1}.$$

12. A two-terminal-pair network is defined by the *g*-parameters g_{11}, g_{12}, and g_{22}. A load with conductance *G* is connected to the output terminals. Show that the ratios I_1/E_1 and I_2/E_1 with the load connected are

$$G_1 = g_{11} - \frac{g_{12}^2}{g_{22} + G} = \frac{I_1}{E_1}$$

and

$$G_{12} = \frac{g_{12}G}{g_{22} + G} = \frac{I_2}{E_1}.$$

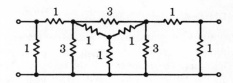

Figure 5–29

13. Reduce the two-terminal-pair network of Fig. 5–29 to three equivalent resistances by means of network transformations.

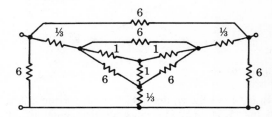

Figure 5–30

14. Reduce the two-terminal-pair network of Fig. 5–30 to three equivalent resistances by Y–Δ and series-parallel transformations.

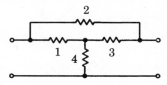

Figure 5–31

15. Find a T-circuit equivalent for the bridged T-circuit of Fig. 5–31.

16. Reduce the network of Fig. 5–32 to a π-network.

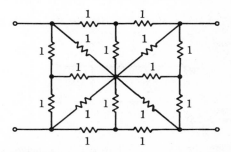

Figure 5–32

SECTION 5–4

17. (a) Find the equivalent r- and g-parameters for the circuit of Fig. 5–33 and give the equivalent T- and π-circuits. (b) Repeat with the series and shunt arms in the lattice interchanged. Use negative resistances in the equivalent circuits. (c) Show that the Y–Δ transformation holds for the negative elements.

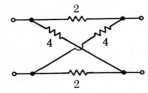

Figure 5–33

18. (a) Find the equivalent T-circuit for the lattice of Fig. 5–34. (b) Find an equivalent π-circuit for the lattice of Fig. 5–34.

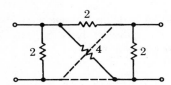

Figure 5–34

19. Find the equivalent lattice for the network of Fig. 5–35.

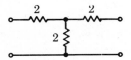

Figure 5–35

20. Find the equivalent lattice for the network of Fig. 5–36.

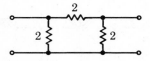

Figure 5–36

21. Find the equivalent lattice for the network of Fig. 5–37.

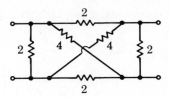

Figure 5–37

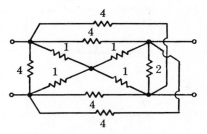

Figure 5–38

22. Reduce the four-terminal network of Fig. 5–38 to a minimum number of resistances while preserving all four terminals.

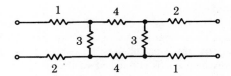

Figure 5–39

23. Reduce the four-terminal network of Fig. 5–39 to an equivalent three-terminal T-circuit.

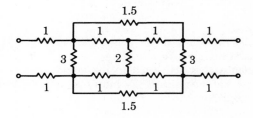

Figure 5–40

24. Change the four-terminal network of Fig. 5–40 to a three-terminal network by means of symmetry principles, and then obtain an equivalent T-network.

Problems

1. A linear passive network has a pair of input terminals and a pair of output terminals. When the input voltage is 10 v the input current is 5 amp, and the current in a short circuit across the output terminals is simultaneously 1 amp. If the voltage source is moved to the output terminals and a 2-ohm resistance is placed across the input terminals, what voltage will occur across the 2-ohm resistance?

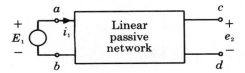

Figure 5–41

2. When the voltage E_1 in the circuit of Fig. 5–41 is 10 v, the current i_1 is 5 amp and the voltage e_2 is 2 v. A 1-ohm resistance added across terminals c–d reduces the voltage there to 1 v. Obtain the r-parameters which describe the circuit, and then find what current would flow in the 1-ohm resistance if it were placed across terminals a–b and the 10-v source were placed across terminals c–d.

3. A current source of value 10 amp is applied to the input terminals of a two-terminal-pair network. The corresponding input voltage is 20 v, and the current flowing in a short circuit at the output terminals is 4 amp at the same time. If the resistance across the output terminals is changed to 1 ohm, the current changes to 2 amp. Find the current which would flow in a 1-ohm resistor placed across the input terminals if the output terminals are driven by a 5-amp current source.

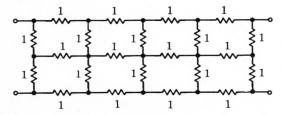

Figure 5–42

4. Make use of symmetry to find r_{11}, r_{22}, and r_{12} for the circuit of Fig. 5–42.

5. By means of symmetry find g_{11}, g_{22}, and g_{12} directly from the circuit of Fig. 5–42.

6. Find an equivalent T for the network of Fig. 5–43.

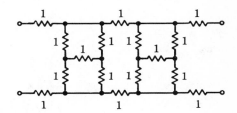

Figure 5–43

7. Find the equivalent lattice for the network of Fig. 5–44.

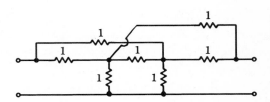

Figure 5–44

8. Find the voltage across the 10-amp source in the circuit of Fig. 5–45 by utilizing the symmetry and resolving the excitation into two 15-amp sources symmetrically applied and two 5-amp sources anti-symmetrically applied.

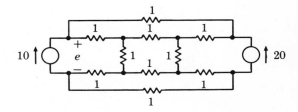

Figure 5–45

CHAPTER 6

DIFFERENTIATION, INTEGRATION, AND SINGULARITY FUNCTIONS

A mathematician is a man who is willing to assume everything except responsibility.

T. von Kármán

6–1 Introduction

Mathematics is an area of idealization. If a mathematical development is to apply to a physical problem, an element of approximation must enter at some point. It is natural for the physicist and engineer, who are dealing with both real devices and the mathematical descriptions of them, to combine the two areas and to develop an "intuitive mathematics" which relies on physical reasoning for some of its validity. This approach is useful in the areas of integration and differentiation and is essential for the application of the singularity functions.

It is not the purpose of this chapter to present a course in calculus. The student should already be familiar with the elements of differentiation and integration. Experience has shown, however, that the concept of differentiation and integration as continuous "operators" is not easily grasped, although it is extremely useful in many engineering problems.

Differentiation and integration can be fitted into the stimulus-response relationship by representing them as "black boxes" which perform operations. The input stimulus is usually a single-valued function of time, and the output response is the instantaneous value of the derivative or the integral of the input waveform. This point of view is closely related to electric circuits. Electrical energy storage elements perform the mathematical operations of differentiation and integration.

The latter part of this chapter deals with the singularity functions. Here the split between mathematical rigor and useful intuition is more pronounced. A rigorous treatment of the singularity functions requires the advanced Lebesgue calculus, which is seldom taught to undergraduates. However, the singularity functions are very useful, because they represent simple idealizations of practical switching operations. A switching operation takes place in a very short interval, but the interval is still finite. Mathematical problems which involve singularity functions can always be resolved by allowing the functions to spread out over a short interval and to occur in a definite sequence. The objective is to obtain the advantages of idealized switching operations, taking place in zero time, without introducing insoluble mathematical difficulties.

6–2 Differentiation of functions

Since differentiation is less difficult than integration, we shall discuss it first. The functional and operational concept of differentiation is illustrated in Fig. 6–1. The input to the black box is the function $f_1(t)$, and the output is the function $f_2(t)$. Differentiation is represented by the black box, which operates on the input so that

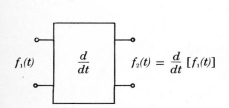

Figure 6–1. Differentiation as a continuous operation.

$$f_2(t) = \frac{d}{dt}[f_1(t)] = f_1'(t). \qquad (6–1)$$

Equation (6–1) states that the output function $f_2(t)$ is at each instant of time equal to the slope, or derivative, of the input function $f_1(t)$. If $f_1(t)$ is a straight line, the slope is a constant equal to the rise divided by the run. If $f_1(t)$ is a more general curve, the slope at any instant is the slope of the tangent drawn to the curve. Note that the derivative *of a point* has no meaning. The nature of the curve on either side of the point determines the derivative; the curve must be known before the derivative *at the point* can be obtained.

Graphical differentiation. A typical curve and its derivative are shown in Fig. 6–2. To the left of the origin the original curve $f(t)$ and its derivative $f'(t)$ are both zero. Between $t = 0$ and $t = 1$ the original curve rises with a constant slope of $+1$. The derivative curve has therefore a constant value of $+1$. Between $t = 1$ and $t = 3$ the original curve drops with a slope of -1, and the corresponding portion of the derivative curve also has a value of -1. From $t = 3$ to $t = 4$ the original curve rises again with a slope

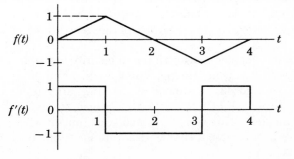

Figure 6–2. A typical curve and its derivative.

of $+1$, and thus the derivative curve again has a value of $+1$. To the right of $t = 4$ the original curve and its derivative are both zero. Note that a function can be zero *at a point* and still have a derivative. For example, at the point $t = 2$ in Fig. 6–2, the curve $f(t)$ is zero but its derivative has a value of -1.

The original function shown in Fig. 6–2 looks rather simple, since it consists of straight lines. Nevertheless, to express it mathematically is difficult, because the derivatives of the function are discontinuous at the sharp corners.

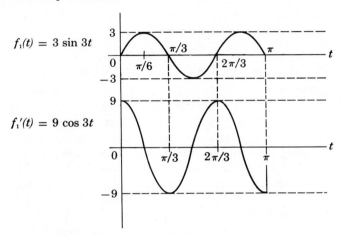

Figure 6–3. The function $f(t) = 3 \sin 3t$ and its derivative.

Analytical differentiation. If an original function can be expressed as a simple mathematical expression, the derivative function can usually be found in standard tables of derivatives. An example is the function

$$f_1(t) = 3 \sin 3t. \tag{6-2}$$

Tables of derivatives show that

$$d (\sin x) = \cos x \, dx.$$

Applying this formula to the function of Eq. (6–2) gives the derivative

$$f_2(t) = \frac{d}{dt} [f_1(t)] = 9 \cos 3t. \tag{6-3}$$

The functions $f_1(t)$ and $f_2(t)$, or $f'(t)$, are plotted in Fig. 6–3 from $t = 0$ to $t = \pi$. The derivative curve can also be obtained by drawing a tangent at each point on the original curve and then plotting the slopes of the tangents. Thus, at $t = \pi/6$ the slope of the tangent is zero, and the corresponding value of the derivative curve is zero. At $t = \pi/4$ the slope of the tangent is negative and has a value of approximately −6.3. Equation (6–3) yields a more accurate value:

$$f_2\left(t = \frac{\pi}{4}\right) = 9\cos\left(\frac{3\pi}{4}\right) = -9 \times 0.707 = -6.363.$$

In general it can be said that the operation of taking a derivative is a straightforward procedure which can be accomplished either analytically or graphically. It is best to think of the graphical procedure as the basic method and to consider the analytical procedure only a method of accomplishing the graphical procedure without actually drawing the curve.

6–3 Integration of functions

Integration is more difficult than differentiation, because the value of an integral at a point involves the entire past history of the function and not just the nature of the function in the immediate vicinity of the point. Another problem in integration is the use of the *indefinite* integral, which is frequently misunderstood by students. We shall use in this textbook only the definite integral representing the area bounded by the curve and the two limits specified by the integral. Usually the lower limit will be minus infinity, which we interpret as a time in the past prior to which the function is zero; the upper limit will be the variable time. Thus the basic integral measures the area under a function from the instant the function began in the remote past until the present time. As time changes, the area changes, and thus traces out a function curve.

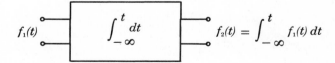

Figure 6–4. Integration as a continuous operation.

$$f_1(t) \qquad \int_{-\infty}^{t} dt \qquad f_2(t) = \int_{-\infty}^{t} f_1(t)\, dt$$

The operational concept of integration is shown in Fig. 6–4. The input function is $f_1(t)$. The operation of integration consists in finding the area under the function curve from the time it began until the present time, t, which is a variable. As time changes the area changes; at any given instant the value of the area is the output function $f_2(t)$. The operation of integration is similar to the accumulation of cash in a bank account. The input function $f_1(t)$ is analogous to the deposits and withdrawals. The output function $f_2(t)$ is analogous to the instantaneous amount, or balance, which is present in the account. The balance is the algebraic sum of all the deposits and withdrawals which have occurred since the instant in the past when the account was opened.

Expressed mathematically, the definite integral of a function is

$$f_2(t) = \int_{-\infty}^{t} f_1(t)\, dt. \tag{6-4}$$

Equation (6–4) states that the value of the function $f_2(t)$ at some time t is the area under the curve $f_1(t)$ from the beginning of time up to the present time t. In any actual problem, it is possible to find a time before which the function $f_1(t)$ is zero. Very often this point is $t = 0$, but to be more general we shall refer to it as $t = a$. Then, the functional integral is

$$f_2(t) = \int_{a}^{t} f_1(t)\, dt. \tag{6-5}$$

Graphical integration. An example of a function which can be integrated easily is shown in Fig. 6–5. It is zero until $t = 0$, has a value of unity from $t = 0$ to $t = 5$, and is zero to the right of $t = 5$. The area accumulated to the left of $t = 0$ is zero. There-fore, the value of the integral curve at $t = 0$ is zero.* At $t = 1$, an area of unity has accumulated; thus the value of the integral curve at this point is 1. At $t = 2$, the total accumulated area is 2; the value of the integral curve is therefore 2. At $t = 3$, the integral curve equals 3; at $t = 4$, it equals 4; and so on. To the right of $t = 5$ the integral curve maintains a value of 5. In terms of the banking analog, a deposit of 1 dollar is made each month for five months, and thus the total accumulation is 5 dollars. This amount remains undisturbed unless further deposits or withdrawals are made.

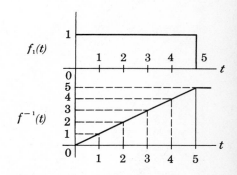

Figure 6–5. Integration of a function.

If the curve to be integrated is arbitrary, it can be approximated by a series of rectangles of varying heights, and the integral can be obtained by adding the areas of the rectangles. Machines called *planimeters* are available for performing such graphical integration, but often it is sufficiently accurate merely to count squares under the curve after it is plotted on graph paper.

Analytical integration. If the analytic form of the original function is known, the integral of the function can be obtained by the use of tables of integrals. The entries in the tables are usually indefinite integrals. An indefinite integral is identical to that of Eq. (6–4), except that an arbitrary constant is added to account for a possible value at $t = -\infty$. Although physical functions are zero at minus infinity, mathematical functions need not be. No practical difficulty

---

* Integrals with respect to time are designated as $f^{-1}(t)$.

arises, because most integrations are effected between two limits, the constant at minus infinity canceling out.

The value under a curve is simply the value of the indefinite integral at the upper limit minus its value at the lower limit. As an example, consider the function

$$f_1(t) = \begin{cases} 3 \sin 3t & \text{for } t > 0, \\ 0 & \text{for } t < 0. \end{cases}$$

The integral of this function is zero for $t < 0$; for $t > 0$ the integral is

$$f_2(t) = \int_0^t 3 \sin 3t \, dt. \tag{6-6}$$

The tabulated indefinite integral is

$$\int \sin x \, dx = -\cos x + C. \tag{6-7}$$

If we substitute $x = 3t$, we can evaluate the integral of Eq. (6-6) as follows:

$$f_2(t) = \left(-\frac{\cos 3t}{1} \right) - \left(-\frac{\cos 0}{1} \right),$$

or

$$f_2(t) = 1 - \cos 3t.$$

The function $3 \sin 3t$ and its integral are plotted in Fig. 6-6. From $t = 0$ to $t = \pi/3$ the function is positive. At the beginning the function has small values, and each successive integrating step contributes very little area; thus the integral curve rises slowly. In the neighborhood of $t = \pi/6$ the function reaches its maximum value, and the integral curve rises at its maximum rate. This rate decreases as the function decreases, until the maximum value of the integral is reached at $t = \pi/3$. Beyond this point the function becomes

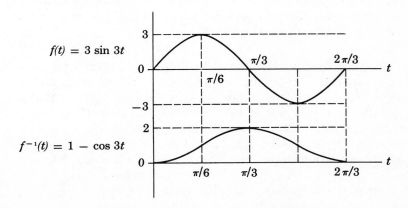

Figure 6-6. The function $f(t) = 3 \sin 3t$ and its integral.

negative, and the negative area is subtracted from the positive area, until the net accumulated area is zero at $t = 2\pi/3$.

An approximate integration of the function in Fig. 6–6 can be obtained by counting squares under its curve. The student should view as basic the concept of an integral as an area and consider tabulated values of integrals only a means of avoiding the counting of squares.

The relationship of differentiation and integration. Differentiation and integration as defined here are inverse operations. Thus, if we take a given curve, integrate it, and differentiate the result, we obtain the original curve. Similarly, if we first differentiate and then integrate, we return to the original curve. These results will be proved by a study of the two curves in Fig. 6–7. In this illustration the lower curve is the integral of the upper curve. In the time interval Δ, the increment of area contributed by the upper curve is $h\Delta$. This value is added to the height of the integral curve at the end of the interval Δ. Now let us reverse the process and obtain the slope of the integral curve. Over the interval Δ the slope is given by the rise in the curve over the corresponding run, that is,

$$\frac{h\Delta}{\Delta} = h,$$

which is the value of the original curve. Since the process works either way, the derivative curve is the inverse of the integral curve and vice versa.

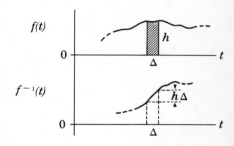

Figure 6–7. The relationship between the derivative and the integral.

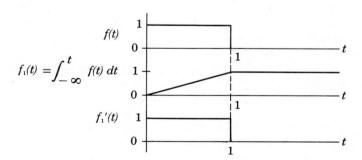

Figure 6–8 shows an example of the inverse relationship between integral and derivative curves. The center curve is the integral of the top curve, and the lowest curve is the derivative of the center curve. Note that the lowest curve is identical to the top curve.

Figure 6–8. The inverse nature of integral and derivative curves.

A second example of the inverse relationship is provided by the analytic expression

$$\int_0^x \sin x \, dx = 1 - \cos x, \qquad (6\text{–}8)$$

and the derivative of the integral curve in Eq. (6–8):

$$\frac{d}{dx}(1 - \cos x) = \sin x. \tag{6–9}$$

Note in Eq. (6–9) that the derivative of the integral curve in Eq. (6–8) equals the original function, sin x. The two functions $1 - \cos x$ and sin x are exact inverses. The sine and cosine functions by themselves are not.

6–4 The singularity functions

Since the publication of Oliver Heaviside's *Electrical Papers* in 1892, electrical engineers and physicists have made use of unit switching functions, or *singularity functions*, on a more or less empirical basis. Laurent Schwartz's *Théorie des Distributions* in 1951 gave a rigorous mathematical representation of singularity functions. However, we shall approach singularity functions from an intuitive point of view.

We idealize switching waveforms in much the same fashion as we idealize network elements, and for much the same reason. It is easier to solve a problem in which a switch has only two positions, open and closed, than it is to solve the actual problem which involves a complicated transition between the two states. The mathematical difficulties associated with idealized switching functions arise from the assumption that the switching takes place in zero time. In our intuitive approach we avoid these difficulties by never quite reaching the limit. In fact, if a switch is closed at time zero, we break this instant into three parts: 0^-, the instant just before the switch is closed; 0, the instant during which the switch is being closed; and 0^+, the instant just after the switch is closed. These three instants are separated by intervals which are negligibly short, but nevertheless finite.

The step function. A constant current or a constant voltage switched into a circuit at time $t = 0$ can be represented by a *step function*. The unit step function is denoted by the symbol $u_{-1}(t)$ and defined by the equations

$$u_{-1}(t) = \begin{cases} 0 & \text{for } t < 0, \\ 1 & \text{for } t > 0. \end{cases} \tag{6–10}$$

A graph of the function is shown in Fig. 6–9(a). The function is zero for negative values of time and unity for positive values of time. The switching operation occurs in the short interval between 0^-, when the function is zero, and 0^+, when it is unity. The value of the func-

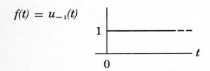

$f(t) = u_{-1}(t)$

(a) The step function

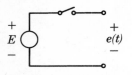

(b) Voltage step

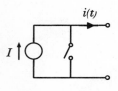

(c) Current step

Figure 6–9. The unit step function.

tion precisely at zero is indeterminate. A voltage source switched into a circuit at $t = 0$ can be represented by means of the unit step function. Consider the source shown in Fig. 6–9(b). Let us say that the switch is closed at $t = 0$. The voltage $e(t)$, which is zero before $t = 0$ and equal to E for t greater than zero, can be expressed analytically as

$$e(t) = Eu_{-1}(t). \qquad (6–11)$$

A current source [Fig. 6–9(c)] switched into a circuit at $t = 0$ can also be expressed in terms of the unit step function. Prior to $t = 0$ the switch is closed, and the current from the source passes through the short circuit. At $t = 0$ the switch is opened, and the current passes through the external circuit. The current $i(t)$, which is zero before $t = 0$ and equal to I for t greater than zero, can be expressed analytically as

$$i(t) = Iu_{-1}(t). \qquad (6–12)$$

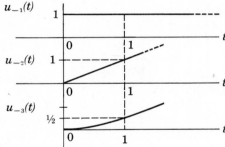

(a) The unit step function

(b) The unit ramp function

(c) The unit parabola

Figure 6–10. The integrals of the unit step function.

The ramp function. Since the circuit elements can produce integrals and derivatives, we are interested in the integrals and derivatives of the step function. The integral of the unit step function is called the *unit ramp function, $u_{-2}(t)$*, where

$$u_{-2}(t) = \int_{-\infty}^{t} u_{-1}(t)\, dt = \int_{0}^{t} dt$$

or $\qquad (6–13)$

$$u_{-2}(t) = \begin{cases} t & \text{for } t > 0, \\ 0 & \text{for } t < 0. \end{cases}$$

A graph of the unit ramp function is shown in Fig. 6–10(b). The slope of the function is unity and its value at $t = 1$ is unity. The integral of a step function with height A is a ramp function having a value of A at $t = 1$, and thus a slope of A.

Other singularity functions can be obtained by taking further integrals. The *unit second-order function*, the integral of the unit ramp, is represented by the symbol $u_{-3}(t)$ and is obtained as follows:

$$u_{-3}(t) = \int_{-\infty}^{t} u_{-2}(t)\,dt = \int_{0}^{t} t\,dt$$

or   (6–14)

$$u_{-3}(t) = \begin{cases} t^2/2 & \text{for } t > 0, \\ 0 & \text{for } t < 0. \end{cases}$$

The graph of the unit second-order function [Fig. 6–10(c)] is zero for negative values of t and a parabola for positive values of t. Additional higher-order functions can be obtained, but they occur rather rarely in circuit theory.

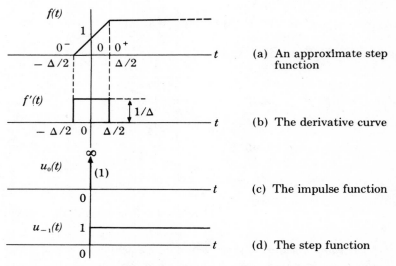

(a) An approximate step function

(b) The derivative curve

(c) The impulse function

(d) The step function

Figure 6–11. The derivative of the step function: the impulse function.

The impulse function. The derivative of the unit step function is called the *impulse function*. Figure 6–11(a) shows a unit step function plotted on an expanded scale between 0^- and 0^+. The derivative [Fig. 6–11(b)] is zero everywhere except between 0^- and 0^+. If we denote this interval as Δ, the derivative is $1/\Delta$. As Δ approaches zero the value of the derivative approaches infinity. In the limit we reach the impulse function [Fig. 6–11(c)], which is zero everywhere except at $t = 0$; at this point it is infinite. The area under the impulse can be obtained from Fig. 6–11(b). It is

$$\frac{1}{\Delta} \times \Delta = 1. \tag{6–15}$$

The significance of Eq. (6–18) lies in the fact that the area under the derivative of the step function is independent of the rise-time, Δ, over which the step occurs. It is convenient to characterize the impulse by the area under it rather than by its height, which is infinite. The graphical symbol for the impulse is shown in Fig. 6–11(c), where the number in parentheses denotes the area under the impulse. The notation $u_0(t)$ is used for the unit impulse.

Since the derivative of the step function is an impulse function, the integral of the impulse function should be a step function. If we integrate the impulse function of Fig. 6–11(c), we obtain no area to the left of the origin. As we go from 0^- to 0^+, however, we pick up the area under the impulse; thus the integral curve jumps from 0 to 1. Since there are no further contributions to the right of the origin, the value of the integral curve remains at unity. This integral curve, shown in Fig. 6–11(d), is obviously the unit step function. The derivative of a step function with height A is an impulse function with area A. When we integrate the impulse, we pick up an area A at the origin, and thus the integral curve jumps up by an amount A. An impulse of current is represented by an area whose dimensions are *amp·sec*, or *coulombs;* an impulse of voltage is represented by an area whose dimensions are *volt·sec*, or *flux linkages.* By definition,

$$u_0(t) = \frac{d}{dt} u_{-1}(t). \qquad (6\text{--}16)$$

The symbol $u_0(t)$ makes the unit impulse, rather than the unit step, the basic singularity function. The response of a network to a unit impulse is a more basic function than its response to a unit step function.

Additional singularity functions can be defined as the derivatives of the unit impulse function. For example, the *unit doublet* is

$$u_1(t) = \frac{d}{dt} u_0(t). \qquad (6\text{--}17)$$

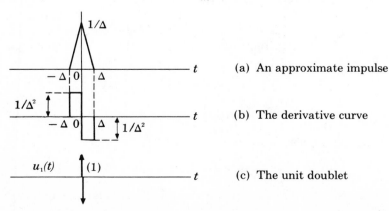

(a) An approximate impulse

(b) The derivative curve

(c) The unit doublet

Figure 6–12. The derivative of the impulse function.

In order to be able to take a derivative of the unit impulse function, we shall view it as a triangular pulse of height $1/\Delta$ and width 2Δ, as shown in Fig. 6–12(a). This is permissible, since the exact shape of an impulse function does not matter so long as its area does not change. The derivative curve [Fig. 6–12(b)] consists of a positive pulse followed by a negative pulse. The pulses have magnitudes of $1/\Delta^2$ and areas of $1/\Delta$. In the limit as Δ approaches zero, the areas become infinite. Thus the unit doublet [Fig. 6–12(c)] consists of an infinite positive impulse followed by an infinite negative impulse. The doublet is characterized by its second integral and has the dimensions of amp·sec^2 for a current doublet, and volt·sec^2 for a voltage doublet.

Other singularity functions can be obtained by taking further derivatives of the unit impulse function. In practice, however, singularity functions of higher order than the doublet seldom occur.

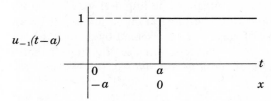

Figure 6–13. A delayed step function.

Singularity functions at arbitrary times. The unit step function $u_{-1}(t)$ is zero for negative t and unity for positive t. Similarly, a unit step function of some other argument is zero for negative values of the argument and unity for positive values of the argument. In order to change the time t at which a step function occurs, we change the variable to $t - a$, and obtain the unit step function

$$u_{-1}(t - a). \tag{6–18}$$

This function is zero when its argument is negative, that is, for t less than a; the function has a value of unity when its argument is positive, that is, when t is greater than a. The result of this substitution is to produce a step function which begins at $t = a$, as shown in Fig. 6–13.

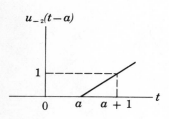

(a) Delayed ramp function

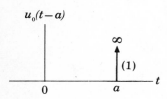

(b) Delayed impulse function

Figure 6–14. A delayed unit ramp function and unit impulse function.

Similarly, a unit ramp function which begins at $t = a$ is

$$u_{-2}(t - a), \tag{6–19}$$

and a unit impulse function which begins at $t = a$ is

$$u_0(t - a). \tag{6–20}$$

The graphs of these functions are shown in Fig. 6–14(a) and 6–14(b).

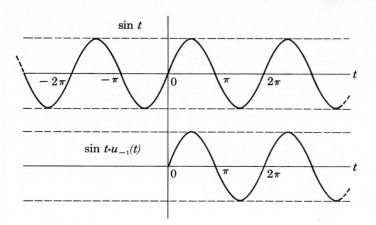

(a) A sine wave

(b) A sectioned sine wave

Figure 6–15. The use of a step function to section a waveform.

Sectioned waveforms. One of the most useful applications of the unit step function is to section or cut off a function for negative values of time. Most mathematical expressions extend over all time from minus infinity to plus infinity. Most actual problems, however, begin at a particular time, usually called zero time, and their solutions are valid only for positive time. One way in which we can indicate that a solution is not valid for negative time is to multiply it by the unit step function. The product is zero for negative time, since the unit step function is zero; the solution remains unchanged for positive time, since the unit step function is unity. Figure 6–15 illustrates this multiplication. The waveform shown in Fig. 6–15(a) is a sine wave which extends over all time. Its mathematical expression is

$$f(t) = \sin t. \tag{6–21}$$

The waveform shown in Fig. 6–15(b) is a sine wave which is zero for negative time. It is said to be *sectioned at the origin*. Its mathematical expression is

$$f(t) = \sin t \times u_{-1}(t). \tag{6–22}$$

The resolution of periodic waveforms. We can express many periodic waveforms in terms of a superposition of singularity functions, each delayed somewhat from the one preceding it. An example is shown in Fig. 6–16. The square wave of Fig. 6–16(a) can be produced by a summation of the unit step functions shown in Fig. 6–16(b). The first step function is positive and occurs at $t = 0$, giving a value of unity from $t = 0$ to $t = 1$; at $t = 1$ a second, negative step function occurs which subtracts from the first to leave a net value of zero between $t = 1$ and $t = 2$; at $t = 2$ a third, positive step function occurs which, when added to the first two, produces a value of unity for the square wave from $t = 2$ to $t = 3$.

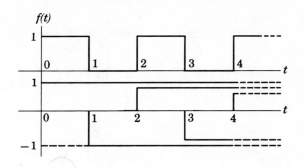

(a) Repeated square wave

(b) Resolution into step functions

Figure 6–16. The resolution of a periodic square wave into step functions.

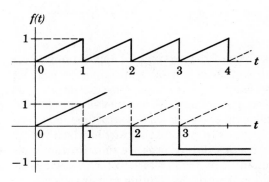

(a) A saw-tooth wave

(b) Resolution into singularity functions

Figure 6–17. The resolution of a saw-tooth wave into singularity functions.

At $t = 3$ a negative step function again occurs, and so on. We can obtain a mathematical expression for the square wave of Fig. 6–16(a) by adding the component step functions of Fig. 6–16(b). Thus,

$$f(t) = u_{-1}(t) - u_{-1}(t - 1) + u_{-1}(t - 2) - u_{-1}(t - 3) + \cdots.$$

$$(6\text{–}23)$$

A slightly more complicated example is shown in Fig. 6–17. From $t = 0$ to $t = 1$ the saw-tooth function [Fig. 6–17(a)] is represented by a unit ramp function which rises to a value of 1. At $t = 1$ a negative unit step function occurs which reduces the saw-tooth function to zero. The initial ramp continues to rise, however, and at $t = 2$, the net value is again unity. A second, negative unit step function occurs at $t = 2$, and so on. The mathematical expression for the saw-tooth function, obtained from Fig. 6–17(b), is

$$f(t) = u_{-2}(t) - u_{-1}(t - 1) - u_{-1}(t - 2) - u_{-1}(t - 3) - \cdots.$$

$$(6\text{–}24)$$

The over-all response of a network to a periodic function can be obtained by the superposition of the responses produced by the component singularity functions.

Summary

Operational derivative (slope at time t)

$$f_1(t) \quad \boxed{\frac{d}{dt}} \quad f_2(t) = \frac{d}{dt} f_1(t) = f_1'(t)$$

Operational integral (area up to time t)

$$f_1(t) \quad \boxed{\int_{-\infty}^{t} dt} \quad f_2(t) = \int_{-\infty}^{t} f_1(t)\, dt = f_1^{-1}(t)$$

Relationship between derivative and integral

$$\frac{d}{dt}[f^{-1}(t)] = f(t)$$

$$\int_{-\infty}^{t} f'(t) = f(t)$$

The singularity functions

$$u_n(t) = \frac{d}{dt}[u_{n-1}(t)] = \int_{-\infty}^{t} u_{n+1}(t)\, dt$$

$$\vdots$$

Unit ramp

$$u_{-2}(t) = \begin{cases} 0 \text{ for } t < 0 \\ t \text{ for } t > 0 \end{cases}$$

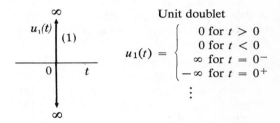

Unit step

$$u_{-1}(t) = \begin{cases} 0 \text{ for } t < 0 \\ 1 \text{ for } t > 0 \end{cases}$$

Unit impulse

$$u_0(t) = \begin{cases} 0 \text{ for } t > 0 \\ 0 \text{ for } t < 0 \\ \infty \text{ for } t = 0 \end{cases}$$

Unit doublet

$$u_1(t) = \begin{cases} 0 \text{ for } t > 0 \\ 0 \text{ for } t < 0 \\ \infty \text{ for } t = 0^- \\ -\infty \text{ for } t = 0^+ \end{cases}$$

$$\vdots$$

Delayed singularity functions

$$u_n(t - a) = u_n(t) \text{ delayed to start at } t = a$$

References

The subjects in this chapter are mathematical. However, the best reference material will be found not in the mathematics field but in the field of electrical engineering. The concept of integration and differentiation as "time operators" has been developed in the field of analog computers. Step and impulse responses have been developed in circuit theory. Listed below are a few selected references for this material.

1. G. B. THOMAS, JR., *Calculus and Analytical Geometry*, Addison-Wesley, Reading, Mass., 1954. A good introductory text to the calculus. Integration is discussed from a number of points of view, both mathematical and physical.

2. D. K. CHENG, *Analysis of Linear Systems*, Addison-Wesley, Reading, Mass., 1959. This text gives an excellent discussion of the impulse function.

3. E. A. GUILLEMIN, *Introductory Circuit Theory*, John Wiley, New York, 1953. Guillemin points out clearly the advantages of using the definite integral from minus infinity to t rather than the indefinite integral.

4. E. A. GUILLEMIN, *The Mathematics of Circuit Analysis*, John Wiley, New York, 1949. This graduate-level text gives a semi-rigorous discussion of the singularity functions.

5. L. SCHWARTZ, *Théorie des Distributions*, Hermann et Cie, Paris, 1950. The original rigorous treatment of singularity functions.

6. B. FRIEDMAN, *Principles and Techniques of Applied Mathematics*, John Wiley, New York, 1956. Friedman gives a useful account of distribution functions.

7. KORN and KORN, *Analog Computers*, McGraw-Hill, New York, 1956. This standard text on analog computers stresses the operational meaning of integration. This point of view is very useful, especially in understanding differential equations.

8. W. K. LINVILL, "Sampled-data Control System," *Trans. AIEE*, Vol. 70, Part II, pp. 1779–1788 (1951).

9. RAGAZZINI and ZADEH, "The Analysis of Sampled-Data Systems," *Trans. AIEE*, Vol. 71, Part II, pp. 225–232 (1952). This paper and that of Reference 8 show the relationship of impulse approximations to the conventional theory of numerical analysis, and introduce a convenient technique for performing it, called Z-transforms.

10. H. A. HELM, "The Z-transform," *B.S.T.J.*, Vol. 38 (Jan. 1959). A rigorous treatment of singularity functions and Z-transforms by means of Lebesgue integrals.

Exercises

SECTION 6-2

1. Sketch the derivative of the function shown in Fig. 6-18.

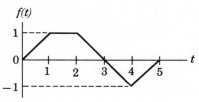

Figure 6-18

2. Sketch the derivative of the function shown in Fig. 6-19.

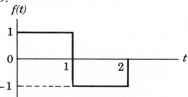

Figure 6-19

3. Sketch the derivative of the function shown in Fig. 6-20.

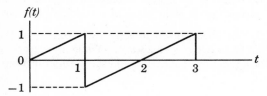

Figure 6-20

4. Sketch the function $f(t) = \sin t$ from $t = 0$ to $t = 2\pi$. Also, obtain and sketch its derivative over the same range.

5. Sketch the function $f(t) = (1 - e^{-t})$ and its derivative from $t = 0$ to infinity.

6. Obtain the first, second, and third derivatives of the function $f(t) = e^{2t}$. Sketch each over all values of time.

7. Obtain the first three derivatives of the function $f(t) = t^n$. Sketch the curves for $n = 1$, $n = 2$, and $n = 3$. What general conclusion can you draw?

8. Find the maximum value of the curve $f(t) = e^{-t} \sin t$, and the point at which it occurs.

SECTION 6-3

9. Sketch the integral of the waveform shown in Fig. 6-18.

10. Sketch the integral of the waveform shown in Fig. 6-19.

11. Sketch the integral of the waveform shown in Fig. 6-20.

12. Sketch the first, second, and third integrals of the function shown in Fig. 6-21.

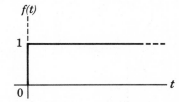

Figure 6-21

13. Differentiate the function shown in Fig. 6-22. Integrate the resulting waveform to obtain the original function.

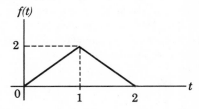

Figure 6-22

14. (a) Differentiate the function $f(t) = \sin t$. Integrate the resulting expression from $t = 0$ to $t = t$. Comment on the inverse property of the curves. (b) Integrate the function $f(t) = \sin t$ from $t = 0$

to $t = t$. Differentiate the resulting expression, and comment on the inverse nature of the curves.

15. Differentiate the function $f(t) = \cos t$. Integrate the resulting expression from $t = 0$ to $t = t$. Comment on the inverse nature of the curves.

16. A curve $f(t)$ is defined by

$$f(t) = \begin{cases} e^t & \text{for } t > 0, \\ 0 & \text{for } t < 0. \end{cases}$$

Note that the derivative of this curve is infinite at $t = 0$. What area must be enclosed under the infinite derivative at $t = 0$ to make the integral of the derivative of $f(t)$ equal to the original function?

SECTION 6–4

17. Sketch the derivative of the function shown in Fig. 6–23. Find the area under the derivative curve. What does the area become when a is allowed to approach zero? What does the derivative become?

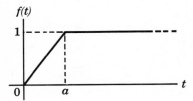

Figure 6–23

18. (a) Write an analytic expression for the waveform shown in Fig. 6–24. (b) Find an analytic expression for the derivative of the waveform shown in Fig. 6–24. Sketch the derivative. (c) Find an analytic expression for the integral of the waveform shown in Fig. 6–24. Sketch the integral.

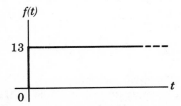

Figure 6–24

19. Sketch the function $f(t) = \cos t \times u_{-1}(t)$. Obtain the derivative from the sketch. Also, obtain the derivative analytically by the formula for the derivative of the product of two functions.

20. (a) Express the waveform of Fig. 6–19 in terms of singularity functions. Express the integral and derivative of the waveform in the same manner. (b) Express the waveform of Fig. 6–20 in terms of singularity functions. Express the integral and derivative of the waveform in the same manner.

21. Find an expression for the pulse shown in Fig. 6–25 in terms of singularity functions.

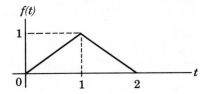

Figure 6–25

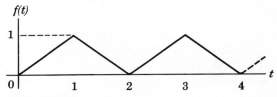

Figure 6–26

22. Write an analytical expression for the waveform in Fig. 6–26 in terms of singularity functions.

23. The pulse shown in Fig. 6–27 consists of the first half-cycle of a sine wave. Obtain an expression for it in terms of sinusoids and singularity functions.

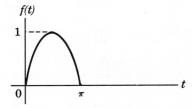

Figure 6–27

24. Sketch the waveform of the expression

$$f(t) = u_{-1}(t) + u_{-1}(t - 1) + u_{-1}(t - 2) + \cdots.$$

Problems

1. Differentiate the function e^t. Show that the integral of the derivative from minus infinity to t regains the original function but the integral from zero to t does not.

2. Show that the integral of the derivative of e^{-t} from minus infinity to t does not converge. Examine the way in which the indefinite integral overcomes this problem.

3. An alternative to using the indefinite integral is to cause all functions to become zero in the vicinity of minus infinity by multiplying them by $u_{-1}(t - A)$, where A is a large negative number which can be made to approach as closely as desired to minus infinity. For the function $u_{-1}(t - A)e^{-t}$ show that the integral of the derivative from minus infinity to t recovers the original curve. Sketch the curve and its derivative.

4. A function is zero for negative values of t and equal to e^{-t} for positive values of t. Find its derivative and show that the integral of the derivative from minus infinity to t reproduces the original curve.

5. (a) Using singularity functions write an analytical expression for the curve which is zero for negative values of t and $\cos t$ for positive values of t. (b) Obtain the formal derivative of this curve. (c) Show that the integral from minus infinity to t of the derivative gives back the original curve.

6. Sketch the waveform of the following expression:

$$f(t) = u_{-2}(t) - 2u_{-2}(t - 1) + u_{-2}(t - 2).$$

7. (a) Write an expression for the triangular wave of Fig. 6–28 in terms of singularity functions. (b) Obtain an approximate expression in terms of five equally spaced step functions. (c) Obtain the integrals and the derivatives of the two expressions for the triangular wave of Fig. 6–28. What conclusion can you draw?

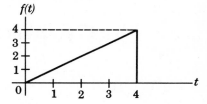

Figure 6–28

8. (a) Approximate the curve of Fig. 6–28 by means of four impulse functions occurring at $t = 1$, 2, 3, and 4, and each one representing the area under the curve in the preceding unit. (b) Obtain and sketch the integral of this approximation and compare it with the integral of the actual curve.

CHAPTER 7

THE TIME RESPONSE FUNCTIONS OF SINGLE ELEMENTS

Mathematics is an experimental science. Since the answers can always be verified, it is not important how they are obtained.

OLIVER HEAVISIDE

7–1 Introduction

The singularity functions were introduced into electrical engineering by Oliver Heaviside. We shall follow his lead and use them to test and describe our networks. Like Heaviside, we shall be more interested in obtaining useful results than in justifying the rigor of our methods. We can apply our intuition to the singularity functions by assuming that they occur not instantaneously but over a short period of time.

The energy-storage elements, L and C, introduce integrals and derivatives into the network equations. A general network, is described by a differential equation, and the solution is a function of time. For the particular case of single elements the networks perform the simple operations of integration, differentiation, and multiplication by a constant. Thus, if we excite them by means of singularity functions, the responses will also be singularity functions.

The excitation can arise from an externally applied source, or from energy stored in the network at the beginning of the problem. It makes very little difference to the behavior of the network whether the energy is externally or internally supplied. Indeed, the internal energy storages at the beginning of a problem can be replaced by step or impulse sources without changing the currents and voltages of the network. This equivalence allows us a choice in the method of solving problems. For the solution of differential equations, we usually remove step and impulse sources and account for their effects by computing the initial values of the variables of interest. In the network-theory point of view we are more likely to replace the initial energy-storage values by equivalent sources, since we can treat these sources by the usual stimulus-response techniques.

The step and the impulse responses of networks are in themselves the solutions of important switching problems. They also represent a way of characterizing or describing the networks in analytical terms. For linear networks the response to an arbitrary time function can be computed from the step or the impulse response.

7–2 The volt-ampere relationships

The volt-ampere relationships of the elements were discussed in Section 1–4. The basic definitions are repeated here for convenience.

Element	Symbol	Direct equation	Inverse equation	
Resistance		$e = iR$	$i = Ge$	(7–1)
Inductance		$e = L\dfrac{di}{dt}$	$i = \dfrac{1}{L}\displaystyle\int_{-\infty}^{t} e\,dt$	(7–2)
Capacitance		$e = \dfrac{1}{C}\displaystyle\int_{-\infty}^{t} i\,dt$	$i = C\dfrac{de}{dt}$	(7–3)

In the first six chapters we have been concerned with the resistance element. In the present chapter we must extend our methods of analysis to include inductance and capacitance. First of all, we should observe that the volt-ampere relationships of Eqs. (7–1), (7–2), and (7–3) represent constraints which the elements impose on the currents and voltages. Either the current or the voltage can be considered to be the stimulus, and the other the response. Neither should be considered basic, and *the volt-ampere equations must be so thoroughly learned that they can be used with equal facility in either form.* The volt-ampere equations are the abc's of circuit theory; we cannot proceed further unless we are completely familiar with them.

Flux linkage and charge. The volt-ampere equations above are written in terms of the current and the voltage. These variables are basic in circuit theory and are the ones most often used. Occasionally, however, it is convenient to have a special name and a special symbol for the integral of the voltage, and another one for the integral of the current. The integral of the voltage is called the *flux linkage* and is represented by the symbol λ. Thus

$$\lambda = \int_{-\infty}^{t} e\,dt, \qquad (7–4)$$

and the current in an inductance is given by

$$i = \frac{\lambda}{L}. \tag{7-5}$$

The integral of the current is perhaps a more familiar concept than the integral of the voltage. It is the electric charge Q. By definition,

$$Q = \int_{-\infty}^{t} i \, dt. \tag{7-6}$$

In terms of the charge Q the voltage across a capacitance can be written as

$$e = \frac{1}{C} Q. \tag{7-7}$$

Duality. Duality for resistive circuits was discussed in Section 3-4. Duality is a transformation in which currents and voltages are interchanged.

Because of the symmetry of Eqs. (7-2) and (7-3) it is apparent that an interchange of current and voltage merely interchanges inductance and capacitance. Thus inductance and capacitance are dual quantities. The dual of a 5-henry inductance is a 5-farad capacitance, and the dual of a $\frac{1}{3}$-farad capacitance is a $\frac{1}{3}$-henry inductance. The duality transformation can be effected by writing the mesh equations of the original network (assumed to be planar), changing the currents to voltages, and interpreting the resulting equations as the node-voltage equations of the dual network. Alternatively, the dual network can be obtained by the geometrical method discussed in Chapter 3. An example of a duality transformation will now be given. The original network is shown in Fig. 7-1(a). The mesh equation for this circuit is

$$e_L + e_R + e_C = e(t)$$

or $\tag{7-8}$

$$3\frac{di}{dt} + 5i + \tfrac{1}{4} \int_{-\infty}^{t} i \, dt = e(t).$$

If voltages and currents are interchanged, Eq. (7-8) becomes

$$3\frac{de}{dt} + 5e + \tfrac{1}{4} \int_{-\infty}^{t} e \, dt = i(t). \tag{7-9}$$

This equation can be interpreted as the circuit of Fig. 7-1(b), consisting of a parallel combination of $C = 3$ farads, $L = 4$ henries, and $R = \frac{1}{5}$ ohm. The broken lines in Fig. 7-1(a) represent the

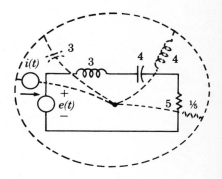

(a) Original circuit

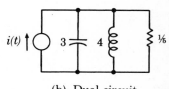

(b) Dual circuit

Figure 7-1. Duality in energy-storage circuits.

geometrical dual. If each broken line is replaced by the dual of the element through which it passes, the circuit of Fig. 7-1(b) is obtained. The current source is directed into the node because the voltage source tended to produce clockwise mesh current.

7-3 Initial energy storage

In circuits with only the resistance element, the currents and voltages are independent of time. As soon as inductance and capacitance are added the currents and voltages become functions of time and a time origin must be selected. Usually a problem begins when a source of energy is switched into the circuit and this instant is taken as $t = 0$. Any energy which is stored in the inductances or the capacitances in the circuit at $t = 0$ also contributes to the solution and must be accounted for. In fact these energy storages are equivalent to sources switched into the circuit at $t = 0$.

Energy in L and in C. Instantaneous power is given by the product of voltage and current. If the power is constant the energy is simply the product of the power and the time. It is given by the integral

$$W = \int_{t_1}^{t_2} e \times i \, dt, \qquad (7\text{-}10)$$

where t_1 and t_2 are the beginning and the ending of the interval over which the energy is to be measured, and W is the energy in watt-sec or joules. To account for the energy which has been stored in the inductance or the capacitance at any time in the past, t_1 must be taken as $-\infty$.

The energy stored in an inductance is

$$W_L = \int_{-\infty}^{t} e \times i \, dt = \int_{-\infty}^{t} L \frac{di}{dt} i \, dt. \qquad (7\text{-}11)$$

It is possible to change the variable in Eq. (7-11) from time to current. If the current is zero at $-\infty$, and at time t has a value of I, the integral becomes

$$W_L = \int_{0}^{I} Li \, di = \tfrac{1}{2}LI^2. \qquad (7\text{-}12)$$

The significance of Eq. (7-12) is that the energy stored in the inductance depends only on the instantaneous value of the current and not on the past history of the device, except as that past history has contributed to the current. A useful conclusion which can be drawn from Eq. (7-12) is that an inductance can be analyzed without a full knowledge of its past history. Indeed, all we need to know is the current which it is carrying at the start of our problem.

A similar situation holds for the capacitance. The energy stored in a capacitance is

$$W_C = \int_{-\infty}^{t} e \times i\, dt = \int_{-\infty}^{t} e \times C \frac{de}{dt}\, dt. \qquad (7\text{--}13)$$

If the voltage at $t = -\infty$ is assumed to be zero, and the voltage at $t = t$ is E, the integral becomes

$$W_C = \int_{0}^{E} Ce\, de = \tfrac{1}{2}CE^2. \qquad (7\text{--}14)$$

The energy in the capacitance depends only on the voltage across it at the instant in question. It is not necessary to know the past behavior of the capacitance in order to be able to predict its future behavior. The past behavior is summed up in the energy stored in the capacitance at the beginning of the problem.

Equivalent sources for initial energy storage. The energy stored in an inductance or a capacitance at the beginning of a problem is capable of exciting the circuit and is equivalent in every respect to an externally applied source. It is very convenient to sum up the whole past behavior of an energy storage element in terms of its energy state at the beginning of a problem, and to replace this energy by an equivalent exciting source for the network.

The inductance element is completely described by the volt-ampere equation

$$i_L = \frac{1}{L} \int_{-\infty}^{t} e\, dt = \frac{1}{L} \int_{-\infty}^{0^+} e\, dt + \frac{1}{L} \int_{0^+}^{t} e\, dt. \qquad (7\text{--}15)$$

In Eq. (7–15) the integral from minus infinity to t represents the present flux linkages stored in the inductance as a summation of all the deposits and withdrawals over all time. The integration can be broken up into two parts. The first part is the net flux linkage which is present at $t = 0^+$ as a result of all the operations prior to this time. This integral divided by the inductance is the initial current in the inductance. The time $t = 0^+$ is used rather than $t = 0$ in order to include the effects of any switching operations which occur between $t = 0^-$ and $t = 0^+$. The second part of the integration is the volt-ampere equation of an inductance which is unfluxed at $t = 0$ and has no initial energy storage. Equation (7–15) thus shows that an inductance with an initial current can be replaced by an inductance without initial current, in parallel with a current source with a value equal to the initial current in the inductance.

An inductance with an initial current is shown in Fig. 7–2(a) and an equivalent circuit which has the same volt-ampere equation for

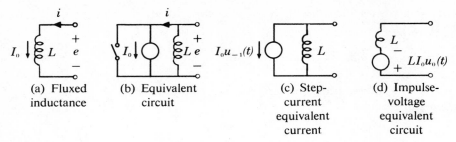

| (a) Fluxed inductance | (b) Equivalent circuit | (c) Step-current equivalent current | (d) Impulse-voltage equivalent circuit |

Figure 7–2. Equivalent circuits for an inductance with an initial current.

$t > 0$ is shown in Fig. 7–2(b). The switch is closed before $t = 0$ and opened at $t = 0$. Before $t = 0$ the voltage e is identically zero and no current can build up in the inductance. When the switch is opened the terminal current is

$$i = \frac{1}{L} \int_{0^+}^{t} e \, dt + I_0. \tag{7-16}$$

Equation (7–16) is identical to Eq. (7–15), and thus verifies the equivalence of Fig. 7–2(a) and (b). The constant current and the switch of Fig. 7–2(b) are equivalent to a step-current source as shown in Fig. 7–2(c). Thus we have shown that

An initial current in an inductance is equivalent to a step-current source of the same value in parallel with the unfluxed inductance.

A final equivalent circuit for the initial current in the inductance is shown in Fig. 7–2(d). It is obtained by applying Thévenin's theorem to the circuit of Fig. 7–2(c). The open-circuit voltage is

$$e_{0C} = L \frac{d}{dt} [I_0 u_{-1}(t)] = L I_0 u_0(t). \tag{7-17}$$

The impulse voltage of Eq. (7–17) appears in series with the un-fluxed inductance.

Similar arguments hold for the capacitance element. It is completely described by the volt-ampere equation

$$e_C = \frac{1}{C} \int_{-\infty}^{+} i \, dt = \frac{1}{C} \int_{-\infty}^{0^+} i \, dt + \frac{t}{C} \int_{0^+}^{t} i \, dt. \tag{7-18}$$

The integral from $-\infty$ to t represents the net charge on the capacitance at time t. If the integration is broken up into two parts, the integral from $-\infty$ to 0 represents the charge at $t = 0^+$, and this integral divided by C is the voltage on the capacitance at $t = 0$.

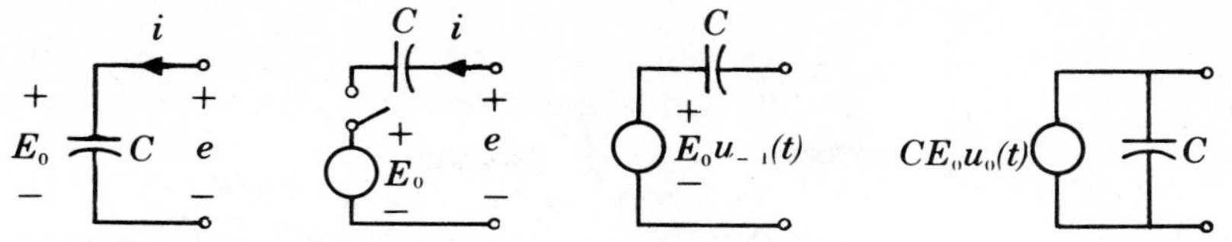

Figure 7–3. Equivalent circuits for a capacitance with an initial voltage.

The integral from $t = 0^+$ to t represents the volt-ampere equation of a capacitance which is uncharged at $t = 0$. Equation (7–18) thus shows that a capacitance with an initial voltage can be replaced by an uncharged capacitance in series with a voltage source with a value equal to the initial voltage on the capacitance.

A capacitance with an initial voltage is shown in Fig. 7–3(a), and an equivalent circuit which has the same volt-ampere equation for $t > 0$ is shown in Fig. 7–3(b). The switch is held open before $t = 0$ and closed at $t = 0$. Before $t = 0$, the current is identically zero so that there is no voltage on the capacitance. When the switch is closed the terminal voltage is

$$e = \frac{1}{C} \int_{0^+}^{t} i \, dt + E_0. \tag{7–19}$$

Equation (7–19) is identical to Eq. (7–18), and the equivalence of Fig. 7–3(a) and (b) is verified. The constant voltage source and the switch of Fig. 7–3(b) are equivalent to the step-voltage source of Fig. 7–3(c). We have thus shown that

An initial voltage on a capacitance is equivalent to a step-voltage source of the same value in series with the uncharged capacitance.

A final equivalent circuit for the initial voltage on the capacitance is shown in Fig. 7–3(d). It is obtained by applying Norton's theorem to the circuit of Fig. 7–3(c). The short-circuit current is

$$i_{sc} = C \frac{d}{dt}[E_0 u_{-1}(t)] = C E_0 u_0(t). \tag{7–20}$$

The impulse current of Eq. (7–20) appears in parallel with the uncharged capacitance.

Computations between 0^- and 0^+. For a variety of reasons it is desirable to compute the initial values of the variables in a problem. By the initial values we mean the values at $t = 0^+$ after the switching operations are over. These values are used directly in solving the differential equations of the circuit, and they serve as convenient check points if the solution is obtained in some other fashion. Fortunately an *R-L-C* circuit reduces to pure resistances between $t = 0^-$ and $t = 0^+$, and the calculations are relatively easy.

Inductance. For an inductance the energy and hence the current cannot be changed in zero time unless an impulse of infinite voltage is applied. The current change between $t = 0^-$ and $t = 0^+$ is given by

$$\Delta i_L = \frac{1}{L} \int_{0^-}^{0^+} e\, dt. \qquad (7\text{–}21)$$

Equation (7–21) is zero unless there is an impulse voltage of area A flux linkages occurring between 0^- and 0^+. Under these circumstances the current changes suddenly by the finite amount

$$\Delta i_L = \frac{A}{L}. \qquad (7\text{–}22)$$

Between $t = 0^-$ and $t = 0^+$ the inductance behaves like an open circuit. A step voltage applied to it creates no initial current. An impulse voltage creates the indeterminate situation of an infinite voltage across an infinite resistance which is resolved by the use of the integral of Eq. (7–21). An initial current in the inductance at $t = 0^-$ adds a current source in parallel with the open-circuit for the interval from $t = 0^-$ to $t = 0^+$. These equivalents are shown in Fig. 7–4.

Capacitance. The energy associated with the voltage on a capacitance cannot be changed in zero time unless an impulse of infinite current occurs. The voltage change between $t = 0^-$ and $t = 0^+$ is given by

$$\Delta e_C = \frac{1}{C} \int_{0^-}^{0^+} i\, dt. \qquad (7\text{–}23)$$

Equation (7–23) is zero unless there is an impulse current of area A coulombs occurring between 0^- and 0^+. Under these circumstances the voltage changes suddenly by the finite amount

$$\Delta e_C = \frac{A}{C}. \qquad (7\text{–}24)$$

Between $t = 0^-$ and $t = 0^+$ the capacitance behaves like a short circuit. A step current applied to it creates no initial voltage. An impulse current creates the indeterminate situation of an infinite current through zero resistance and the indeterminacy must be re-

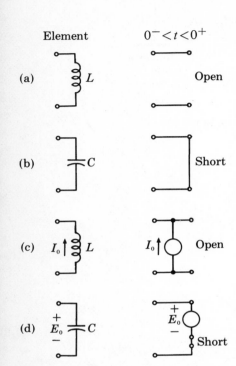

Figure 7–4. The behavior of inductance and capacitance between $t = 0^-$ and $t = 0^+$.

solved by the use of the integral of Eq. (7–23). An initial voltage on the capacitance at $t = 0$ adds a voltage source in series with the short circuit for the interval from $t = 0^-$ to $t = 0^+$. These equivalents are shown in Fig. 7–4.

As an example, we will compute the "initial" values (values at $t = 0^+$) just after a switching operation, for the circuit of Fig. 7–5(a). The switch is closed upon the direct voltage source at $t = 0^-$. The currents and voltages are to be found at the instant just after the switch is closed, $t = 0^+$. At this instant the inductance is an open circuit and the capacitance is a short circuit. The equivalent resistive circuit for computations between $t = 0^-$ and $t = 0^+$ is shown in Fig. 7–5(b). The currents and voltages computed from this circuit are

$$i_1 = 5 \text{ amp}, \quad i_2 = 2.5 \text{ amp}, \quad i_3 = 2.5 \text{ amp},$$

$$e_L = 5 \text{ volts}.$$

A second example of computations at $t = 0^+$ is shown in Fig. 7–6(a). The initial energy stored in the capacitance is replaced by a constant voltage source. The equivalent resistive circuit at $t = 0^+$ is shown in Fig. 7–6(b). Because the inductance is an open circuit, the current is

$$i(0^+) = 0.$$

Although the current is zero, its derivative is not zero. By Kirchhoff's law, the voltage across the inductance is

$$e_L = 5 \text{ volts},$$

and hence

$$\frac{di}{dt} = \frac{1}{L} e_L = \tfrac{5}{3} \text{ volts}.$$

By using Kirchhoff's laws and the volt-ampere equations of the elements, and by differentiating them as many times as necessary, we can find as many derivatives as we wish.* We shall pursue the matter only as far as the second derivative of the current.

By Kirchhoff's law, for the circuit of Fig. 7–6(a) we write

$$e_L + e_R + e_C = 10$$

or

$$L \frac{di}{dt} + Ri + \frac{1}{C} \int_{-\infty}^{t} i \, dt = 10.$$

---

* An expression for the unknown current or voltage can then be written, of course, in terms of Maclaurin's series.

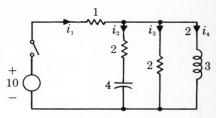

(a) Complete circuit, switch closed at $t = 0$

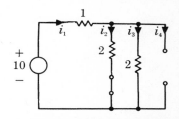

(b) Equivalent resistive circuit at $t = 0^+$

Figure 7–5. An example of computations between $t = 0^-$ and $t = 0^+$.

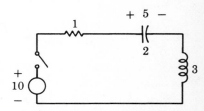

(a) Circuit with initial energy storage, switch closed at $t = 0$

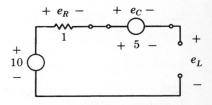

(b) Equivalent circuit for $t = 0^+$

Figure 7–6. Computations at $t = 0^+$ for a circuit with initial energy storage.

The integral from $-\infty$ to 0 is the initial voltage of 5 volts on the capacitance, and hence we can write

$$L\frac{di}{dt} + Ri + \frac{1}{C}\int_0^t i\,dt = 5 \text{ volts.}$$

This result could have been obtained more directly from the equivalent circuit of Fig. 7–6(b). To obtain a second derivative we must differentiate both sides of this equation. In order to avoid any questions which might arise right at the switching instant, we will perform the differentiation at $t = 0^+$. Since the upper limit of the integral is a variable, the derivative of the integral is the integrand. After $t = 0$ the applied voltages are constant and the derivative of the right side of the equation is zero. Thus we obtain

$$L\frac{d^2i}{dt^2} + R\frac{di}{dt} + \frac{i}{C} = 0,$$

and the value of the second derivative at $t = 0$ is

$$\frac{d^2i}{dt^2} = \frac{1}{L}\left(-R\frac{di}{dt} - i\right)$$
$$= \tfrac{1}{3}(-1 \times \tfrac{5}{3} - 0)$$
$$= -\tfrac{5}{9}\text{ amp/sec/sec.}$$

Computations at $t = \infty$***.*** When a switching operation takes place at $t = 0$ in a circuit, there is a redistribution of energy and the currents and voltages change over a period of time. If we wait long enough, however, the transient variations die out and the currents and voltages reach new steady values. The voltage across each inductance drops to zero and the current in each capacitance drops to zero. The inductance is thus indistinguishable from a short circuit, and the capacitance is indistinguishable from an open circuit. This equivalence applies to all real physical sources and circuits, but it cannot be applied to idealized sources which continue to vary indefinitely nor to idealized lossless circuits in which transient variations would never die out. The equivalent circuits are shown in Fig. 7–7.

The computation of "final" values (values at $t = \infty$) for the circuit of Fig. 7–8(a) proceeds as follows. After all the transients have died out the currents and voltages can be found from the purely resistive circuit of Fig. 7–8(b). The values are

$$i_L = 5 \text{ amp}, \qquad e_C = 5 \text{ volts.}$$

The energy stored in the two elements at $t = \infty$ can be computed

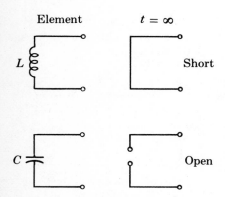

Figure 7–7. The behavior of inductance and capacitance at $t = \infty$.

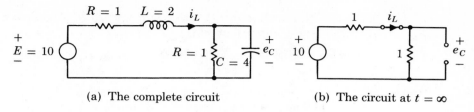

(a) The complete circuit   (b) The circuit at $t = \infty$

Figure 7–8. An example of computations at $t = \infty$.

from these values, even though the values themselves are determined strictly by the resistive circuit. The energy in the inductance is

$$W_L = \tfrac{1}{2}Li_L^2 = \tfrac{1}{2} \times 2 \times (5)^2 = 25 \text{ joules.}$$

The energy in the capacitance is

$$W_C = \tfrac{1}{2}Ce_C^2 = \tfrac{1}{2} \times 4 \times (5)^2 = 50 \text{ joules.}$$

At $t = 0^+$ and at $t = \infty$ the most complicated circuits involving resistance, inductance, and capacitance reduce to pure resistance circuits and can be solved with relative ease. Most of the methods for solving general circuit problems make use of this fact. In the solution of differential equations the initial values of the variable and its derivatives must be known. For the method of matching a known characteristic behavior to the boundary conditions at $t = 0$ and at $t = \infty$, the initial and final values are, of course, essential. Even for the transform methods considered in the latter part of this book, the initial conditions must be specified.

7–4 Single-element response functions

We shall obtain the step responses of the elements and then the impulse responses, because step functions are inherently simpler and represent many practical switching problems. We have a dual point of view: A response may be the solution to an actual physical problem, or it may be a method of characterizing the network. The step response is more important than the impulse response from the first point of view but less important from the second.

Step-responses of the single elements. *Resistance.* The resistance element has the property of relating voltage and current by a constant multiplier. It does not change the waveform. Thus a step-function excitation gives rise to a step-function response with a different amplitude. If a current $i(t) = Iu_{-1}(t)$ is applied to a resistance of value R, the voltage response is

$$e(t) = IRu_{-1}(t). \tag{7–25}$$

If a voltage $e(t) = Eu_{-1}(t)$ is applied to a resistance of value R, the resulting current is

$$i(t) = \frac{E}{R} u_{-1}(t). \tag{7–26}$$

Inductance. The inductance element has the volt-ampere equations

$$e_L = L\frac{di}{dt} \quad \text{and} \quad i_L = \frac{1}{L}\int_{-\infty}^{t} e\, dt.$$

When a step function of voltage, $e(t) = Eu_{-1}(t)$, is applied, the response current is the integral, or*

$$i_L = \frac{E}{L} u_{-2}(t). \tag{7–27}$$

When the input is a current step, $i(t) = Iu_{-1}(t)$, the response voltage is the derivative, or

$$e_L = LIu_0(t). \tag{7–28}$$

According to Eq. (7–27), if a voltage of value E is suddenly connected to an inductance, the current builds up at a linear rate of E/L amp per sec, and continues to increase so long as the voltage is present. Equation (7–28) shows that if a step function of current is forced through an inductance, an infinite voltage is produced across the inductance for a very short time. The LI flux linkages equal the area under the impulse.

Both these response functions have practical applications. A stalled starter-motor in a car represents practically a pure inductance. When the battery is connected to it, the current rises to a very large value. In Eq. (7–28), the very high voltage which exists for a short time is the basis of the automobile ignition system. A step current is applied to a coil, and the very large voltage which occurs across it produces the spark.

Capacitance. The capacitance element has the volt-ampere equations

$$e_C = \frac{1}{C}\int_{-\infty}^{t} i\, dt \quad \text{and} \quad i_C = C\frac{de}{dt}.$$

If the input is a step current, $i(t) = Iu_{-1}(t)$, the voltage response is

$$e_C = \frac{I}{C} u_{-2}(t). \tag{7–29}$$

The voltage in Eq. (7–29) rises linearly at a rate of I/C volts per sec.

---

* The student is cautioned against memorizing these results. There are too many of them! They should be worked out as needed from the volt-ampere equations.

This result is utilized in producing *sweep* voltages to move the light spot across cathode ray and television tubes. If the input is a step voltage, $e(t) = Eu_{-1}(t)$, the current response is

$$i_C = ECu_0(t). \tag{7-30}$$

When the capacitance is connected across the constant voltage it becomes charged in a very short time to the value of the voltage source. The amount of charge required to produce the voltage is

$$Q = EC. \tag{7-31}$$

The charge is the area under the impulse current. The amount of charge is important, but the exact shape of the current-versus-time curve is of very little consequence. One practical application of this sort of impulse current is in "flash" photography. A capacitance is charged to a high voltage and then discharged through the low resistance of a gas tube. The impulse current causes the gas tube to produce a flash of visible light.

Impulse responses of the single elements. Although the step response can be used to characterize a network, the impulse response is more useful. Some students find the impulse response more difficult to visualize than the step response. In this connection it is well to remember that an *impulse current is a charge, Q, which flows during a short time*, and an *impulse voltage is a flux linkage, λ, which attaches itself to a circuit in a brief time.*

Resistance. A resistance element changes an impulse current into an impulse voltage and vice versa, but it does not change the time function. If the stimulus is the current $i(t) = Qu_0(t)$, the response is the voltage

$$e_R(t) = QRu_0(t). \tag{7-32}$$

If the stimulus is the voltage $e(t) = \lambda u_0(t)$, the response is the current

$$i_R(t) = \frac{\lambda}{R} u_0(t). \tag{7-33}$$

In Eq. (7-32) the impulse current of Q coulombs is changed into an impulse voltage of QR flux linkages. In Eq. (7-33) the impulse voltage of λ flux linkages is changed into an impulse current of λ/R coulombs.*

Inductance. When the impulse voltage $e(t) = \lambda u_0(t)$ is applied to an inductance the response current is

$$i_L = \frac{1}{L} \int_{-\infty}^{t} \lambda u_0(t)\, dt = \frac{\lambda}{L} u_{-1}(t). \tag{7-34}$$

---

* One problem with the singularity functions is that they are not dimensionless. For example, $u_0(t)$ has the dimensions 1/time.

The impulse voltage causes a current to start instantly in the inductance, and the current continues to flow forever. Both these conclusions may seem strange. It is as though we had a paper bag full of flux linkages which we threw at the coil at time $t = 0$. The bag breaks when it strikes the coil, and the flux linkages attach themselves to the coil in zero time. Since each flux linkage is associated with a current, the current is established in zero time.

The current flowing indefinitely in the circuit is a consequence of the assumption of an ideal inductance. Most physical inductors are constructed from wire which has loss characteristics; therefore the energy is gradually dissipated and the current decays to zero. Certain "superconductors" at very low temperatures verify the theory. If a current is created in a superconductive coil, which has zero loss below a particular temperature, the current continues for months or even years with no measurable decay.

When the impulse current $i(t) = Qu_0(t)$ is applied to an inductance the response voltage is

$$e(t) = L \frac{d[Qu_0(t)]}{dt} = LQu_1(t). \qquad (7\text{–}35)$$

The impulse current produces a doublet of voltage. While the infinite current is being established an infinite voltage is produced across the inductance, opposing the current flow; when the current is removed an infinite voltage is produced in the opposite direction, and this voltage tends to keep the current flowing.

Capacitance. When an impulse current $i(t) = Qu_0(t)$ is applied to a capacitance the response voltage is

$$e(t) = \frac{1}{C} \int_{-\infty}^{t} Qu_0(t)\, dt = \frac{Q}{C} u_{-1}(t). \qquad (7\text{–}36)$$

The impulse current causes a voltage to appear immediately on the capacitance, and the voltage remains there indefinitely. The voltage rises on the capacitance, because the coulombs suddenly appear there. It is as though we had a bucket of coulombs which we suddenly dumped into the capacitance at $t = 0$. As soon as the coulombs appear on the capacitance the voltage rises to its new value.*

We are much more used to the idea of perfect capacitance than to the idea of perfect inductance, and it is not surprising that volt-

---

* A capacitance may be likened to a bathtub, and the coulombs which fill the capacitance may be likened to water which fills the tub. A step current applied to the capacitance is analogous to a tap turned on in the tub. The tub fills at a linear rate. An impulse current applied to the capacitance is analogous to a bucket of water dumped suddenly into the tub. The water level rises in essentially zero time.

age remains on the capacitance indefinitely. A perfect capacitance has zero leakage, or an infinite resistance across its plates. Practical capacitors can very closely approach the ideal; they can hold their charge for hours, days, or even months.

When the impulse voltage $e(t) = \lambda u_0(t)$ is applied to a capacitance the response current is

$$i(t) = C\frac{d[\lambda u_0(t)]}{dt} = C\lambda u_1(t). \qquad (7\text{–}37)$$

The impulse voltage produces a doublet of current. While the infinite voltage is being established a large current must flow in the positive direction. In order for the voltage to drop to zero again the current must reverse and carry away the charge which accumulated on the capacitance.

The impulse responses which we have considered in this section are somewhat more difficult than the step responses. The mathematical expressions are sufficiently straightforward, but the circuit interpretations involve some indeterminate forms. A voltage impulse applied to an inductance starts up a current in zero time, even though the inductance is an open circuit at $t = 0$. A current impulse applied to a capacitance instantly produces a voltage across it, even though the capacitance is a short circuit at $t = 0$. We shall make use of these results in later chapters.

Summary

The volt-ampere equations

Resistance

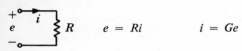

$$e = Ri \qquad i = Ge$$

Inductance

$$e = L\frac{di}{dt} \qquad i = \frac{1}{L}\int_{-\infty}^{t} e\,dt$$

Capacitance

$$e = \frac{1}{C}\int_{-\infty}^{t} i\,dt \qquad i = C\frac{de}{dt}$$

Duality

L and C are dual quantities.

Initial conditions as singularity functions

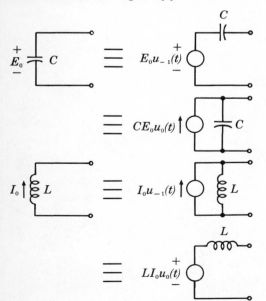

Computations at $t = 0$ and $t = \infty$

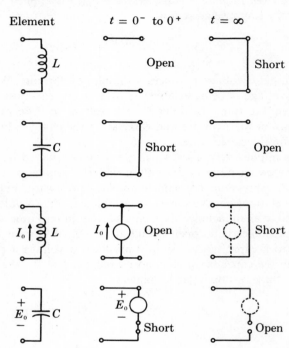

Element	$t = 0^-$ to 0^+	$t = \infty$
L	Open	Short
C	Short	Open
I_0 L	I_0 Open	Short
E_0 C	E_0 Short	Open

Step function responses of single elements

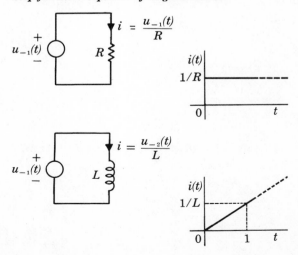

$$i = \frac{u_{-1}(t)}{R}$$

$$i = \frac{u_{-2}(t)}{L}$$

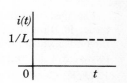

$i = Cu_0(t)$

$u_{-1}(t)$ C

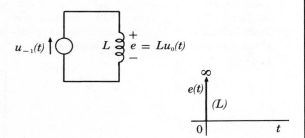

$u_{-1}(t)$ R $e = Ru_{-1}(t)$

$u_{-1}(t)$ L $e = Lu_0(t)$

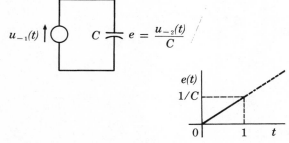

$u_{-1}(t)$ C $e = \dfrac{u_{-2}(t)}{C}$

Impulse responses of single elements

$u_0(t)$ R $i = \dfrac{u_0(t)}{R}$

$i = \dfrac{u_{-1}(t)}{L}$

$u_0(t)$ L

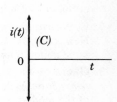

$i = Cu_1(t)$

$u_0(t)$ C

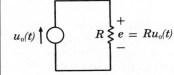

$u_0(t)$ R $e = Ru_0(t)$

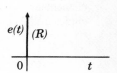

$u_0(t)$ L $e = Lu_1(t)$

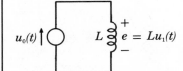

$u_0(t)$ C $e = \dfrac{u_{-1}(t)}{C}$

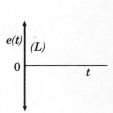

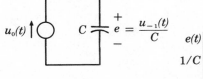

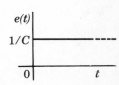

References

The best references for the formulation of the basic differential equations of electric circuits are the books which present the theory of Laplace transforms. Specific references are listed below.

1. D. K. CHENG, *Analysis of Linear Systems*, Addison-Wesley, Reading, Mass., 1959. Cheng gives a brief but excellent treatment of the formulation of the differential equations for circuits and the evaluation of initial conditions.

2. E. WEBER, *Linear Transient Analysis*, John Wiley, New York, 1954. This text covers essentially the same material as does Cheng's.

3. GARDNER and BARNES, *Transients in Linear Systems*, John Wiley, New York, 1942. The first of the modern texts on Laplace transforms. The treatment of source transformations is especially complete.

4. M. E. VAN VALKENBURG, *Network Analysis*, Prentice-Hall, New Jersey, 1955. A slightly more elementary version of Laplace transforms. Includes initial conditions and mutual inductance.

5. SESHU and BALABANIAN, *Linear Network Analysis*, John Wiley, New York, 1959. This text is one of the few to discuss initial conditions in the presence of impulses.

6. E. A. GUILLEMIN, *Introductory Circuit Theory*, John Wiley, New York, 1953. Guillemin gives the general volt-ampere relationships of the elements and an elementary treatment of circuits based on the singularity functions.

7. H. G. BOOKER, *An Approach to Electrical Science*, McGraw-Hill, New York, 1959. The first section of this book is concerned with pure capacitance networks and the second with pure resistance networks. The third section contains a chapter on pure inductance networks.

8. BRENNER and JAVID, *Analysis of Electric Circuits*, McGraw-Hill, New York, 1959. Brenner and Javid begin their book with a discussion of single-element circuits. They consider impulses only as responses.

Exercises

SECTION 7–2

1. Sketch the currents in the circuits of Fig. 7–9 as functions of time. The switches are closed at $t = 0$.

2. Sketch the voltages which appear across the elements in the circuits of Fig. 7–10 as functions of time. The switches are opened at $t = 0$.

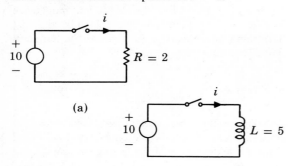

(a)

(b)

Figure 7–9

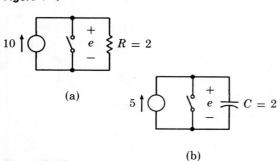

(a)

(b)

Figure 7–10

3. The switches in the circuits of Fig. 7–11 are closed at $t = 0$. Find the analytic expressions for the currents which flow after $t = 0$.

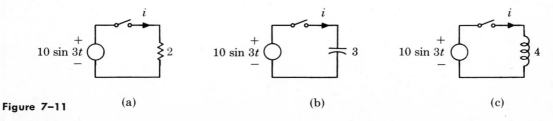

(a)

(b)

(c)

Figure 7–11

4. The switches in the circuits of Fig. 7–12 are opened at $t = 0$. Find the analytic expressions for the voltages which appear across the elements for $t > 0$.

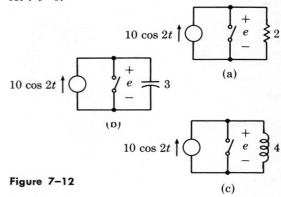

(a)

(b)

(c)

Figure 7–12

5. (a) The switch in the circuit of Fig. 7–13 is closed at $t = 0$. How much charge flows from the battery to the capacitor? How long does it take? (b) The switch in the circuit of Fig. 7–14 is opened at $t = 0$. How many flux linkages are created in the inductance? How long before they appear?

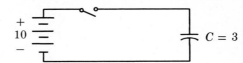

Figure 7–13

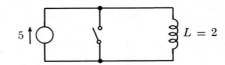

Figure 7–14

6. (a) A constant current of 4 amp is fed into a capacitance of 2 f, starting at $t = 0$. How much energy is stored after 10 sec? How much after 100 sec? (The capacitance has no leakage resistance.) (b) A constant voltage of 6 v is connected across an inductance of 2 h. What is the energy stored after 5 sec? What is it after 10 sec? (Assume a perfect inductance with no series resistance.)

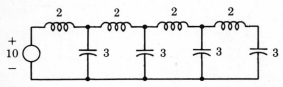

Figure 7-15

7. Find the dual of the circuit of Fig. 7-15.

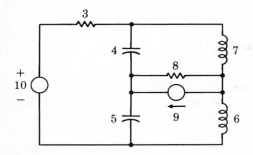

Figure 7-16

8. Find the dual of the circuit of Fig. 7-16.

SECTION 7-3

9. The switch in the circuit of Fig. 7-17 is closed at $t = 0$. Give the voltage-source equivalent circuit for the network to the left of the terminals a-b. Give also the current-source equivalent circuit.

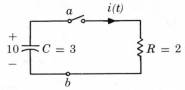

Figure 7-17

10. The switch in the circuit of Fig. 7-18 is opened at $t = 0$. Draw the equivalent voltage-source cir-

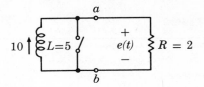

Figure 7-18

cuit for the network to the left of the terminals a-b. Also draw the equivalent current-source circuit.

11. Show that the circuits used to represent the initial energy stored in the capacitance and inductance in Figs. 7-17 and 7-18 can be obtained by applying Thévenin's and Norton's theorems at the terminal-pair a-b in each case.

12. What is the initial current which flows at $t = 0^+$ in the circuit of Fig. 7-17? What is the derivative of this current at $t = 0^+$?

13. What is the initial voltage produced across the resistance at $t = 0^+$ in the circuit of Fig. 7-18? What is the derivative of this voltage at $t = 0^+$?

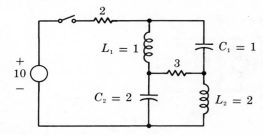

Figure 7-19

14. The switch in the circuit of Fig. 7-19 is closed at $t = 0$. Compute the voltage across each inductance at $t = 0$ and the voltage across each capacitance at $t = \infty$.

15. (a) In the circuit of Fig. 7-20 compute the current at $t = 0^+$ by replacing the impulse voltage and

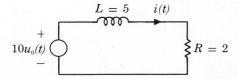

Figure 7-20

the inductance by an inductance with an initial energy storage. (b) As an alternative, treat the inductance as an open circuit from $t = 0^-$ to $t = 0^+$, and compute the current established in it by the infinite impulse voltage by means of the voltage-current equation for the inductance.

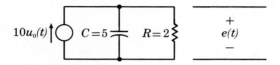

Figure 7–21

16. (a) In the circuit of Fig. 7–21 compute the initial voltage at $t = 0^+$ by replacing the impulse current source and the uncharged capacitance by the equivalent charged capacitance. (b) Obtain the same result by treating the capacitance as a short circuit for the interval from $t = 0^-$ to $t = 0^+$ and evaluate the voltage established in it by the infinite current by means of the volt-ampere equation of the capacitance.

SECTION 7–4

17. (a) A step voltage of value $e(t) = 100u_{-1}(t)$ is applied to (i) a resistance of 10 ohms, (ii) an inductance of 3 h, and (iii) a capacitance of $\frac{1}{6}$ f. In each case give the resulting currents in analytic form and sketch them. (b) A step current of $i(t) = 100u_{-1}(t)$ is applied to (i) a resistance of 3 ohms, (ii) an inductance of 7 h, and (iii) a capacitance of 4 f. In each case give analytical expression for the resulting voltage and sketch it.

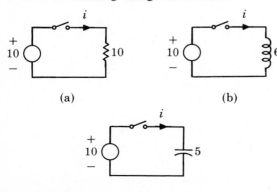

Figure 7–22

18. (a) In the circuits of Fig. 7–22 the switches are closed at $t = 0$. Give analytical expressions for the resulting currents in terms of the singularity functions. (b) In the circuits of Fig. 7–23 the switches are opened at $t = 0$. Give expressions for the voltages in terms of the singularity functions.

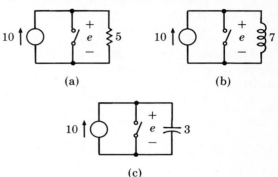

Figure 7–23

19. (a) The voltage

$$e(t) = 10u_{-1}(t) - 10u_{-1}(t - 1)$$

is applied to the parallel combination of $R = 5$, $L = 5$, and $C = \frac{1}{5}$. Give the analytical expression for the input current and sketch it. (b) The current $i(t) = 10u_{-1}(t) - 10u_{-1}(t - 1)$ is applied to the series combination of $R = \frac{1}{5}$, $L = \frac{1}{5}$, and $C = 5$. Give the analytical expression for the voltage across the combination and sketch the waveform.

20. (a) A certain two-terminal device has the following current response to a step-voltage stimulus:

$$i(t) = 5u_{-1}(t) + 6u_0(t) + 3u_{-2}(t).$$

Give a possible circuit which could represent the device. (b) A certain two-terminal device has the following voltage response to an applied step-current stimulus:

$$e(t) = 3u_{-1}(t) + \tfrac{1}{3}u_0(t) + \tfrac{7}{8}u_{-2}(t).$$

Give a possible circuit which could represent the device.

21. (a) An impulse voltage $e(t) = 100u_0(t)$ is applied to (i) a resistance of 10 ohms, (ii) an inductance of 3 h, and (iii) a capacitance of 5 f. Write an analytical expression for the current which flows

in each case and sketch it. (b) An impulse current $i(t) = 13u_0(t)$ is applied to (i) a resistance of 4 ohms, (ii) an inductance of 5 h, and (iii) a capacitance of $\frac{1}{3}$ f. Write an analytical expression for the voltage which occurs in each case and sketch it.

22. (a) The voltage $e(t) = 10u_0(t) - 10u_0(t - 1)$ is applied to the parallel combination of $R = 2$, $L = 5$, and $C = \frac{1}{4}$. Give the analytical expression for the current drawn from the source and sketch it. (b) The current $i(t) = 10u_0(t) - 10u_0(t - 1)$ is applied to the series combination of $R = \frac{1}{2}$, $L = \frac{1}{4}$, and $C = 5$. Give the analytical expression for the voltage produced across the combination and sketch it.

23. (a) A voltage $e(t) = 10u_0(t) - 10u_1(t)$ is applied to a parallel combination of $R = 2$, $L = 2$,

and $C = \frac{1}{2}$. Write an expression for the input current and sketch it. (b) A current $i(t) = 5u_0(t) - 10u_{-1}(t)$ is applied to a series combination of $R = 2$, $C = \frac{1}{4}$, and $L = 1$. Find the resulting voltage as a function of time, and sketch it.

24. (a) The response of a two-terminal network to an input impulse voltage is the current

$$i(t) = 10u_{-1}(t) + 5u_0(t) + 3u_1(t).$$

What is a possible network which would give this response? (b) The response of a two-terminal network to an impulse-current excitation is the voltage

$$e(t) = 7u_1(t) + \tfrac{1}{3}u_0(t) + \tfrac{1}{15}u_{-1}(t).$$

What is a possible network which would have this response?

Problems

1. The switch in the circuit of Fig. 7–24 is opened at $t = 0$. Previous to this time a steady-state condition has been attained. Find the voltage and the first derivative of the voltage across the capacitance just after the switch is opened. What value will it have at $t = \infty$?

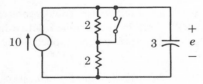

Figure 7–24

2. The switch in the circuit of Fig. 7–25 is closed at $t = 0$, at which time steady-state conditions are present in the network to the left of the switch. Find the initial current through the switch, its first derivative, and its value at $t = \infty$.

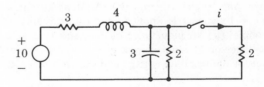

Figure 7–25

3. The switch in the circuit of Fig. 7–26 is opened at $t = 0$. Find the initial value of the voltage, $e(t)$, and its first three derivatives.

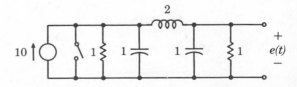

Figure 7–26

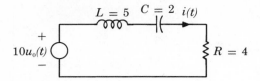

Figure 7–27

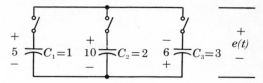

Figure 7–30

4. (a) Find $i(0^+)$ and $di(0^+)/dt$ for the circuit of Fig. 7–27. (b) Formulate and solve the dual problem of part (a).

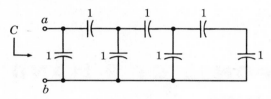

Figure 7–28

5. (a) Derive the formula for combining capacitances in series and in parallel. (b) Find the equivalent capacitance C at terminal-pair a–b in the circuit of Fig. 7–28.

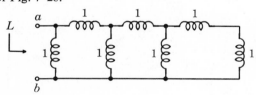

Figure 7–29

6. (a) Derive the formulas for combining inductances in series and in parallel. (b) Find the equivalent inductance L at the terminal-pair a–b in the circuit of Fig. 7–29.

7. In the circuit of Fig. 7–30 the capacitance C_1 has a voltage of 5 v, the capacitance C_2 has a voltage of 10 v, and the capacitance C_3 has a voltage of -6 v. The three capacitances are connected at $t = 0$. What will the voltage be across the combination for $t > 0$?

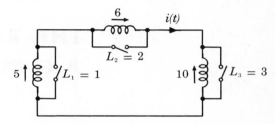

Figure 7–31

8. In the circuit of Fig. 7–31 the three switches are opened at $t = 0$. Previous to this time there is a current in L_1 of 5 amp, a current in L_2 of 6 amp, and a current in L_3 of -10 amp. What current will flow through the three series inductances for $t > 0$?

CHAPTER **8**

THE RESPONSE OF *R-L* AND *R-C* CIRCUITS

The theory of differential equations is the most important branch of mathematics. It occupies a central position from which lines of development extend in many directions.

SOPHUS LIE

8–1 Introduction

Electric circuits are described by linear differential equations with constant coefficients. Since differential equations represent circuits, the concepts of stimulus and response are applicable. The simplest sort of stimulus for a network is provided by energy initially stored in one of the circuit elements. The stored energy causes currents to flow in the circuit. As the currents flow, the energy is dissipated in the resistances, and eventually the currents decrease to zero. The response of a network to an initial energy storage is a characteristic of the network, known as the network's *natural behavior*, or its *transient response*. The term *force-free behavior* is also applied to this response function, since it is produced by the network without an externally applied source. From a mathematical standpoint the natural behavior is the solution of the differential equation with the sources equated to zero. This solution is called the *complementary function*. All four of these names are in general use, and we shall make no distinction among them.

The response of a network to an impulse source is very similar to the network's natural behavior. The impulse exists only between $t = 0^-$ and $t = 0^+$. The impulse stores energy during this interval and the stored energy produces the natural behavior of the network after the impulse is over. Thus, *after $t = 0^+$ the impulse response of a network is equal to its natural behavior.*

The response of a network to excitation by a step function can be found by integration of the impulse response. In this case a final value, or *steady-state solution*, exists which is proportional to the excitation and does not decrease to zero with time. The steady-state value is simply the solution for the network at $t = \infty$; it is identical to the direct-current value treated in earlier chapters. The *complete solution* of a network differential equation is the sum of the natural behavior and the steady-state solution. The transient solution provides a smooth transition from the initial energy state of the network, as represented by the initial values of the currents and voltages, to the final energy state, as represented by the final values of the currents and voltages. The steady-state solution is also called *the forced solution* or the *particular integral* of the differential equation.

8–2 The first-order differential equation

An electric circuit with a single energy-storage element is represented by a first-order differential equation. The problem, however, is not completely described by the differential equation. The energy initially stored must also be stated. A knowledge of the stored energy is required to compute the initial value of the variable of interest in the problem. In summary, the specification of a problem concerned with single energy storage requires:

1. The statement of the differential equation.
2. The initial value of the variable.

The differential equation is written by using Kirchhoff's laws. The initial value of the variable is computed (by the methods described in Chapter 7) from the purely resistive circuit which holds at $t = 0$. We will now consider the solution of the differential equation.

R-L circuit. An example of a single-energy-storage circuit is the resistance-inductance combination shown in Fig. 8–1. The differential equation for this circuit is

$$L\frac{di}{dt} + Ri = 0. \qquad (8–1)$$

To solve the equation we separate the variables:

$$\frac{di}{i} = \frac{-R}{L}\,dt. \qquad (8–2)$$

The current function on the left side of Eq. (8–2) is identically equal to the time function on the right side. The integrals are equal provided we integrate each function between corresponding limits. Thus if we integrate from $t = 0$ to $t = t$ on the right side, we must integrate from the value of the current at $t = 0$, namely, i_0, to the value of the current at $t = t$, namely, i. Accordingly

$$\int_{i_0}^{i} \frac{di}{i} = \int_{0}^{t} \left(\frac{-R}{L}\right) dt,$$

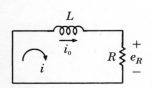

Figure 8–1. An *R-L* circuit with initial energy storage.

from which

$$\log i - \log i_0 = \frac{-R}{L} t,$$

or

$$i = i_0 e^{-Rt/L}. \qquad (8\text{–}3)$$

Equation (8–3) shows that the natural behavior of the current in the R-L circuit is a damped exponential curve which starts at the initial value i_0 and decays to zero, as shown in Fig. 8–2. At $t = L/R$ the value of the current is

$$i = i_0 e^{-1} = \frac{i_0}{e}, \qquad (8\text{–}4)$$

or about one-third of the initial value. The time L/R is called the *time constant* of the circuit. An alternative interpretation of the time constant can be obtained from the derivative of the current:

$$\frac{di}{dt} = \frac{-Ri_0}{L} e^{-Rt/L},$$

the value of which at $t = 0$ is

$$\frac{di(0)}{di} = \frac{-Ri_0}{L}. \qquad (8\text{–}5)$$

If the exponential curve continued to fall (after $t = 0$) at the rate given by Eq. (8–5) for one time constant, L/R seconds, it would drop by i_0 amperes. Thus the time constant is the time at which the extension of the initial derivative cuts the t-axis.

All the currents and voltages in the circuit have equations in the form of damped exponentials, which are characterized by their initial values and time constants and represented by an equation of the form

$$f(t) = f(0)e^{-t/T}, \qquad (8\text{–}6)$$

where $f(0)$ = initial value of the function and $T = L/R$ (time constant).

R-C circuit. The R-C circuit shown in Fig. 8–3 is also represented by a differential equation of the first order:

$$Ri + \frac{1}{C} \int_{-\infty}^{t} i \, dt = 0, \qquad (8\text{–}7)$$

or

$$R \frac{di}{dt} + \frac{i}{C} = 0. \qquad (8\text{–}8)$$

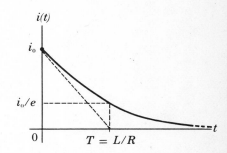

Figure 8–2. The damped exponential curve $i = i_0 e^{-Rt/L}$

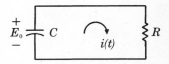

Figure 8–3. An R-C circuit with initial energy storage.

Equation (8–8), being similar to Eq. (8–1), is solved in a similar manner. The solution is

$$i = I_0e^{-t/RC} = I_0e^{-t/T}, \qquad (8\text{–}9)$$

where I_0 = initial value of the current and $T = RC$ (time constant). The initial value of the current is computed from the state of the circuit at $t = 0$. At this instant, the voltage on the capacitance is E_0. Since this voltage also appears across the resistance, the initial current is E_0/R. Thus, as a function of time the current is

$$i = \frac{E_0}{R}e^{-t/T}. \qquad (8\text{–}10)$$

In the circuit of Fig. 8–3 the voltage across R and the voltage across C are both given by expressions having the form

$$e_R = E_0e^{-t/RC}. \qquad (8\text{–}11)$$

The natural behavior of a single-energy-storage circuit involving capacitance is a damped exponential, having the form

$$f(t) = Ae^{-t/T}, \qquad (8\text{–}12)$$

where A = initial value of the variable and $T = RC$ (time constant).

Impulse excitation of the inductive circuit. Since an impulse is zero for t greater than zero it does not appear in the differential equation, which describes the variable only for t greater than zero. The impulse affects the solution only through the initial value of energy storage which it establishes during its short active interval. An inductive circuit excited by an impulse is shown in Fig. 8–4(a). The state of the circuit for t greater than zero is shown in Fig. 8–4(b). The differential equation for the circuit of Fig. 8–4(a) is

$$L\frac{di}{dt} + Ri = u_0(t).$$

For t greater than zero this equation becomes

$$L\frac{di}{dt} + Ri = 0, \qquad (8\text{–}13)$$

and the solution is

$$i = I_0e^{-Rt/L}. \qquad (8\text{–}14)$$

The impulse can affect the solution only through the value of I_0. At $t = 0^-$, before the impulse strikes, the circuit is at rest and the current is zero. At $t = 0$, when the impulse is acting, the inductance behaves as an open circuit, and all the voltage appears across it.

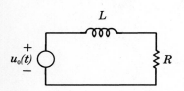

(a) Circuit excited by an impulse

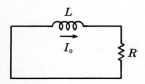

(b) Circuit for $t > 0$

Figure 8–4. An *R-L* circuit excited by an impulse.

The current established in the inductance between $t = 0^-$ and $t = 0^+$ is

$$i(0^+) = \frac{1}{L} \int_{0^-}^{0^+} u_0(t)\, dt. \qquad (8\text{–}15)$$

By definition, the area under the impulse curve from 0^- to 0^+ is unity. Thus

$$i(0^+) = \frac{1}{L}. \qquad (8\text{–}16)$$

Substituting the value of the current in Eq. (8–16) for I_0 in Eq. (8–14), the general expression for the natural behavior of the circuit, results in the impulse response

$$i = \frac{1}{L} e^{-tR/L}. \qquad (8\text{–}17)$$

Thus the current response to an impulse voltage has the same form as the natural behavior of the circuit.

Impulse excitation of the capacitive circuit. An *R-C* circuit excited by a parallel impulse of current is shown in Fig. 8–5(a). The state of the circuit for t greater than zero is shown in Fig. 8–5(b). The differential equation for the circuit of Fig. 8–5(a) is

$$C\frac{de}{dt} + \frac{e}{R} = u_0(t), \qquad (8\text{–}18)$$

and for the circuit of Fig. 8–5(b) is

$$C\frac{de}{dt} + \frac{e}{R} = 0. \qquad (8\text{–}19)$$

The solution of Eq. (8–19) is

$$e = E_0 e^{-t/RC}. \qquad (8\text{–}20)$$

The impulse can affect Eq. (8–20) only through the initial value of the voltage, E_0. The voltage produced by the action of the impulse is

$$e_C(0^+) = \frac{1}{C} \int_{0^-}^{0^+} u_0(t)\, dt. \qquad (8\text{–}21)$$

Since the area under the impulse curve from $t = 0^-$ to $t = 0^+$ is unity, we write

$$e_C(0^+) = \frac{1}{C}. \qquad (8\text{–}22)$$

Substituting $1/C$ for the initial voltage, E_0, in Eq. (8–20), we

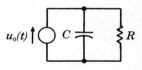

(a) Circuit excited by an impulse

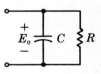

(b) Circuit for $t > 0$

Figure 8–5. An *R-C* circuit excited by an impulse.

obtain the expression for the impulse response of the circuit:

$$e = \frac{1}{C} e^{-t/RC}. \qquad (8\text{–}23)$$

Again, the impulse response has the same analytical form as the natural behavior of the circuit.

In the classical theory of differential equations emphasis is placed on the natural, or force-free, behavior of a differential equation. In circuit theory the impulse response is used more often, since a stimulus-response relationship of this sort can characterize a network.

Step excitation of an inductive circuit. If a first-order circuit is suddenly excited by a constant value (step function), it produces a response which is the sum of its natural behavior and a steady-state value proportional to the excitation. The steady-state value, which remains after the natural behavior has disappeared, is the value of the circuit response at $t = \infty$.

A series *L-R* circuit excited by a step function of voltage is shown in Fig. 8–6. Assume the switch is closed at $t = 0$. For t greater than zero the differential equation is

$$L \frac{di}{dt} + Ri = E. \qquad (8\text{–}24)$$

When the variables are separated, we find

$$\frac{di}{E/R - i} = \frac{R}{L} dt. \qquad (8\text{–}25)$$

Since the two functions in Eq. (8–25) are equal, the right side can be integrated from $t = 0$ to $t = t$, and the left side from the current value at $t = 0$ to the current value at $t = t$. Thus

$$\int_{I_0}^{i} \frac{di}{E/R - i} = \int_{0}^{t} \frac{R}{L} dt,$$

from which

$$\log \left(\frac{E/R - i}{E/R - I_0} \right) = \frac{-R}{L} t,$$

and, since I_0 is zero for the given excitation,

$$i = \frac{E}{R} (1 - e^{-Rt/L}). \qquad (8\text{–}26)$$

The first term in Eq. (8–26) is the steady-state, or constant, value and the second term is the transient. The function is zero when

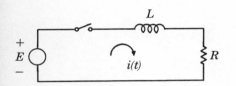

Figure 8–6. An *R-L* circuit excited by a step function of voltage.

$t = 0$ and rises to a final value of E/R when t is very large. The transition between the two states is accomplished smoothly by means of the natural response function $e^{-Rt/L}$, as indicated by Fig. 8–7(a). In one time constant the curve comes within approximately one-third of its final value; to be accurate, it reaches $(1 - 1/e)$ of the final value, E/R. If the derivative at $t = 0$ is extended it reaches the final value at $t = L/R$, that is, in one time constant. The final value is the direct current which flows at $t = \infty$, at which time the inductance is treated as a short circuit.

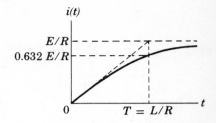

Figure 8–7. The rising exponential curve $i(t) = (E/R)(1 - e^{-Rt/L})$.

As a second example of the response of a circuit to a suddenly applied constant excitation, we shall consider the circuit of Fig. 8–8. Again, the switch is closed at $t = 0$. For t greater than zero the differential equation is

$$Ri + \frac{1}{C}\int_{-\infty}^{t} i\, dt = E,$$

or

$$R\frac{di}{dt} + \frac{i}{C} = 0. \tag{8–27}$$

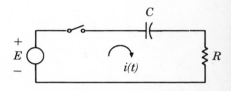

Figure 8–8. An *R-C* circuit excited by a step function of voltage.

Since this differential equation is identical to Eq. (8–8), the solution is

$$i = I_0 e^{-t/RC}. \tag{8–28}$$

In this case the steady-state solution is zero. At $t = 0$ the capacitance acts as a short circuit, the voltage appears across the resistance, and the current is

$$I_0 = \frac{E}{R}. \tag{8–29}$$

Substituting E/R for I_0 in Eq. (8–28), we obtain the step response

$$i = \frac{E}{R} e^{-t/RC}. \tag{8–30}$$

A step response may have a constant term, as in Eq. (8–26), or it may not, as in Eq. (8–30), depending on the value of the response at $t = \infty$. The transient term, consisting of a damped exponential, takes up the initial difference between the value of the response at $t = 0$ and the steady-state value which the circuit will eventually reach at $t = \infty$.

8–3 Step and impulse responses of *R-L* circuits

The step and impulse responses of *R-L* circuits are completely determined by an initial value, a final value, and a time constant. The circuit is capable only of moving from an initial value to a final value along an exponential curve. It is neither necessary nor desirable to write the differential equation. It is sufficient to find the initial value, $f(0)$, the final value, $f(\infty)$, and the time constant, T, and to match the solution to one of the canonical forms.

Rising: $f(t) = f(0)e^{-t/T};$ (8–31)

Decaying: $f(t) = [f(\infty) - f(0)](1 - e^{-t/T}).$ (8–32)

As an example, consider the circuit of Fig. 8–9(a) in which an R-L circuit is excited by a voltage impulse. We have previously solved the differential equation for the current in this circuit. Now let us find the current and the voltage across the inductance by inspection.

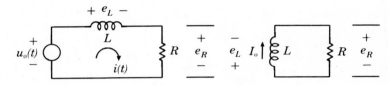

(a) Impulse-excited circuit   (b) The circuit for $t > 0$

Figure 8–9. An R-L series circuit excited by an impulse voltage.

The circuit for $t > 0$ is shown in Fig. 8–9(b). The impulse affects the circuit for $t > 0$ through the initial current which it establishes in the inductance between $t = 0^-$ and $t = 0^+$. During this interval the inductance is an open circuit and the impulse voltage appears across it.* The current established in the inductance is

$$i_L(0^+) = \frac{1}{L}\int_{0^-}^{0^+} e\, dt = \frac{1}{L}\int_{0^-}^{0^+} u_0(t)\, dt = \frac{1}{L}.$$ (8–33)

The initial value of the current is $1/L$, the final value of the current is zero, and the time constant is L/R. By inspection we can write the equation for the current, as

$$i_L(t) = \frac{1}{L}e^{-Rt/L} \qquad \text{for} \quad t > 0,$$ (8–34)

which is plotted in Fig. 8–10(a).

The voltage across the inductance is interesting. For $t > 0$ the inductance and the resistance are in parallel, and the voltage across the inductance is the negative of the voltage across the resistance. In addition to this voltage there is the original impulse across the

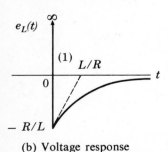

(a) Current response

(b) Voltage response

Figure 8–10. The response functions for the R-L circuit of Fig. 8–9.

———————

* A finite voltage also appears across R, but the voltage across L is still infinite.

inductance at $t = 0$. Thus the complete expression for the voltage across the inductance is

$$e_L(t) = u_0(t) - \frac{R}{L} e^{-Rt/L} \cdot u_{-1}(t). \qquad (8\text{–}35)$$

A plot of Eq. (8–35) is shown in Fig. 8–10(b).

A second example, an impulse current source in parallel with an inductance and resistance, is shown in Fig. 8–11(a). In this circuit it is necessary to distinguish very carefully the instants $t = 0^-$ and $t = 0^+$. At exactly $t = 0^-$ the impulse strikes, and the inductance is an open circuit, as shown in Fig. 8–11(b). By $t = 0^+$ the impulse has become inactive, and the dead current source is an open circuit which takes the form shown in Fig. 8–11(c). This circuit is identical to that in Fig. 8–9(b). The problem lies in the calculation of the initial value of the current in the inductance. Referring to Fig. 8–11(b), we note that the impulse current passes through the resistance, producing the voltage

$$e = Ru_0(t).$$

This voltage also appears across the inductance, and thus the current established in the inductance between $t = 0^-$ and $t = 0^+$ is

$$i_L(0^+) = \frac{1}{L} \int_{0^-}^{0^+} Ru_0(t)\,dt = \frac{R}{L}.$$

This current exists at $t = 0^+$ and excites the circuit of Fig. 8–11(c). The initial voltage is negative and has the value

$$e(0^+) = -R^2/L.$$

The final value for the voltage is

$$e(\infty) = 0,$$

and the time constant, T, is L/R. Thus for $t > 0$ the voltage across the parallel circuit is

$$e(t) = \frac{-R^2}{L} e^{-Rt/L}.$$

In addition to this voltage there is the impulse $Ru_0(t)$ which occurs at $t = 0$. The complete expression for the voltage is

$$e(t) = Ru_0(t) - \frac{R^2}{L} e^{-Rt/L} \cdot u_{-1}(t). \qquad (8\text{–}36)$$

A sketch of Eq. (8–36) is shown in Fig. 8–12.

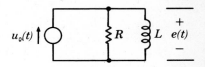

(a) The circuit with impulse excitation

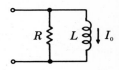

(b) The circuit at $t = 0$

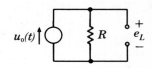

(c) The circuit for $t > 0$

Figure 8–11. A parallel R-L circuit excited by an impulse current.

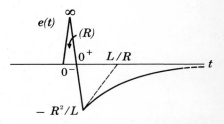

Figure 8–12. The response function for the circuit of Fig. 8–11.

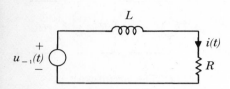

Figure 8–13. A series *R-L* circuit excited by a unit step of voltage.

As a third example we shall apply the method of matching the initial and final values, or boundary conditions, to a series *R-L* circuit excited by a step function of voltage as shown in Fig. 8–13. At $t = 0^+$ the inductance is an open circuit, and the current is

$$i(0^+) = 0.$$

At $t = \infty$ the inductance is a short circuit, the current is

$$i(\infty) = 1/R,$$

and the time constant is

$$T = L/R.$$

Since $f(\infty)$ is larger than $f(0)$ the response equation has the form of Eq. (8–31). The expression for the current can be written by inspection, as

$$i(t) = \frac{1}{R}(1 - e^{-Rt/L}) \qquad \text{for} \quad t > 0$$

$$= \frac{1}{R}(1 - e^{-Rt/L})u_{-1}(t). \tag{8–37}$$

A plot of Eq. (8–37) is shown in Fig. 8–14. The curve can easily be sketched from the initial value, the final value, and the time constant. In about five time constants the curve is essentially equal to its final value.

Figure 8–14. The response function for the circuit of Fig. 8–13.

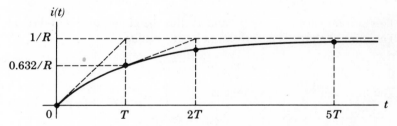

The rising exponential curve is characteristic of step-function responses which possess a final value at $t = \infty$. In other cases the final value is zero and the step response is a decaying exponential. A circuit with a response of this sort is shown in Fig. 8–15. At $t = 0$ the inductance is an open circuit, and the unit step current passes through the resistance. The voltage produced at $t = 0^+$ is

$$e(0^+) = R.$$

At $t = \infty$ the inductance is a short circuit. The step current flows through the short circuit, and the voltage produced is

$$e(\infty) = 0.$$

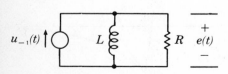

Figure 8–15. A parallel *R-L* circuit excited by a step current.

The time constant is

$$T = L/R.$$

The response is completely determined by the initial value, the final value, and the time constant. Its equation has the form of Eq. (8–31):

$$e(t) = Re^{-Rt/L} \cdot u_{-1}(t). \tag{8–38}$$

8–4 Step and impulse responses of R-C circuits

The response functions which occur in $R\text{-}C$ circuits are essentially the same as those which occur in $L\text{-}R$ circuits. The principal difference is that the time constant is now $T = RC$ instead of $T = L/R$.

In order to write an answer by inspection, it is necessary to compute only the initial value, the final value, and the time constant.

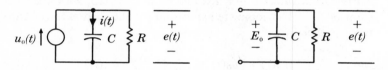

(a) An $R\text{-}C$ circuit driven by an impulse   (b) The circuit for $t > 0$

Figure 8–16. The impulse response of a parallel $R\text{-}C$ circuit.

Impulse excitation affects the $R\text{-}C$ circuit through the energy it stores during the interval $t = 0^-$ to $t = 0^+$. In the circuit of Fig. 8–16(a) a current impulse is applied to a parallel combination of R and C. After $t = 0$ the impulse is zero, and the circuit is that shown in Fig. 8–16(b). The principal problem is the computation of the initial voltage on the capacitance. At $t = 0^-$ the circuit is at rest; at $t = 0$ the impulse strikes, and the capacitance acts as a short circuit. During the interval $t = 0^-$ to $t = 0^+$ current flows into the capacitance and produces the voltage

$$e(0^+) = \frac{1}{C} \int_{0^-}^{0^+} u_0(t)\, dt = \frac{1}{C}. \tag{8–39}$$

The final value of the voltage is

$$e(\infty) = 0,$$

and the time constant is

$$T = RC.$$

The system fits Eq. (8–31), and the voltage is

$$e(t) = \frac{1}{C} e^{-t/RC} \cdot u_{-1}(t). \tag{8–40}$$

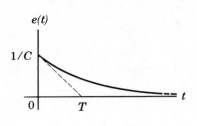

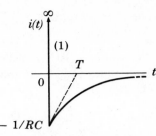

Figure 8–17. The response functions for the circuit of Fig. 8–16.

(a) The voltage response   (b) The capacitance current response

The damped exponential curve of Eq. (8–40) is plotted in Fig. 8–17(a).

The current in the capacitance of Fig. 8–16(a) can be obtained by a similar process. At $t = 0$ the capacitance receives the impulse current. After $t = 0$, current flows out of the capacitance. It starts with a value of $-1/RC$ and decays to zero, with a time constant of RC. The complete expression for the current in the capacitance is therefore

$$i(t) = u_0(t) - \frac{1}{RC} e^{-t/RC} \cdot u_{-1}(t). \qquad (8\text{--}41)$$

The curve for Eq. (8–41) is sketched in Fig. 8–17(b). It can also be obtained from Eq. (8–40) by formal differentiation of the two time functions. Thus

$$i(t) = C \frac{de}{dt} = C \frac{d}{dt} \left[\frac{e^{-t/RC}}{C} \cdot u_{-1}(t) \right]$$

$$= e^{-t/RC} \cdot u_0(t) - \frac{1}{RC} e^{-t/RC} \cdot u_{-1}(t). \qquad (8\text{--}42)$$

In Eq. (8–42) the unit impulse causes the first term to be zero at all time t except at $t = 0$. At this instant the exponential has a value of unity. Therefore Eq. (8–42) is exactly the same as Eq. (8–41).

A series *R-C* circuit excited by an impulse is shown in Fig. 8–18(a). The circuit which holds from $t = 0^-$ to $t = 0^+$ is shown in Fig. 8–18(b). The capacitance acts as a short circuit. After $t = 0^+$ the impulse is inactive, the dead voltage source is replaced by a short circuit, and the capacitance is charged. The circuit for $t > 0$ is shown in Fig. 8–18(c). The problem is one of computing the initial current in the circuit. Precisely at $t = 0$, when the voltage impulse strikes and the capacitance is a short circuit, the current is

$$i(0) = \frac{1}{R} u_0(t). \qquad (8\text{--}43)$$

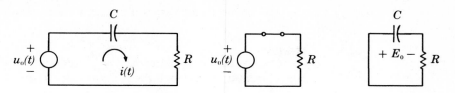

(a) Circuit excited by an impulse   (b) Circuit at $t = 0$ (c) Circuit for $t > 0$

Figure 8–18. A series R-C circuit excited by an impulse voltage.

This current passes through the capacitance and in doing so produces a voltage

$$e_C = \frac{1}{C}\int_{0^-}^{0^+} \frac{1}{R} u_0(t)\, dt = \frac{1}{RC}. \tag{8-44}$$

In the circuit of Fig. 8–18(c) this voltage has a negative polarity, and it causes a negative current to flow with an initial value of

$$i(0^+) = -\frac{1}{R^2 C}. \tag{8-45}$$

The final value of the current is zero, and the time constant is RC. Thus the complete expression for the current is

$$i(t) = \frac{1}{R} \cdot u_0(t) - \frac{1}{R^2 C} e^{-t/RC} \cdot u_{-1}(t). \tag{8-46}$$

Equation (8–46) consists of a positive impulse and a negative exponential which decays to zero with a time constant of RC. A sketch of Eq. (8–46) is shown in Fig. 8–19.

As a third example we will apply the method of matching boundary conditions to the step-function excitation of Fig. 8–20(a). The source is connected at $t = 0$, and a unit step of current is applied to the parallel R-C circuit. At $t = 0$ the capacitance is a short circuit, and

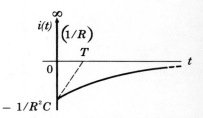

Figure 8–19. The response current for the circuit of Fig. 8–18.

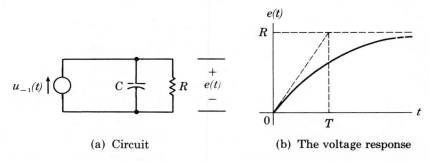

(a) Circuit   (b) The voltage response

Figure 8–20. A parallel R-C circuit excited by a step function of current.

the voltage produced across it by the finite current is zero. Thus

$$e(0^+) = 0.$$

After a long interval the capacitance becomes an open circuit, and the current flows through the resistance R. The final voltage is

$$e(\infty) = R,$$

and the time constant of the circuit is

$$T = RC.$$

Since these data fit Eq. (8–32), the current is

$$i(t) = R(1 - e^{-t/RC})u_{-1}(t). \tag{8–47}$$

This current starts at zero and rises at an exponential rate to a final value of R amperes. A sketch of the curve is shown in Fig. 8–20(b).

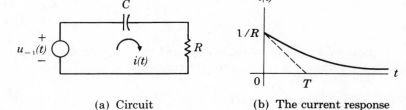

(a) Circuit

(b) The current response

Figure 8–21. A series *R-C* circuit excited by a step function of voltage.

A series *R-C* circuit excited by a step voltage is shown in Fig. 8–21(a). At $t = 0$ the capacitance is a short circuit, and the current in this fourth example is

$$i(0^+) = 1/R.$$

After a long interval the capacitance becomes an open circuit, and the final value of the current is

$$i(\infty) = 0.$$

The time constant of the circuit is

$$T = RC.$$

These data fit Eq. (8–31), and thus the current is

$$i(t) = \frac{1}{R} e^{-t/RC} \cdot u_{-1}(t). \tag{8–48}$$

The circuits which we have considered in the two preceding sections consist of one energy-storage element and one resistive element.

If a network can be separated into two sections, one which is purely inductive or purely capacitive and one which is purely resistive, and if the two sections are joined by only two wires, the network can be treated as a single-energy-storage circuit. The resistive branch is reduced to an equivalent resistance and the energy-storage branch is reduced to a single equivalent branch. The single time constant of the network is obtained in terms of the equivalent energy-storage element and the equivalent resistance.

The ability to solve simple single-time-constant circuits by inspection is a useful one. A surprising number of the practical circuits are of this type. For example, as a first approximation, most motors and generators and most coupling circuits for vacuum tubes and transistors are single-time-constant circuits.

Summary

General types of exponential behavior

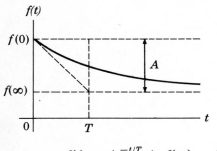

$$f(t) = Ae^{-t/T} + f(\infty) \quad \text{for} \quad t > 0$$

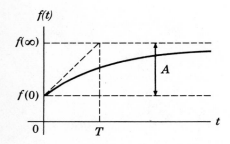

$$f(t) = A(1 - e^{-t/T}) + f(0) \quad \text{for} \quad t > 0$$

The impulse response of R-L circuits

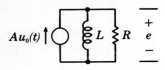

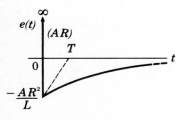

$$e(t) = ARu_0(t) - \frac{AR^2}{L} e^{-Rt/L} \cdot u_{-1}(t)$$

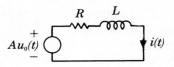

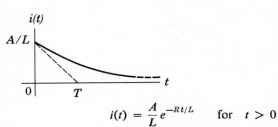

$$i(t) = \frac{A}{L} e^{-Rt/L} \quad \text{for} \quad t > 0$$

The step response of R-L circuits

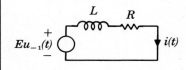

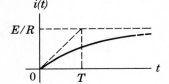

$$i(t) = \frac{E}{R} (1 - e^{-Rt/L}) u_{-1}(t)$$

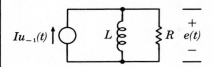

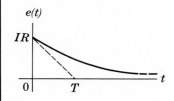

$$e(t) = IRe^{-Rt/L} \cdot u_{-1}(t)$$

The impulse response of R-C circuits

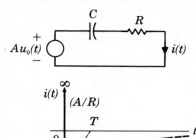

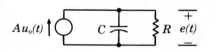

$$i(t) = \frac{A}{R}u_0(t) - \frac{A}{R^2C}e^{-t/RC} \cdot u_{-1}(t)$$

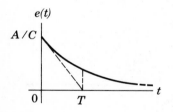

$$e(t) = \frac{A}{C}e^{-t/RC} \cdot u_{-1}(t)$$

The step response of R-C circuits

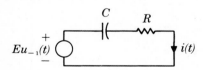

$$i(t) = \frac{E}{R}e^{-t/RC} \cdot u_{-1}(t)$$

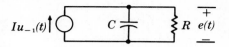

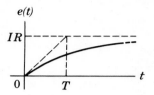

$$e(t) = IR(1 - e^{-t/RC})u_{-1}(t)$$

Responses to ramp excitation

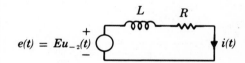

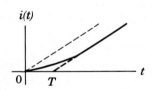

$$i(t) = \frac{E}{R}\left[t - \frac{L}{R}(1 - e^{-Rt/L})\right]u_{-1}(t)$$

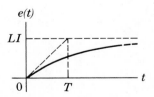

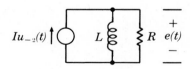

$$e(t) = LI(1 - e^{-Rt/L})u_{-1}(t)$$

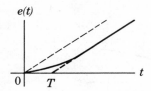

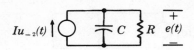

$$e(t) = IR[t - RC(1 - e^{-t/RC})]u_{-1}(t)$$

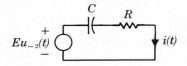

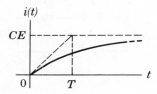

$$i(t) = CE(1 - e^{-t/RC})u_{-1}(t)$$

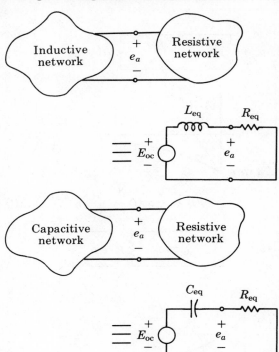

References

In this chapter we have tried to present differential equations from both the point of view of the mathematician and of the electrical engineer. The mathematical point of view has the advantage that it is general and applies to equations which arise from all sorts of physical problems. The electrical engineering point of view has the advantage that it provides concrete illustrations of the abstract concepts of differential equations. One-energy-storage circuits occur frequently in practice, and the method of matching the boundary conditions by inspection is the preferred one for solving them. Differential equations and Laplace transforms amount to "driving the tack with the sledge hammer."

1. SALVADORI and SCHWARTZ, *Differential Equations In Engineering Problems*, Prentice-Hall, New York, 1954. This relatively modern text gives a very complete discussion of linear equations and many examples from dynamics, statics, heat transfer, chemical action, and electric circuits.

2. H. B. PHILLIPS, *Differential Equations*, John Wiley, New York, 1922. A standard text in applied mathematics. It is devoted to linear equations and their applications in physical problems.

3. E. A. GUILLEMIN, *Communications Networks*, Vol. 1, John Wiley, New York, 1931. This text is the most complete treatment of linear equations, from the point of view of the electrical engineer, which is available in the English language. It is very readable, even in the sections devoted to advanced material.

4. G. B. THOMAS, JR., *Calculus and Analytical Geometry*, Addison-Wesley, Reading, Mass., 1954. The last chapter of this introductory text gives a brief account of the essentials of linear differential equations.

5. E. A. GUILLEMIN, *Introductory Circuit Theory*, John Wiley, New York, 1953. The method of writing the transient response by inspection, in terms of the initial value, final value, and time constant, is implied in Guillemin's book.

6. MIT EE Staff, *Electric Circuits*, John Wiley, New York, 1943. This text gives the classical treatment of R–L and R–C circuits with step excitation, but not with impulse excitation.

Exercises

SECTION 8-2

1. A current is given by the equation

$$i(t) = 10e^{-t/10}.$$

(a) Find the current values at $t = 0$, $t = 10$, $t = 20$, and $t = \infty$, and sketch the curve. (b) What is the time constant? (c) Find the derivative of the curve and sketch it. (d) What is the time constant? (e) If the curve were to continue as a straight line with the same slope as that of the actual curve at $t = 0$, how long would it take to reach zero?

2. A voltage is given by the equation

$$e(t) = 10(1 - e^{-t/10}).$$

(a) Find the voltage values at $t = 0$, $t = 10$, $t = 20$, and $t = \infty$, and sketch the curve. (b) What is the time constant? (c) Find the derivative of the curve and sketch it. (d) What is its time constant? (e) If the curve were to continue as a straight line with the same slope as that of the actual curve at $t = 0$, how long would it take to reach the final value of 10?

3. Solve the following differential equation, subject to the given initial condition:

$$6\frac{di}{dt} + 4i = 0, \qquad i(0) = 5.$$

4. Solve the following differential equation, subject to the given initial condition:

$$2\frac{de}{dt} + e = 0, \qquad e(0) = -10.$$

5. Solve the following differential equation, subject to the given initial condition:

$$5\frac{di}{dt} + 3i = 7u_{-1}(t), \qquad i(0^-) = 0.$$

6. Solve the following differential equation, subject to the given initial condition:

$$\frac{de}{dt} + 3e = 10u_{-1}(t), \qquad e(0^-) = 0.$$

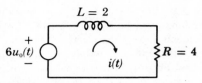

Figure 8-22

7. Write and solve the differential equation for the current in the circuit of Fig. 8-22 for $t > 0$.

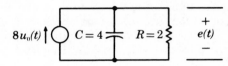

Figure 8-23

8. Write and solve the differential equation for the voltage in the circuit of Fig. 8-23 for $t > 0$.

SECTION 8-3

9. In the circuit of Fig. 8-24 the current in the inductance at $t = 0$ is 6 amp. What is the current as a function of time? [*Note:* There is no point in converting the initial energy storage to a source, since the initial value of the current is the desired quantity.]

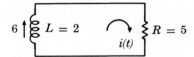

Figure 8-24

10. In the circuit of Fig. 8-25 the current in the inductance at $t = 0$ is 16 amp. At the end of 3 sec the switch is closed. What is the voltage across the resistance R_1 as a function of time?

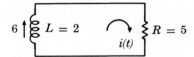

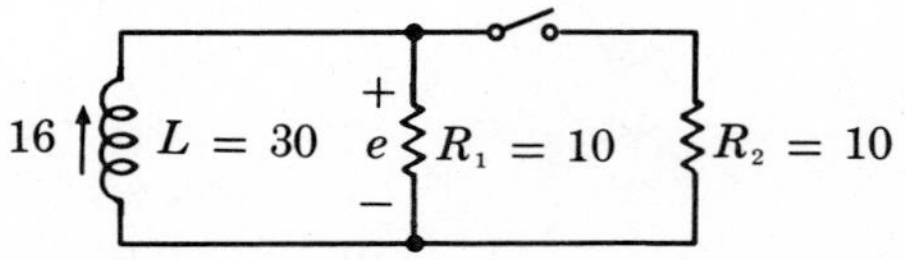

Figure 8-25

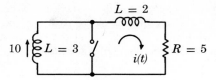

Figure 8–26

11. In the circuit of Fig. 8–26 the current in the 3-h inductance at $t = 0$ is 10 amp. The switch is opened at $t = 0$. What is the current in the circuit for $t > 0$?

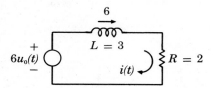

Figure 8–27

12. In the circuit of Fig. 8–27 the current in the inductance just prior to the occurrence of the impulse is 6 amp. Find the current in the circuit as a function of time after the impulse occurs.

13. A 4-h inductance and a 3-ohm resistance are connected in parallel. The current in the inductance is 2 amp at $t = 0$. (a) Replace the initial current in the inductance by a parallel current source and obtain the current in the resistance as a function of time. (b) Compute the initial value of the current, the final value of the current, and the time constant, and thus obtain the current directly.

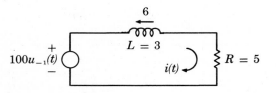

Figure 8–28

14. In the circuit of Fig. 8–28 the current in the inductance is —6 amp at $t = 0$. (a) Find the current as a function of time by computing the initial value, final value, and time constant. (b) Find the current by superposition.

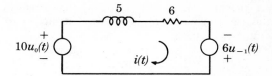

Figure 8–29

15. (a) Find the current in the circuit of Fig. 8–29 as a function of time by computing the initial value, the final value, and the time constant. (b) Find the current by superposition.

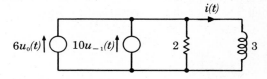

Figure 8–30

16. (a) Find the current in the inductance in the circuit of Fig. 8–30 by computing its initial value, its final value, and its time constant. (b) Verify the result of part (a) by superposition.

SECTION 8–4

17. An impulse voltage source $e(t) = 10u_0(t)$ is connected in series with a resistance of 2 ohms and a capacitance of $\frac{1}{2}$ f. Give the time constant, the current at $t = 0^+$, and the current at $t = \infty$. Sketch the current and give an analytic expression for it. Include the impulse which occurs at $t = 0$.

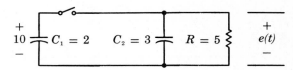

Figure 8–31

18. In the circuit of Fig. 8–31 the switch is closed at $t = 0$. At this time there is a voltage on C_1 of 10 v. Find the voltage $e(t)$ for $t > 0$.

19. A 3-f capacitance and a 5-ohm resistance are connected in series. At $t = 0$ there is a voltage on the capacitance of 15 v. (a) Replace the initial energy storage by a step-voltage source, and find

the current in the circuit. (b) Find the current by a direct computation of its initial value, final value, and time constant.

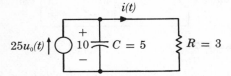

Figure 8–32

20. In the circuit of Fig. 8–32 the voltage on the capacitance just before the impulse strikes is 10 v. Find the current in the resistance for $t > 0$.

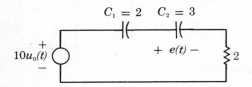

Figure 8–33

21. In the circuit of Fig. 8–33 find the voltage $e(t)$ as a function of time.

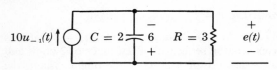

Figure 8–34

22. In the circuit of Fig. 8–34 there is a voltage of -6 v on the capacitance at $t = 0$, when the step-current source is applied. Find the voltage across the resistance as a function of time for $t > 0$.

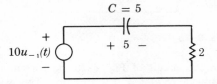

Figure 8–35

23. The capacitance in the circuit of Fig. 8–35 has a voltage of 5 v at $t = 0$, when the step voltage is applied. Find the voltage on the capacitance as a function of time.

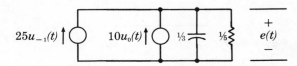

Figure 8–36

24. (a) Solve for the voltage $e(t)$ in the circuit of Fig. 8–36 by computing its initial value, final value, and time constant. (b) Verify the result of part (a) by superposition.

Problems

1. (a) Find the solution to the following differential equation:

$$7\frac{de}{dt} + 2e = 8u_{-1}(t).$$

(b) Draw the circuit which it represents and obtain the solution from the initial value, the final value, and the time constant.

2. (a) Find the solution to the following differential equation:

$$3\frac{di}{dt} + 2i = 6u_0(t).$$

(b) Draw the circuit which it represents and obtain the solution from the initial value, the final value, and the time constant.

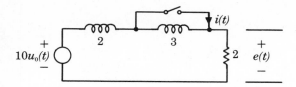

Figure 8–37

3. In the circuit of Fig. 8–37 the switch is closed at $t = 0^+$, just after the impulse is over. What is the voltage $e(t)$ for $t > 0$, and what is the current in the switch?

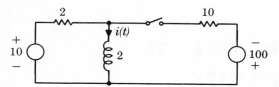

Figure 8–38

4. In the circuit of Fig. 8–38 a steady state is reached with the switch open. At $t = 0$ the switch is closed. Write an expression for the current in the inductance as a function of time from this instant.

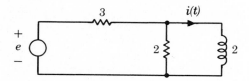

Figure 8–39

5. In the circuit of Fig. 8–39 the inductance represents the deflection coil of a television tube. The current in it must be a linear ramp, or sweep, with a value $i(t) = 10t$. What voltage source will produce the required value?

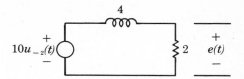

Figure 8–40

6. A ramp voltage is applied to the circuit of Fig. 8–40. Find the voltage across the resistance as a function of time. Find also the steady-state, or ramp-function, component of this voltage.

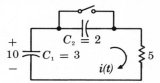

Figure 8–41

7. The switch in the circuit of Fig. 8–41 is opened at $t = 0$. At this time there is a voltage of 10 v on C_1 and no voltage on C_2. Find the current $i(t)$ and the voltage across C_2 as functions of time.

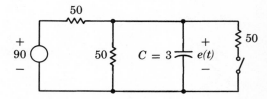

Figure 8–42

8. The switch in Fig. 8–42 is closed at $t = 0$ after a steady state has been attained in the remainder of the circuit. Find the voltage $e(t)$ across the capacitance as a function of time from the moment of the closing of the switch.

CHAPTER **9**

THE RESPONSE OF
R-L-C CIRCUITS

Men eat birds, birds eat worms, worms eat men again.

SAMUEL BUTLER

9–1 Introduction

The conservation of energy is one of the basic laws of the universe. Many energy changes are cyclical, like that observed by Samuel Butler. Electric circuits which contain two types of energy-storage elements exhibit such cyclical behavior. Energy is first stored in the electric field of a capacitance, is transferred to the magnetic field of an inductance, and is then returned to the electric field of the capacitance. The process continues indefinitely until the energy is dissipated by the resistive losses of the system. Many of the interesting properties of electrical systems, such as resonance and wave propagation, are consequences of the two types of energy which can be stored and the "swapping" of energy from one type to the other and back again.

A circuit with resistance, inductance, and capacitance is described by a second-order differential equation of the form

$$\frac{d^2y}{dt^2} + 2\alpha \frac{dy}{dt} + \omega_0^2 y = f(t). \tag{9–1}$$

A pendulum or a swing satisfies the same differential equation and illustrates the behavior which we can expect from it. Energy is stored initially in either of two ways. If the pendulum is lifted up from its rest position the energy is potential; if it is given an initial velocity the energy is kinetic. In either case the pendulum will continue to swing back and forth at a constant frequency until the initial energy is dissipated by windage and friction. These decaying oscillations constitute the natural behavior of the system. If the friction is small they may be of almost constant amplitude, or undamped. If the friction is large, the pendulum may be overdamped and sink exponentially to rest. The transition point between oscillations and exponential behavior is called critical damping.

In this chapter we will be concerned with the step and impulse responses of *R-L-C* circuits. These responses have the same form as the natural behavior except for the possible addition of a constant term, or steady-state solution, in the step response. The case of sinusoidal excitation, in which the steady-state solution is also sinusoidal, will be treated in a later chapter.

9–2 The second-order differential equation

Excitation by initial energy storage. We cannot integrate a second-order equation as easily as a first-order equation. The response to an arbitrary excitation, however, still consists of two parts: a transient, or homogeneous, solution and a steady-state solution, or particular integral. The homogeneous solution is the solution of the differential equation without an external driving force connected to the circuit. It is the natural behavior of the circuit produced by internally stored energy. The natural behavior of a first-order system contains one arbitrary constant to accommodate the single, arbitrary energy storage. The natural behavior of a second-order system contains two arbitrary constants, one for each of the arbitrary energy storages. In order to evaluate these two constants we need to know the values of the two energy storages in the circuit, or more conveniently the values of the response function and its first derivative at $t = 0$. Thus the specification of a two-energy-storage system by means of a second-order differential equation requires:

1. The statement of the differential equation.
2. The initial value of the variable and of its first derivative.

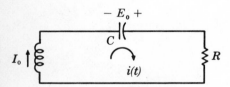

Figure 9–1. An *R-L-C* circuit excited by an initial energy storage.

A second-order circuit excited by energy initially stored in the elements is shown in Fig. 9–1. The differential equation for the circuit is

$$L \frac{di}{dt} + Ri + \frac{1}{C} \int_{-\infty}^{t} i \, dt = 0$$

or

$$L \frac{d^2 i}{dt^2} + R \frac{di}{dt} + \frac{i}{C} = 0. \tag{9–2}$$

The initial value of i and its derivative are determined by the energy stored in the inductance and capacitance. The initial current is

$$i(0) = I_0, \tag{9–3}$$

and the initial voltage on C is

$$\frac{1}{C} \int_{-\infty}^{0} i \, dt = E_0.$$

At $t = 0$ Eq. (9–2) becomes

$$L \frac{di(0)}{dt} + Ri(0) + E_0 = 0$$

or

$$\frac{di(0)}{dt} = -\frac{1}{L}(RI_0 + E_0). \tag{9–4}$$

There is no direct procedure for solving the second-order differential equation. Essentially one guesses a solution and verifies it by substitution in the equation. By analogy with the first-order equation and knowing that we need two arbitrary constants, we can make a reasonable guess of the form

$$i = A_1 e^{p_1 t} + A_2 e^{p_2 t}, \tag{9–5}$$

where the A's and p's are constants to be found. The first and second derivatives of Eq. (9–5) are

$$\frac{di}{dt} = A_1 p_1 e^{p_1 t} + A_2 p_2 e^{p_2 t},$$

$$\frac{d^2 i}{dt^2} = A_1 p_1^2 e^{p_1 t} + A_2 p_2^2 e^{p_2 t}. \tag{9–6}$$

If Eq. (9–5) is a solution it must satisfy the differential equation. Substituting in Eq. (9–2) we obtain

$$A_1 e^{p_1 t} \left(L p_1^2 + R p_1 + \frac{1}{C}\right) + A_2 e^{p_2 t} \left(L p_2^2 + R p_2 + \frac{1}{C}\right) = 0. \tag{9–7}$$

Since neither $A_1 e^{p_1 t}$ nor $A_2 e^{p_2 t}$ can be zero if we are to have a second-order solution, the two terms in parentheses must be zero. Thus each of the p's must satisfy an equation of the form

$$p^2 + \frac{R}{L} p + \frac{1}{LC} = 0. \tag{9–8}$$

The two p-values are

$$p_{1,2} = -\frac{R}{2L} \pm \sqrt{\left(\frac{R}{2L}\right)^2 - \frac{1}{LC}}$$

or

$$p_{1,2} = -\alpha \pm \sqrt{\alpha^2 - \omega_0^2}, \tag{9–9}$$

where

$$\alpha = \frac{R}{2L} \quad \text{and} \quad \omega_0^2 = \frac{1}{LC}. \tag{9–10}$$

Equation (9–9) gives the values of p_1 and p_2 which make Eq. (9–5) a solution of the differential equation. The two constants A_1 and

A_2 are obtained from the initial conditions in each problem. There are three general types of solution, depending on whether $\alpha > \omega_0$, $\alpha = \omega_0$, or $\alpha < \omega_0$. These three solutions are called respectively the overdamped case, the critically damped case, and the underdamped case.

Overdamped case ($\alpha > \omega_0$). When $\alpha > \omega_0$ the two values of p are real and negative, and the solution consists of the sum of two damped exponential terms. We shall obtain the transient solution for the initial conditions of

$$i(0) = I_0 \qquad \text{and} \qquad \frac{di(0)}{dt} = 0 \quad \text{(that is, } E_0 = I_0 R \text{).}$$

From Eq. (9–5) the general solution is

$$i(t) = A_1 e^{p_1 t} + A_2 e^{p_2 t}, \tag{9–11}$$

and the derivative is

$$\frac{di}{dt} = A_1 p_1 e^{p_1 t} + A_2 p_2 e^{p_2 t}. \tag{9–12}$$

The values of the A's are determined from the initial conditions and Eqs. (9–11) and (9–12). At $t = 0$

$$i(0) = I_0 = A_1 + A_2,$$

$$i'(0) = 0 = A_1 p_1 + A_2 p_2,$$

from which

$$A_1 = \frac{p_2 I_0}{p_2 - p_1} \qquad \text{and} \qquad A_2 = \frac{-p_1 I_0}{p_2 - p_1}.$$

The transient solution for the overdamped case is therefore

$$i(t) = I_0 \frac{p_2}{p_2 - p_1} e^{p_1 t} - I_0 \frac{p_1}{p_2 - p_1} e^{p_2 t}, \tag{9–13}$$

where $p_1 = -\alpha + \sqrt{\alpha^2 - \omega_0^2}$ and $p_2 = -\alpha - \sqrt{\alpha^2 - \omega_0^2}$.

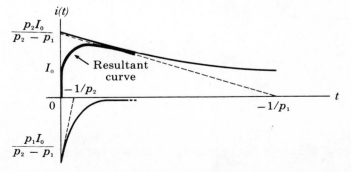

Figure 9–2. The overdamped current
$i(t) = [p_2 I_0/(p_2 - p_1)]e^{p_1 t}$
$+ [Lp_1 I_0/(p_2 - p_1)]e^{p_2 t}.$

A sketch of the response function is shown in Fig. 9–2. The beginning of the curve is influenced most strongly by the negative term, which has a short time constant. The final disposition of the curve is determined by the positive term, which has a long time constant. It is characteristic of overdamped systems that a pulse is produced whose rise time is controlled by one time constant and whose fall time is controlled by another.

Critically damped case ($\alpha = \omega_0$). It might seem that the case of $\alpha = \omega_0$ would be the simplest to solve, since the p-values are equal and only one term occurs in the transient solution. The reverse is true, however, since we need two terms for a second-order solution in order to account for the two arbitrary energy storages. Somehow we must find a second solution! Let us restrict ourselves to the initial conditions considered in the case $\alpha > \omega_0$; that is, the initial value of the current is I_0 and the initial derivative is zero. Then, according to Eq. (9–13), the general solution for the current is

$$\frac{i(t)}{I_0} = \frac{p_2}{p_2 - p_1} e^{p_1 t} - \frac{p_1}{p_2 - p_1} e^{p_2 t}. \tag{9–14}$$

If in Eq. (9–14) we let $p_1 = p_2$, the mathematical difficulty is at once evident. The two exponentials become equal, but their coefficients become infinite, making the difference indeterminate. To evaluate the indeterminacy we let

$$p_1 = -\alpha, \qquad p_2 = p_1 + \delta,$$

where δ is a small number which later will be allowed to become zero. Substituting $p_1 + \delta$ for p_2 in Eq. (9–14), we obtain

$$\frac{i(t)}{I_0} = \frac{p_1 + \delta}{p_1 + \delta - p_1} e^{p_1 t} - \frac{p_1}{p_1 + \delta - p_1} e^{p_2 t + \delta t}$$

$$= \frac{e^{p_1 t}}{\delta} [p_1 + \delta - p_1 (1 + \delta t + \cdots)]$$

$$= e^{p_1 t} \left(\frac{\delta - \delta p_1 t}{\delta} + \cdots \right). \tag{9–15}$$

Now, as δ is allowed to approach zero, Eq. (9–15) approaches the limit

$$\frac{i(t)}{I_0} = e^{-\alpha t}(1 + \alpha t). \tag{9–16}$$

The waveform for Eq. (9–16) is sketched in Fig. 9–3. Note that the maximum value occurs at $t = 0$. Equation (9–16) was developed for a particular set of initial conditions. In the more general

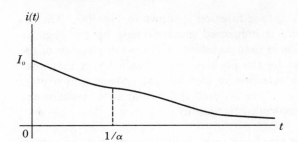

Figure 9-3. The critically damped current $i(t) = I_0 e^{-\alpha t}(1 + \alpha t)$.

case the terms $e^{-\alpha t}$ and $te^{-\alpha t}$ remain, but the multiplying constants are arbitrary, as in the following expression:

$$i(t) = e^{-\alpha t}(A_1 + A_2 t). \qquad (9\text{-}17)$$

Underdamped case ($\alpha < \omega_0$). When $\alpha < \omega_0$ the p-roots become conjugate complex numbers, and the whole character of the solution changes. For this case it is convenient to write the p-values in the form

$$\begin{aligned} p_1 &= -\alpha + j\sqrt{\omega_0^2 - \alpha^2} = -\alpha + j\omega_d, \\ p_2 &= -\alpha - j\sqrt{\omega_0^2 - \alpha^2} = -\alpha - j\omega_d. \end{aligned} \qquad (9\text{-}18)$$

With the initial conditions, $i(0) = I_0$ and $i'(0) = 0$. The general solution as given in Eq. (9-14) is

$$\frac{i(t)}{I_0} = \frac{p_2}{p_2 - p_1} e^{p_1 t} - \frac{p_1}{p_2 - p_1} e^{p_2 t}.$$

Substitution of the p-values from Eq. (9-18) gives

$$\begin{aligned} \frac{i(t)}{I_0} &= \frac{-\alpha - j\omega_d}{-2j\omega_d} e^{-\alpha t} e^{j\omega_d t} - \frac{-\alpha + j\omega_d}{-2j\omega_d} e^{-\alpha t} e^{-j\omega_d t} \\ &= \frac{e^{-\alpha t}}{2j\omega_d}[\alpha(e^{j\omega_d t} - e^{-j\omega_d t}) + j\omega_d(e^{j\omega_d t} + e^{-j\omega_d t})]. \end{aligned} \qquad (9\text{-}19)$$

By Euler's formula

$$\frac{e^{+j\theta} + e^{-j\theta}}{2} = \cos\theta, \qquad \frac{e^{j\theta} - e^{-j\theta}}{2j} = \sin\theta.$$

Therefore Eq. (9-19) can be written in the form

$$\frac{i(t)}{I_0} = e^{-\alpha t}\left(\frac{\alpha}{\omega_d}\sin\omega_d t + \cos\omega_d t\right). \qquad (9\text{-}20)$$

An alternative form of Eq. (9-20) can be obtained by trigonometric manipulation. If we let $\alpha = \omega_0 \sin\theta$ and $\omega_d = \omega_0 \cos\theta$, we can write Eq. (9–20) in the form

$$\frac{i(t)}{I_0} = \frac{e^{-\alpha t}\omega_0}{\omega_d}(\cos \omega_d \cos \theta + \sin \omega_d \sin \theta)$$

$$= \frac{\omega_0}{\omega_d}e^{-\alpha t}\cos(\omega_d t - \theta), \tag{9–21}$$

where ω_d is the damped natural frequency in rad/sec (it is the number of radians through which the oscillation passes each second), ω_0 is the value of ω_d when the resistance term which produces the damping becomes zero (it is the undamped natural frequency in rad/sec), and α is the damping constant (the reciprocal of the time constant of the envelope curve). A sketch of the waveform of Eq. (9–21) is shown in Fig. 9–4. Notice that it is a damped sine wave. The envelope of the curve is the damped exponential $e^{-\alpha t}$. The initial value of the current is I_0, and the period of the sinusoidal oscillation is $t_d = 2\pi/\omega_d$. The phase angle is $-\theta$, which means that the cosine term has not reached its maximum value at $t = 0$.

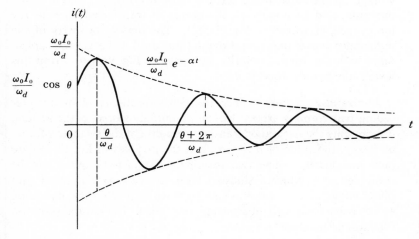

Figure 9–4. The undamped current $i(t) = (\omega_0 I_0/\omega_d)\cos(\omega_d t - \theta)e^{-\alpha t}$.

For different initial conditions the nature of the second-order response function remains the same, but the amplitude and the phase of the resulting damped sine wave change. A general expression is

$$i(t) = e^{-\alpha t}(A_1 \sin \omega_d t + A_2 \cos \omega_d t) \tag{9–22}$$

or

$$i(t) = Ae^{-\alpha t}\cos(\omega_d t + \theta),$$

where

$$\omega_d = \sqrt{\omega_0^2 - \alpha^2}\,.$$

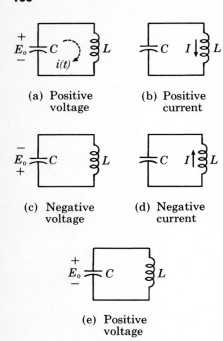

(a) Positive
voltage

(b) Positive
current

(c) Negative
voltage

(d) Negative
current

(e) Positive
voltage

Figure 9–5. The oscillation of energy in an L-C circuit.

9–3 Impulse and step response of an L-C circuit

A lossless L-C circuit is the electrical analog of a lossless (frictionless) mechanical pendulum. In the electric circuit the energy "swaps" back and forth from magnetic to electrical energy; in the mechanical system it oscillates between potential energy and kinetic energy. An intuitive understanding of the operation of the electric circuit can be obtained from Fig. 9–5. The five illustrations show the state of the same circuit at successive instants of time. In Fig. 9–5(a) the energy is stored in the capacitance. No current is flowing, and no energy is stored in the inductance. The voltage on the capacitance causes a current to start flowing in the positive direction, and at the instant represented by Fig. 9–5(b) the capacitance is discharged and a maximum current is flowing in the inductance. The energy is stored in the inductance. The "inertia" of the current in the inductance causes it to continue until the capacitance is charged in the opposite direction, as shown in Fig. 9–5(c). At this instant the current is zero, and the energy is again stored in the capacitance. The voltage on the capacitance starts a current flowing in the opposite direction, and eventually all the energy is transferred back to the inductance, as shown in Fig. 9–5(d). The inertial property of the inductance causes the current to continue until it charges the capacitance with the original polarity, as shown in Fig. 9–5(e). From this instant the process repeats itself.

The impulse response. Since the behavior discussed in the preceding paragraph is excited by energy initially stored in the system, it represents the natural or transient response of the system. Mathematically, the value of α is zero, and the p-values in Eq. (9–18) are pure imaginaries. The two imaginary exponential terms can be combined to produce a sinusoid with an arbitrary amplitude and phase angle, or the sum of a sine term with an arbitrary amplitude and a cosine term with an arbitrary amplitude. The natural response function is therefore*

$$f(t) = A_1 \cos \omega_0 t + A_2 \sin \omega_0 t$$
$$= A \cos (\omega_0 t + \theta) \qquad \text{for} \quad t > 0, \qquad (9\text{–}23)$$

where $\omega_0 = 1/\sqrt{LC}$, and A_1, A_2, A, and θ are constants determined by the initial conditions.

We will match the natural response function of Eq. (9–23) to the initial values of the function and its first derivative. For our first example, consider the circuit of Fig. 9–5(a), which has an initial voltage E_0 on the capacitance. This voltage can be treated

---

* This equation is also Eq. (9–22) with $\alpha = 0$.

as a step function applied in series with the two elements. The inductance at $t = 0$ acts as an open circuit, and therefore the initial current is

$$i(0^+) = 0.$$

The voltage across the inductance is E_0, however, and the rate of change of current is

$$\frac{di(0^+)}{dt} = \frac{E_0}{L}.$$

The assumed form of the current function for $t > 0$ is

$$i(t) = A_1 \cos \omega_0 t + A_2 \sin \omega_0 t, \qquad (9\text{–}24)$$

from which

$$\frac{di}{dt} = -A_1\omega_0 \sin \omega_0 t + A_2\omega_0 \cos \omega_0 t. \qquad (9\text{–}25)$$

When $t = 0^+$, Eqs. (9–24) and (9–25) must yield the initial values of the current and its derivative. Hence

$$i(0^+) = A_1 = 0,$$

$$\frac{di(0^+)}{dt} = A_2\omega_0 = \frac{E_0}{L},$$

from which

$$A_1 = 0, \qquad A_2 = \frac{E_0}{\omega_0 L}.$$

Having evaluated the constants in Eq. (9–24), we obtain

$$i(t) = \frac{E_0}{\omega_0 L} \sin \omega_0 t \qquad \text{for} \quad t > 0 \qquad (9\text{–}26)$$

or

$$i(t) = \frac{E_0}{\omega_0 L} \sin \omega_0 t \cdot u_{-1}(t). \qquad (9\text{–}27)$$

A sketch of the function is shown in Fig. 9–6. The maximum amplitude of the oscillation is $E_0/\omega_0 L$ and its period is $2\pi/\omega_0$.

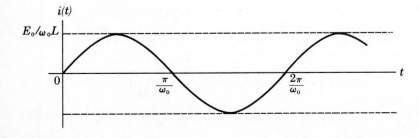

Figure 9–6. A sketch of the response function $i(t) = (E_0/\omega_0 L)\sin \omega_0 t \cdot u_{-1}(t)$.

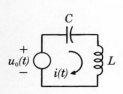

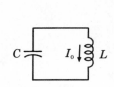

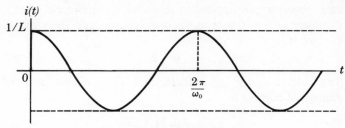

(a) Circuit with
    impulse excitation

(b) Circuit for
    $t > 0$

(c) The current response function

Figure 9–7. A series *L-C* circuit excited by a voltage impulse.

Another *L-C* circuit, in which the natural response is excited by an impulse voltage, is shown in Fig. 9–7(a). Again, we shall assume the form of the solution and evaluate the arbitrary constants from the initial conditions in the problem. At $t = 0$, when the impulse strikes, the capacitance is a short circuit, and the inductance is an open circuit. The impulse voltage appears across the inductance. The current produced is indeterminate and must be evaluated from the integral

$$i_L(0^+) = \frac{1}{L} \int_{0^-}^{0^+} e \, dt = \frac{1}{L} \int_{0^-}^{0^+} u_0(t) \, dt = \frac{1}{L}. \qquad (9\text{--}28)$$

The circuit which holds for $t > 0$ is shown in Fig. 9–7(b). At $t = 0^+$ in this circuit the capacitance is a short circuit, and the voltage across it is zero. The inductance is in parallel with the capacitance, and the voltage across it is also zero. Hence

$$\frac{di(0^+)}{dt} = \frac{e_L}{L} = 0.$$

We will assume a general form for the current and its first derivative, as given by Eqs. (9–24) and (9–25). At $t = 0^+$ the values of the equations must match those which we have computed from the circuit. Therefore

$$i(0^+) = A_1 = 1/L, \qquad di(0^+)/dt = A_2\omega_0 = 0,$$

from which

$$A_1 = 1/L, \qquad A_2 = 0.$$

The current response function for the circuit of Fig. 9–7(a) is therefore

$$i(t) = \frac{1}{L} \cos \omega_0 t \cdot u_{-1}(t). \qquad (9\text{--}29)$$

This function is plotted in Fig. 9–7(c). It starts at $t = 0$ with a maximum value of $1/L$ and oscillates sinusoidally with a period of $2\pi/\omega_0$.

The step response. The step response of an L-C circuit consists of the transient response plus a constant or steady-state value. A general expression for the step response is therefore

$$f(t) = A_1 \cos \omega_0 t + A_2 \sin \omega_0 t + B \qquad \text{for} \quad t > 0, \qquad (9\text{–}30)$$

where $\omega_0^2 = 1/LC$, and A_1, A_2, and B are constants. The first two terms in Eq. (9–30) constitute the transient response, and the third term is the steady-state value. A minor problem arises here, because the transient response does not die out with time. The original oscillations in the circuit, produced when the source is switched in, continue undiminished in amplitude and thus obscure the steady-state value. To avoid this difficulty it is convenient to imagine a very small amount of dissipation in the circuit, which causes the transient response to damp out as time approaches infinity. Then, the steady-state value B is the value of the variable at $t = \infty$. The dissipation added is vanishingly small and does not have any effect on B. We can evaluate the arbitrary constants in the general solution by computing the initial and final values of the variable from the resistive circuits at $t = 0$ and $t = \infty$. The circuit of Fig. 9–8 will illustrate the method.

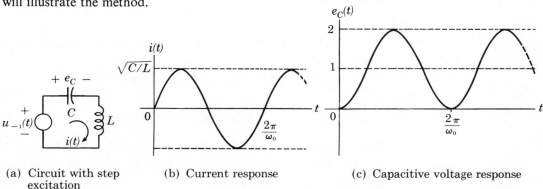

(a) Circuit with step   (b) Current response   (c) Capacitive voltage response
    excitation

Figure 9–8. The step response of a series L-C circuit.

At $t = 0$, when the step voltage is applied, the capacitance is a short circuit, and the inductance is an open circuit. The initial current is therefore $i(0^+) = 0$. The applied voltage appears across the inductance. Hence the rate of change of current is

$$\frac{di(0^+)}{dt} = \frac{e_L}{L} = \frac{1}{L}.$$

At $t = \infty$ the capacitance is an open circuit, and the inductance is a short circuit. If we imagine enough dissipation to damp out the oscillations, the current at $t = \infty$ is

$$i(\infty) = 0.$$

The solution for the current response is assumed to be of the form given by Eq. (9–30):

$$i(t) = A_1 \cos \omega_0 t + A_2 \sin \omega_0 t + B \qquad \text{for} \quad t > 0, \qquad (9\text{–}31)$$

from which

$$\frac{di}{dt} = -A_1 \omega_0 \sin \omega_0 t + A_2 \omega_0 \cos \omega_0 t.$$

The three circuit conditions which we have computed are sufficient to determine the three constants A_1, A_2, and B. Since we assumed that the transients have died out

$$i(\infty) = 0 = B.$$

At $t = 0^+$,

$$i(0^+) = A_1 = 0,$$

$$di(0^+)/dt = A_2 \omega_0 = 1/L,$$

from which

$$A_1 = 0, \qquad A_2 = 1/L\omega_0.$$

The current-response function of the circuit in Fig. 9–8(a) is therefore

$$i(t) = 1/L\omega_0 \sin \omega_0 t \qquad \text{for} \quad t > 0$$

or

$$i(t) = \sqrt{C/L} \sin \omega_0 t \cdot u_{-1}(t). \qquad (9\text{–}32)$$

The response function of Eq. (9–32) is sketched in Fig. 9–8(b). It is a sine wave starting at $t = 0$ and having a maximum amplitude of $\sqrt{C/L}$ and a period of $2\pi/\omega_0$.

The voltage across the capacitance in Fig. 9–8(a) can be obtained by integrating Eq. (9–32) from $t = 0$ to $t = t$. It can also be obtained by the general procedure. At $t = 0$ the capacitance is a short circuit, and the voltage across it is zero. The current through the capacitance is also zero, and thus the derivative of the voltage is zero:

$$e_C(0^+) = 0, \qquad \frac{de_C(0^+)}{dt} = 0.$$

Since both the function and its derivative are zero at $t = .0$, it might appear that the response is zero. Such is not the case, however, because the response includes the steady-state term B. At $t = \infty$ the capacitance is an open circuit, and the inductance is a short circuit. Since the applied voltage appears across the capacitance,

$$e_C(\infty) = 1 = B. \qquad (9\text{--}33)$$

The general expression for the voltage across the capacitance is

$$e_C(t) = A_1 \cos \omega_0 t + A_2 \sin \omega_0 t + B, \qquad (9\text{--}34)$$

from which

$$\frac{de_C}{dt} = -A_1 \omega_0 \sin \omega_0 t + A_2 \omega_0 \cos \omega_0 t.$$

The value of B is given by Eq. (9–33). The two initial conditions, applied to Eq. (9–34), yield

$$e_C(0^+) = A_1 + B = 0, \qquad \frac{de_C(0^+)}{dt} = A_2 \omega_0 = 0,$$

from which

$$A_1 = -B = -1, \qquad A_2 = 0.$$

The complete voltage-response function is

$$e_C(t) = (1 - \cos \omega_0 t) \qquad \text{for} \quad t > 0$$

or

$$e_C(t) = (1 - \cos \omega_0 t)u_{-1}(t). \qquad (9\text{--}35)$$

The response function of Eq. (9–35) is sketched in Fig. 9–8(c). It is a negative cosine wave with its horizontal axis displaced upwards by unity.

The *L-C* response functions which we have obtained in this section are particular cases of the more general *R-L-C* response functions. All real physical circuits have resistance, and the oscillations in them eventually die out. A circuit in which there are a large number of oscillations within one time constant of the exponential envelope curve can be considered to be lossless for the first few cycles of the oscillation. A quantity called the Q of the circuit is a measure of this property. By definition,

$$Q = \frac{\omega_0}{2\alpha}. \qquad (9\text{--}36)$$

The larger the Q, the more nearly a system is lossless, and the more nearly the undamped oscillations approximate the true natural behavior. We shall meet the quantity Q in a number of other applications. It is an important natural parameter of a system.

9–4 Impulse and step responses of the R-L-C circuit

Three-element circuits, involving resistance, inductance, and capacitance lead to increased complexity for two reasons. The first is that the nature of the response depends on the relative values of the three elements. The R-L-C circuit must represent an R-L circuit (with its damped exponential type of response) to which a small amount of C has been added. Alternatively, the R-L-C circuit must represent an L-C circuit (with its pure sine-wave response) to which a small amount of resistance has been added.

The second reason for the added complexity is that the nature of the response depends on the geometry of the circuit. For the two-element circuit the natural response function is the same with the elements connected in series or in parallel. For the R-L-C circuit it makes a difference whether the elements are connected in series or in parallel.

For our first example, consider the series R-L-C circuit shown in Fig. 9–9. This circuit is excited by energy initially stored in the capacitance. In order to evaluate the constants in the natural behavior we must determine the initial value of the current and of its first derivative. At $t = 0$ the inductance is an open circuit, and the charged capacitance is equivalent to a voltage source in series with a short circuit. The current is

$$i(0^+) = 0.$$

Since the voltage across the resistance is zero the voltage across the inductance must be equal to the voltage across the capacitance. The rate of change of current is therefore

$$\frac{di}{dt} = \frac{e_L}{L} = \frac{E_0}{L}.$$

Having the initial conditions we now proceed to evaluate the constants in the three possible response functions.

Overdamped response $(\alpha > \omega_0)$. If the circuit is overdamped, the response function for the R-L-C series circuit (Eq. 9–11) is

$$i(t) = A_1 e^{p_1 t} + A_2 e^{p_2 t}, \qquad (9\text{–}37)$$

where

$$p_{1,2} = -\alpha \pm \sqrt{\alpha^2 - \omega_0^2}, \qquad \alpha = \frac{R}{2L}, \qquad \omega_0^2 = \frac{1}{-C},$$

from which

$$\frac{di}{dt} = A_1 p_1 e^{p_1 t} + A_2 p_2 e^{p_2 t}.$$

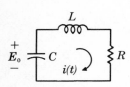

Figure 9–9. A series R-L-C circuit excited by initial energy stored on the capacitance.

At $t = 0$,

$$i(0^+) = A_1 + A_2 = 0,$$

$$\frac{di(0^+)}{dt} = A_1 p_1 + A_2 p_2 = \frac{E_0}{L},$$

from which

$$A_1 = \frac{-E_0}{L(p_2 - p_1)}, \qquad A_2 = -A_1.$$

The overdamped response function is therefore

$$i(t) = \frac{-E_0}{L(p_2 - p_1)} (e^{p_1 t} - e^{p_2 t}) \qquad \text{for} \quad t > 0. \quad (9\text{–}38)$$

Both p_1 and p_2 in Eq. (9–38) are negative, and the magnitude of p_2 is greater than the magnitude of p_1. The difference $p_2 - p_1$ is therefore negative and the multiplying coefficient in the equation is positive. The over-all response starts at zero, as shown in Fig. 9–10(a). The initial rise time of the curve is determined by the value of p_2. The later values of the curve are determined primarily by the value of p_1.

Critically damped response ($\alpha = \omega_0$). If the circuit is critically damped the response function has the form from Eq. (9–17):

$$i(t) = e^{-\alpha t}(A_1 + A_2 t),$$

from which

$$\frac{di}{dt} = e^{-\alpha t} A_2 - \alpha e^{-\alpha t}(A_1 + A_2 t).$$

At $t = 0$,

$$i(0^+) = A_1 = 0,$$

$$\frac{di(0^+)}{dt} = A_2 - \alpha A_1 = \frac{E_0}{L},$$

from which

$$A_1 = 0, \qquad A_2 = \frac{E_0}{L}.$$

The critically damped response function is therefore

$$i(t) = \frac{E_0}{L} t e^{-\alpha t} \qquad \text{for} \quad t > 0. \qquad (9\text{–}39)$$

At $t = 0$ the value of the current in Eq. (9–39) is zero, and at $t = \infty$ it is again zero. The maximum value of the current is $E_0 e^{-1}/L\alpha$, and it occurs at $t = 1/\alpha$, which is one time constant on the exponential envelope curve. A sketch of the response function is shown in Fig. 9–10(b). The general form of the curve is similar to the overdamped case, and a smooth transition occurs between them.

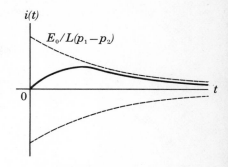

(a) Overdamped response

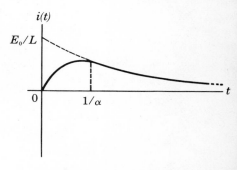

(b) Critically damped response

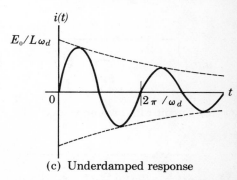

(c) Underdamped response

Figure 9–10. The natural response functions for the circuit of Fig. 9–9.

Underdamped response ($\alpha < \omega_0$). If the circuit is underdamped the response function has the form from Eq. (9–22):

$$i(t) = e^{-\alpha t}(A_1 \cos \omega_d t + A_2 \sin \omega_d t),$$

from which

$$\frac{di}{dt} = e^{-\alpha t}(-A_1 \omega_d \sin \omega_d t + A_2 \omega_d \cos \omega_d t)$$
$$- \alpha e^{-\alpha t}(A_1 \cos \omega_d t + A_2 \sin \omega_d t).$$

At $t = 0$,

$$i(0^+) = A_1 = 0,$$
$$\frac{di(0^+)}{dt} = A_2 \omega_d - A_1 \alpha = \frac{E_0}{L},$$

from which

$$A_1 = 0, \qquad A_2 = \frac{E_0}{L\omega_d}.$$

The underdamped response function is therefore

$$i(t) = \frac{E_0}{L\omega_d} e^{-\alpha t} \sin \omega_d t \qquad \text{for} \quad t > 0. \tag{9–40}$$

The function of Eq. (9–40) is sketched in Fig. 9–10(c). The exponential envelope of the oscillations has a maximum value of $E_0/L\omega_d$ at $t = 0$, and it decays to zero with a time constant of $1/\alpha$. The oscillations start at zero (when $t = 0$) and have a constant period of $2\pi/\omega_d$.*

The impulse response of the series R-L-C circuit. An R-L-C circuit excited by an impulse voltage is shown in Fig. 9–11(a). At $t = 0^-$ the circuit is at rest. At $t = 0$, when the impulse strikes, the inductance is an open circuit and the capacitance is a short circuit. All the impulse voltage appears across the inductance. A finite voltage does occur across the resistance, but this voltage is negligible in comparison with the infinite voltage of the impulse. Between $t = 0^-$ and $t = 0^+$ the impulse voltage creates a current in the inductance whose value is

$$i(0^+) = \frac{1}{L} \int_{0^-}^{0^+} u_0(t) \, dt = \frac{1}{L}. \tag{9–41}$$

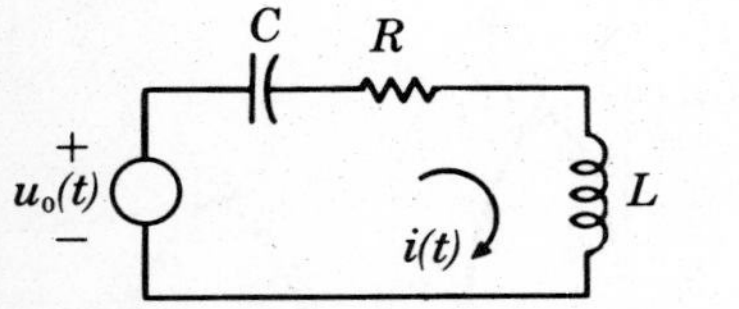

(a) Circuit with impulse voltage

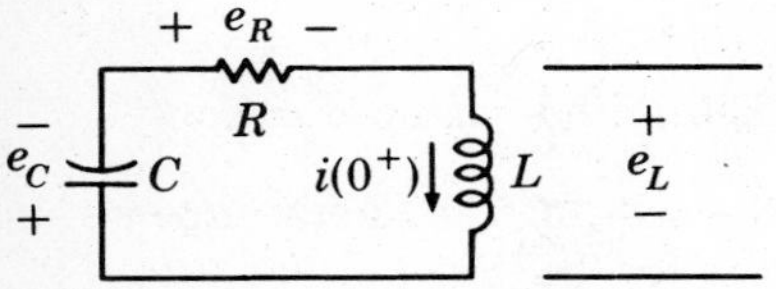

(b) Circuit for $t > 0$

Figure 9–11. An R-L-C circuit excited by an impulse voltage.

The derivative of the current at $t = 0^+$ is computed from the circuit which holds for $t > 0$, as shown in Fig. 9–11(b). The voltage on the capacitance is zero, because as yet no charge has accumulated.

---

* The discovery that damped oscillations have a constant period was first made by Galileo, by watching the chandeliers in church!

The voltage across the resistance is

$$e_R = R \times \frac{1}{L}.$$

The voltage across the inductance is the negative of the voltage across the resistance:

$$e_L = -\frac{R}{L}.$$

The derivative of the current is found from the voltage across the inductance:

$$\frac{di(0^+)}{dt} = \frac{e_L(0^+)}{L} = -\frac{R}{L^2}. \qquad (9\text{-}42)$$

The initial conditions are sufficient to determine the two constants in the general solution as illustrated in the previous example.

The impulse response of the parallel R-L-C circuit. The parallel *R-L-C* circuit is the dual of the series *R-L-C* circuit. In terms of ω_d and α the response functions are identical. Interchanging L with C and R with G, however, changes the definitions of ω_d and α for the parallel *R-L-C* circuit to

$$\omega_0 = \frac{1}{\sqrt{LC}},$$

$$\alpha = \frac{1}{2RC}, \qquad (9\text{-}43)$$

$$\omega_d^2 = \omega_0^2 - \alpha^2.$$

We again obtain the solutions by matching the initial conditions to the known form of the transient behavior. Because of the three possible types of behavior, the solution in any given problem is best carried out numerically. As an example, consider the circuit of Fig. 9–12.

At $t = 0^-$ in this circuit everything is at rest. At $t = 0$ the impulse strikes, with the capacitance acting as a short circuit and the inductance acting as an open circuit. All the impulse current enters the capacitance. A finite current flows in the resistance, but since the capacitive current during the impulse is infinite it is not sensibly diminished by the current in the resistance. The voltage acquired by the capacitance, while the impulse current is flowing from $t = 0^-$ to $t = 0^+$, is

$$e_C(0^+) = \frac{1}{C} \int_{0^-}^{0^+} u_0(t)\, dt = \frac{1}{C}. \qquad (9\text{-}44)$$

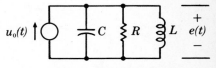

(a) Circuit excited by impulse

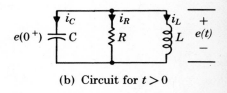

(b) Circuit for $t > 0$

Figure 9–12. An *R-L-C* circuit excited by an impulse current.

The derivative of the voltage at $t = 0^+$ is obtained from the circuit shown in Fig. 9–12(b), which holds after the impulse is over. No current is flowing in the inductance at $t = 0^+$, but a current

$$i_R(0^+) = \frac{1}{RC}$$

is flowing in the resistance. By Kirchhoff's current law this same current must be flowing out of the capacitance. Hence

$$i_C(0^+) = \frac{-1}{RC}.$$

The rate of change of the voltage depends on the current from the capacitance and is given by

$$\frac{de(0^+)}{dt} = \frac{i_C}{C} = \frac{-1}{RC^2}. \tag{9–45}$$

Suppose that $L = C = R = 1$. Then

$$\omega_0 = \frac{1}{\sqrt{LC}} = 1,$$

$$\alpha = \frac{1}{2RC} = \frac{1}{2}.$$

Since $\alpha < \omega_0$ the response is of the underdamped type. The damped natural frequency is

$$\omega_d = \sqrt{\omega_0^2 - \alpha^2} = \sqrt{1 - \tfrac{1}{4}} = \frac{\sqrt{3}}{2} = 0.866.$$

We will assume the cosine form of the underdamped response function, in which the unknown constants are the amplitude and the phase angle. Thus

$$e(t) = Ae^{-\alpha t} \cos(\omega_d t + \theta) \quad \text{for} \quad t > 0, \tag{9–46}$$

from which

$$\frac{de}{dt} = -A\omega_d e^{-\alpha t} \sin(\omega_d t + \theta) - \alpha Ae^{-\alpha t} \cos(\omega_d t + \theta).$$

The initial conditions, from Eqs. (9–44) and (9–45), are

$$e(0^+) = \frac{1}{C} = 1 \text{ volt},$$

$$\frac{de(0^+)}{dt} = -\frac{1}{RC^2} = -1 \text{ volt/sec.} \tag{9–47}$$

Equation (9–46) and its derivative must reduce to the initial values given by Eq. (9–47) when $t = 0$. Hence

$$e(0^+) = A \cos \theta = 1,$$

$$\frac{de(0^+)}{dt} = -A\omega_d \sin \theta - \alpha A \cos \theta = -1, \qquad (9\text{–}48)$$

from which

$$A \cos \theta = 1, \qquad A \sin \theta = \frac{1}{1.732}. \qquad (9\text{–}49)$$

The ratio of these equations gives an expression for the angle θ:

$$\frac{\sin \theta}{\cos \theta} = \tan \theta = \frac{1}{1.732}.$$

The magnitude of the angle is 30°. If A is taken to be positive, $\sin \theta$ is positive and $\cos \theta$ is positive. The angle is therefore in the first quadrant:

$$\theta = 30°.$$

The value of A can now be obtained:*

$$A = \frac{1}{\cos \theta} = 1.15.$$

The final expression for the impulse response of the circuit of Fig. 9–12(a), with all the parameters equal to unity, is

$$e(t) = 1.15e^{-\alpha t} \cos (0.866t + 30°) \qquad \text{for} \quad t > 0. \qquad (9\text{–}50)$$

The step response of the series R-L-C circuit. The step response of the series *R-L-C* circuit differs little in complexity from the impulse response or the natural behavior. A steady-state value can occur in the circuit, and this appears as a constant added to the solution. The *R-L-C* transient decays with time, and therefore the constant can be obtained as the value of the variable at infinity.

As an example to illustrate the method of solution we will obtain the step response of the series *R-L-C* circuit in Fig. 9–13, in which $R = L = C = 1$ and the applied voltage is a unit step. For this circuit

$$\alpha = \frac{R}{2L} = \frac{1}{2},$$

$$\omega_0 = \frac{1}{\sqrt{LC}} = 1,$$

$$\omega_d = \sqrt{\omega_0^2 - \alpha^2} = 0.866.$$

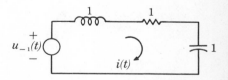

Figure 9–13. The step response of a series *R-L-C* circuit.

---

* The value of A can also be obtained by squaring and adding Eq. (9–49).

Since $\alpha < \omega_0$, the response function is underdamped. The initial conditions in the problem can be obtained from the circuit. At $t = 0$, when the step is applied, the inductance is an open circuit and the capacitance is a short circuit. The current is therefore

$$i(0^+) = 0. \tag{9–51}$$

The applied voltage appears across the inductance and determines the rate of change of the current:

$$\frac{di(0^+)}{dt} = \frac{e_L}{L} = \frac{1}{L} \text{ amp/sec.} \tag{9–52}$$

The response function has the form

$$i(t) = e^{-\alpha t}(A_1 \cos \omega_d t + A_2 \sin \omega_d t) + B, \tag{9–53}$$

from which

$$\frac{di}{dt} = e^{-\alpha t}(-A_1 \omega_d \sin \omega_d t + A_2 \omega_d \cos \omega_d t)$$
$$- \alpha e^{-\alpha t}(A_1 \cos \omega_d t + A_2 \sin \omega_d t).$$

When we match the initial conditions of Eqs. (9–51) and (9–52) with the initial values of Eq. (9–53) and its derivative we obtain

$$i(0^+) = A_1 + B = 0,$$
$$\frac{di(0^+)}{dt} = A_2 \omega_d - A_1 \alpha = \frac{1}{L}. \tag{9–54}$$

The value of B can be obtained from the value of the current in the circuit at $t = \infty$. Since the capacitance is an open circuit the current is zero, and thus

$$B = i(\infty) = 0.$$

From Eq. (12–44) we obtain

$$A_1 = 0, \qquad A_2 = \frac{1}{\omega_d L} = 1.15.$$

The current response to the applied step voltage is therefore

$$i(t) = 1.15 e^{-t/2} \sin 0.866t \qquad \text{for} \quad t > 0. \tag{9–55}$$

The function of Eq. (9–55) is a damped sine wave. The time constant of the envelope is 2 sec and the period of the wave is 7.22 sec. Very few cycles are produced before the wave becomes vanishingly small.

The step response of a parallel R-L-C circuit. The parallel R-L-C circuit-response functions to a step-current source are similar to the impulse-response functions, except for the addition of a constant to represent the steady-state value at $t = \infty$.

As an example of the application of these equations we shall find the current through the inductance in the circuit of Fig. 9–14, which is excited by a unit step current. For the given values of the parameters in the circuit,

$$\alpha = \frac{1}{2RC} = \frac{1}{2},$$

$$\omega_0 = \frac{1}{\sqrt{LC}} = 1,$$

$$\omega_d = \sqrt{\omega_0^2 - \alpha^2} = 0.866.$$

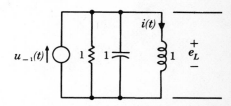

Figure 9–14. The step response of a parallel R-L-C circuit.

Since $\alpha < \omega_0$, the response is underdamped. Therefore

$$i(t) = e^{-\alpha t}(A_1 \cos \omega_d t + A_2 \sin \omega_d t) + B, \qquad (9\text{–}56)$$

from which

$$\frac{di}{dt} = e^{-\alpha t}(-A_1 \omega_d \sin \omega_d t + A_2 \omega_d \cos \omega_d t)$$
$$- \alpha e^{-\alpha t}(A_1 \cos \omega_d t + A_2 \sin \omega_d t).$$

The value of B can be obtained from the circuit response at $t = \infty$. At this time the capacitance is an open circuit, and the inductance is a short circuit. All the current from the source must pass through the inductance. It follows that

$$B = i(\infty) = 1 \text{ amp.} \qquad (9\text{–}57)$$

The constants A_1 and A_2 are obtained from the initial conditions. At $t = 0$ the capacitance is a short circuit and the inductance is an open circuit. All the current flows into the capacitance, and none flows into the inductance. Hence

$$i(0^+) = 0. \qquad (9\text{–}58)$$

Furthermore, at $t = 0$ the voltage across the capacitance is zero, since there is as yet no charge in it, and therefore the voltage across the inductance is also zero. The rate of change of the current is obtained from the voltage across the inductance:

$$\frac{di(0^+)}{dt} = \frac{e_L}{L} = 0. \qquad (9\text{–}59)$$

Because Eq. (9–56) and its derivative must satisfy the boundary conditions at $t = 0$, we find

$$i(0^+) = A_1 + B = 0,$$

$$\frac{di(0^+)}{dt} = A_2\omega_d - A_1\alpha = 0,$$

from which

$$A_1 = -B = -1, \qquad A_2 = -\alpha/\omega_d.$$

The complete expression for the current response in the inductance is

$$i(t) = e^{-t/2}\left(-\cos \omega_d t - \frac{\alpha}{\omega_d}\sin \omega_d t\right) + 1 \qquad \text{for} \quad t > 0$$

$$= 1 - e^{-t/2}(\cos 0.866t + 0.577 \sin 0.866t). \qquad (9\text{–}60)$$

In Eq. (9–60) the first term is the steady-state value, and the second term is the transient. The transient is a damped sine wave with an envelope-time-constant of 2 sec and an oscillatory period of 7.22 sec.

The transient p-plane. A circuit with a single energy-storage element results in a first-order differential equation, and its natural response function is a damped exponential. A general expression for the damped exponential is

$$f(t) = Ae^{pt}, \qquad (9\text{–}61)$$

where p is a negative real number.

A system containing two independent energy-storage elements, for example an inductance and a capacitance, is described by a second-order differential equation. The natural response function requires two exponential terms of the sort given by Eq. (9–61) and has the general form

$$f(t) = A_1 e^{p_1 t} + A_2 e^{p_2 t}. \qquad (9\text{–}62)$$

In Eq. (9–62) the actual nature of the response depends on the p-values. If they are both negative real numbers the response is the sum of two damped exponentials; if they are pure imaginary numbers the response is an undamped sinusoid; and if they are complex numbers the response is a damped sinusoid.

Systems with n independent energy-storage elements are described by a differential equation of order n, and the general solution is

$$f(t) = A_1 e^{p_1 t} + A_2 e^{p_2 t} + \cdots + A_n e^{p_n t}. \qquad (9\text{–}63)$$

Each separate term in Eq. (9–63) is determined by the value of p. If p is a negative real number the response is a damped exponential;

if p is a pure imaginary the response of a pair of the terms is an undamped sinusoid; and if p is a complex number two terms can be combined to give a damped sinusoidal response. The p-values determine the nature of the response functions. The arbitrary multiplying constants associated with each term are determined by the values of the variable and its first $n - 1$ derivatives at $t = 0^+$. *The arbitrary constants are characteristic of the excitation and not of the network. It is the p-values which are characteristic of the network and which in fact completely describe it so far as its stimulus-response relationship is concerned.*

The dimensions of p must be the reciprocal of time, or frequency, in order that the power of the exponential be a dimensionless number. In general the p-values are complex and are therefore complex natural resonant frequencies. It is convenient to record the p-values as points in a complex plane. Several representative p-values are shown in Fig. 9–15, along with the sort of transient responses which they represent. A p-value or natural frequency of $-\alpha$ represents a damped exponential with a time constant of $1/\alpha$. A pair of values on the imaginary axis at $\pm j\omega_0$ represents an undamped sine wave of angular frequency ω_0 and period $2\pi/\omega_0$. A pair of complex values at $-\alpha \pm j\omega_d$ represents a damped sinusoid with an envelope-time-constant of $1/\alpha$, an angular frequency of ω_d, and a period of $2\pi/\omega_d$.

For the moment, the complex frequency plane is to be viewed as simply a convenient place to record essential information about the transient behavior of a circuit. The transient natural frequencies will return to prominence and take a central role in our treatment of Fourier and Laplace transforms.

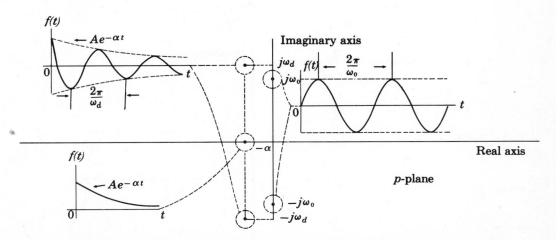

Figure 9–15. The complex-frequency plane and the various types of transient responses.

Summary

Second-order equation—transient solution

Equation

$$\frac{d^2x}{dt^2} + 2\alpha\frac{dx}{dt} + \omega_0^2 x = 0$$

Initial values

$$x(0) = X_0 \quad \text{and} \quad \frac{dx(0)}{dt} = X_0'$$

Overdamped solution ($\alpha > \omega_0$)

$$x = A_1 e^{p_1 t} + A_2 e^{p_2 t},$$

where $p_1 = -\alpha + \sqrt{\alpha^2 - \omega_0^2}$,

$\qquad p_2 = -\alpha - \sqrt{\alpha^2 - \omega_0^2}$,

A_1 and A_2 are constants.

Critically damped solution ($\alpha = \omega_0$)

$$x = Ae^{-\alpha t}(A_1 + A_2 t), \quad \text{with} \quad \alpha = \omega_0$$

Underdamped solution ($\alpha < \omega_0$)

$$x = e^{-\alpha t}(A_1 \sin \omega_d t + A_2 \cos \omega_d t)$$
$$= Ae^{-\alpha t}\cos(\omega_d t + \theta),$$

where $\omega_d = \sqrt{\omega_0^2 - \alpha^2}$,

A_1, A_2, A, and θ are constants.

Second-order equation—step-function excitation

Equation

$$\frac{d^2x}{dt^2} + 2\alpha\frac{dx}{dt} + \omega_0^2 x = Cu_{-1}(t)$$

Initial values

$$x(0) = X_0 \quad \text{and} \quad \frac{dx(0)}{dt} = X_0'$$

Final value

$$x(\infty) = C/\omega_0^2$$

Overdamped solution

$$x = A_1 e^{p_1 t} + A_2 e^{p_2 t} + B$$

Critically damped solution

$$x = e^{-\alpha t}(A_1 + A_2 t) + B$$

Underdamped solution

$$x = e^{-\alpha t}(A_1 \sin \omega_d t + A_2 \cos \omega_d t) + B$$
$$= Ae^{-\alpha t}[\cos(\omega_d t + \theta)] + B,$$

where $B = x(\infty) = C/\omega_0^2$.

Natural behavior of L-C circuit

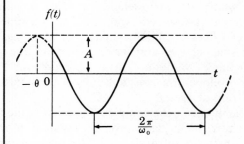

$$f(t) = A\cos(\omega_0 t + \theta) = A_1 \cos \omega_0 t + A_2 \sin \omega_0 t$$
$$\omega_0 = 1/\sqrt{LC}$$
$$A_1 = A\cos\theta \qquad A_2 = -A\sin\theta$$

Impulse response of L-C circuit

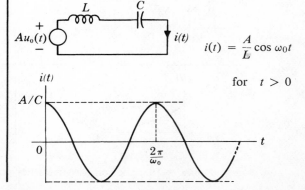

$$i(t) = \frac{A}{L}\cos\omega_0 t$$

for $t > 0$

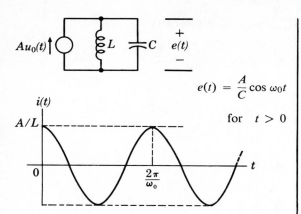

$$e(t) = \frac{A}{C} \cos \omega_0 t$$

for $t > 0$

Step response of L-C circuit

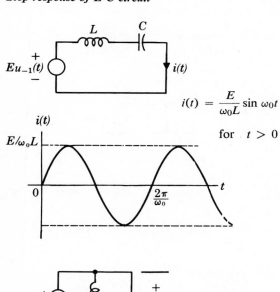

$$i(t) = \frac{E}{\omega_0 L} \sin \omega_0 t$$

for $t > 0$

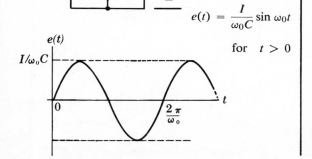

$$e(t) = \frac{I}{\omega_0 C} \sin \omega_0 t$$

for $t > 0$

Natural behavior of R-L-C circuit

(a) Overdamped

$$f(t) = A_1 e^{-p_1 t} + A_2 e^{-p_2 t}$$
for $t > 0$

$$p_1 = -\alpha + \sqrt{\alpha^2 - \omega_0^2}$$

$$p_2 = -\alpha - \sqrt{\alpha^2 - \omega_0^2}$$

(b) Critically damped

$$f(t) = e^{-\alpha t}(A_1 + A_2 t)$$
for $t > 0$

$$\omega_0 = 1/\sqrt{LC}$$

$$\alpha = \begin{cases} R/2L \text{ for series circuit} \\ 1/2RC \text{ for parallel circuit} \end{cases}$$

(c) Underdamped

$$f(t) = A e^{-\alpha t} \cos(\omega_d t + \theta)$$
$$= e^{-\alpha t}(A_1 \cos \omega_d t + A_2 \sin \omega_d t)$$
for $t > 0$

$$A_1 = A \cos \theta$$

$$A_2 = -A \sin \theta$$

$$\omega_d = \sqrt{\omega_0^2 - \alpha^2}$$

(Response waveform shown on page 206.)

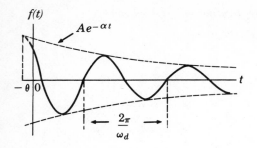

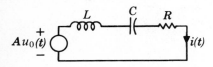

Impulse response of series R-L-C circuit $(\alpha = R/2L)$

(a) Overdamped

$$i(t) = \frac{A}{2L\sqrt{\alpha^2 - \omega_0^2}}(p_1 e^{p_1 t} - p_2 e^{p_2 t})$$

$$\text{for} \quad t > 0$$

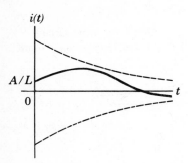

(b) Critically damped

$$i(t) = \frac{A}{L}e^{-\alpha t}(1 - \alpha t)$$

$$\text{for} \quad t > 0$$

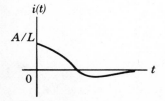

(c) Underdamped

$$i(t) = \frac{A\omega_0}{L\omega_d}e^{-\alpha t}\cos(\omega_d t + \theta)$$

$$\text{for} \quad t > 0$$

$$\theta = \cos^{-1}\frac{\omega_d}{\omega_0}$$

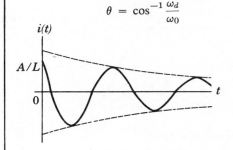

Impulse response of parallel R-L-C circuit
$(\alpha = 1/2RC)$

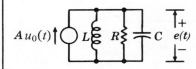

(a) Overdamped

$$e(t) = \frac{A}{2C\sqrt{\alpha^2 - \omega_0^2}}(p_1 e^{p_1 t} - p_2 e^{p_2 t})$$

$$\text{for} \quad t > 0$$

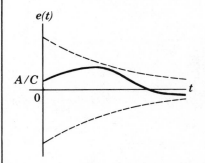

(b) Critically damped

$$e(t) = \frac{A}{C}e^{-\alpha t}(1 - \alpha t) \quad \text{for} \quad t > 0$$

(Response waveform shown on page 207.)

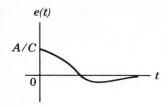

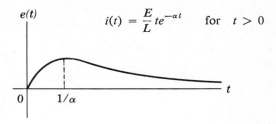

(b) Critically damped

$$i(t) = \frac{E}{L} t e^{-\alpha t} \quad \text{for} \quad t > 0$$

(c) Underdamped

$$e(t) = \frac{A\omega_0}{C\omega_d} e^{-\alpha t} \cos(\omega_d t + \theta)$$

$$\text{for} \quad t > 0$$

$$\theta = \cos^{-1} \frac{\omega_d}{\omega_0}$$

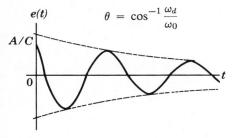

(c) Underdamped

$$i(t) = \frac{E}{L\omega_d} e^{-\alpha t} \sin \omega_d t$$

$$\text{for} \quad t > 0$$

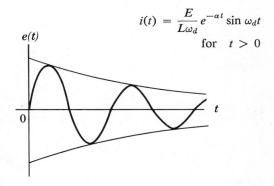

Step response of series R-L-C circuit ($\alpha = R/2L$)

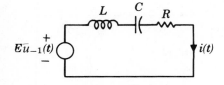

(a) Overdamped

$$i(t) = \frac{E}{2L\sqrt{\alpha^2 - \omega_0^2}} (e^{p_1 t} - e^{p_2 t})$$

$$\text{for} \quad t > 0$$

Step response of parallel R-L-C circuit ($\alpha = 1/2RC$)

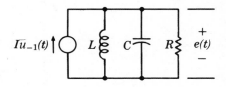

(a) Overdamped

$$e(t) = \frac{I}{2C\sqrt{\alpha^2 - \omega_0^2}} (e^{p_1 t} - e^{p_2 t})$$

$$\text{for} \quad t > 0$$

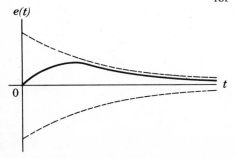

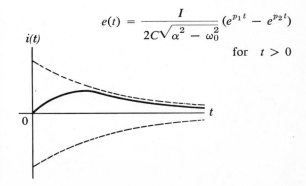

(b) Critically damped

$$e(t) = \frac{I}{C} t e^{-\alpha t} \quad \text{for} \quad t > 0$$

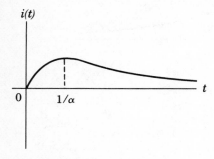

(c) Underdamped

$$e(t) = \frac{I}{C\omega_d} e^{-\alpha t} \sin \omega_d t$$
$$\text{for} \quad t > 0$$

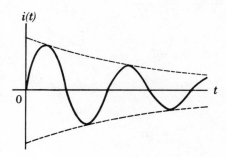

The complex-frequency plane

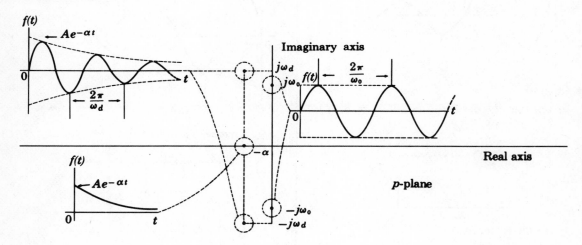

References

Chapter 9 presents *R-L-C* transients in terms of initial values, final values, and natural frequencies. Alternative points of view will be found in the references listed here.

1. E. A. GUILLEMIN, *Introductory Circuit Theory*, John Wiley, New York, 1953. Guillemin develops the *L-C* and *R-L-C* transients principally to expose the types of natural behavior which a circuit can exhibit. Both step and impulse responses are treated.

2. MIT EE Staff, *Electric Circuits*, John Wiley, New York, 1943. This text presents *R-L-C* circuits from the point of view of differential equations. Only the step response is considered.

3. BRENNER and JAVID, *Analysis of Electric Circuits*, McGraw-Hill, New York, 1959. Brenner and Javid separate the source-free behavior and the step and impulse responses.

4. D. K. CHENG, *Analysis of Linear Systems*, Addison-Wesley, Reading, Mass., 1959. A Laplace transform approach.

5. H. H. SKILLING, *Electrical Engineering Circuits*, John Wiley, New York, 1957. Skilling uses the *R-L-C* circuit to discuss the natural modes of a circuit and to introduce the Laplace transform.

Exercises

SECTION 9–2

1. A current is given by the equation

$$i(t) = 10e^{-t/e} - 10e^{-t}.$$

Find the current values at $t = 0$ and $t = \infty$. What is the maximum value and where does it occur? Sketch the curve.

2. A voltage is given by the equation

$$e(t) = 2te^{-t/2}.$$

Find the voltage values at $t = 0$ and $t = \infty$. What is the maximum value and where does it occur? Sketch the curve.

3. A current is given by the equation

$$i(t) = e^{-t/2} \cos (2\pi t + 45°).$$

Find the current values at $t = 0$, $t = 1$, $t = 2$, and $t = \infty$. What is the time constant of the envelope? What is the period of the wave and what is its frequency? What is the phase at $t = 0$? Sketch the waveform.

4. Solve the following differential equation, subject to the given initial conditions:

$$\frac{d^2i}{dt^2} + 5\frac{di}{dt} + 6i = 0,$$

$$i(0) = 0, \qquad i'(0) = 10.$$

5. Solve the following differential equation, subject to the given initial conditions:

$$\frac{d^2e}{dt^2} + 4\frac{de}{dt} + 4e = 0,$$

$$e(0) = 0, \qquad e'(0) = 10.$$

6. Solve the following differential equation, subject to the given initial conditions:

$$\frac{d^2i}{dt^2} + 8\frac{di}{dt} + 25i = 0,$$

$$i(0) = 10, \qquad i'(0) = -10.$$

7. Solve the following differential equation, subject to the given initial conditions:

$$\frac{d^2i}{dt^2} + 5\frac{di}{dt} + 4i = 8,$$

$$i(0) = 0, \qquad i'(0) = 0.$$

8. Solve the following differential equations subject to the given initial conditions:

(a) $\dfrac{d^2e}{dt^2} + 6\dfrac{de}{dt} + 9e = 9,$ $\qquad e(0) = e'(0) = 0.$

(b) $\dfrac{d^2i}{dt^2} + 1.414\dfrac{di}{dt} + i = 10,$ $\qquad i(0) = i'(0) = 0.$

SECTION 9–3

9. A sinusoidal current is given by

$$i(t) = 10 \cos (2\pi t + 45°).$$

(a) Sketch the waveform. (b) Give the maximum amplitude. (c) Give the frequency. (d) Give the period. (e) Give the angular frequency ω. (f) Give the phase relative to a cosine function. (g) Resketch for a frequency of $\omega = 2\pi \times 10^6$.

10. A series circuit is composed of $L = \frac{1}{4}$ h, and $C = \frac{1}{16}$ f. At $t = 0$ there is a current of 1 amp in the inductance and no voltage on the capacitance. (a) Find $i(0^+)$, $di(0^+)/dt$, and ω_0. (b) Match the values in part (a) to the known form of the transient, $i(t) = A_1 \cos \omega t + A_2 \sin \omega t$.

11. In the circuit of Fig. 9–16 the current is 1 amp and the voltage on the capacitance is 1 v at $t = 0$. Find $i(t)$.

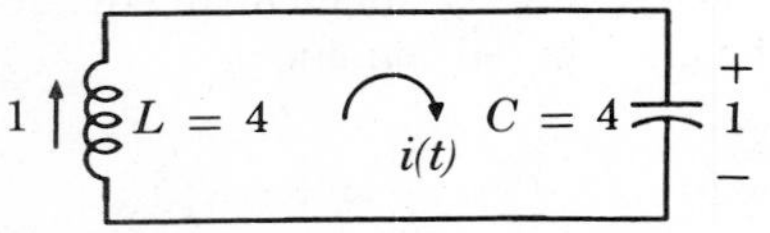

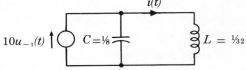

Figure 9–16

12. An impulse voltage source of 10 volt·sec is applied in series with an inductance of $\frac{1}{4}$ h and a capacitance of $\frac{1}{4}$ f. There is no initial energy stored in the circuit. Find $i(0^+)$, $di(0^+)/dt$, ω_0, and the expression for $i(t)$.

13. In the circuit of Fig. 9–17 the switch is closed at $t = 0$, when the current in L_1 is 10 amp and the voltage across C is zero. Find the voltage on C

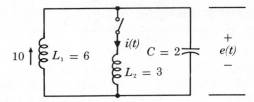

Figure 9–17

as a function of time from the instant the switch is closed. Also find the current through the switch.

14. A 10-v battery is switched in series with a 3-h inductance and a 12-f capacitance at $t = 0$. There is no energy in the circuit at $t = 0$. (a) Find $i(0^+)$, $di(0^+)/dt$, and ω_0. (b) Find $i(\infty)$ (assuming a small resistance). (c) Find $i(t)$. (d) Suppose that at $t = 0$ there is a voltage on the capacitance of 5 v, with a polarity which opposes the applied voltage around the mesh. Find $i(0^+)$, $di(0^+)/dt$, $i(\infty)$, and ω_0. From these values obtain $i(t)$.

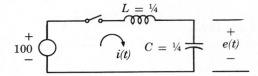

Figure 9–18

15. The switch in the circuit of Fig. 9–18 is closed at $t = 0$. At this time there is no energy stored in the circuit. (a) Find the voltage $e(t)$ by finding the current and integrating. (b) Find the voltage from $e(0^+)$, $de(0^+)/dt$, $e(\infty)$, and ω_0.

16. Find the current $i(t)$ in the circuit of Fig. 9–19.

Figure 9–19

SECTION 9–4

17. A damped sinusoidal current is given by $i(t) = 10e^{-t} \cos (2\pi t + 45°)$. (a) Sketch the waveform. (b) Give the angular frequency, cyclic frequency, and period. (c) What is the time constant of the

envelope? (d) What is the phase relative to a cosine?

18. A series circuit consists of an inductance of 10 h, a resistance of 2 ohms, and a capacitance of 5 f. At $t = 0$ the voltage on the capacitance is 10 v, and the current is zero. (a) Give the values of $i(0^+)$, $di(0^+)/dt$, and $i(\infty)$. (b) Assume a response current of the form $i(t) = Ae^{-\alpha t} \cos(\omega_d t + \theta) + B$ and evaluate the constants. (c) Sketch the current waveform.

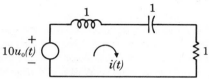

Figure 9–20

19. The circuit of Fig. 9–20 is at rest when it is excited by an impulse voltage. Give the current as a function of time from this instant.

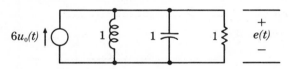

Figure 9–21

20. Find $e(t)$ in the circuit of Fig. 9–21.

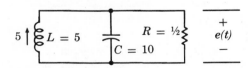

Figure 9–22

21. (a) At $t = 0$ in the circuit of Fig. 9–22 there is a current of 5 amp in the inductance and no voltage on the capacitance. Find $e(0^+)$, $de(0^+)/dt$, $e(\infty)$ and a response of the form

$$e(t) = Ae^{-\alpha t} \cos(\omega_d t + \theta) + B.$$

(b) In the circuit of Fig. 9–22 at $t = 0$ there is a voltage $e(t)$ of 5 v across the capacitance and no current in the inductance. Give the voltage $e(t)$ which will ensue. (c) In the circuit of Fig. 9–21 at $t = 0$ the current in the inductance is 5 amp and the voltage across the capacitance is 5 v. Find $e(t)$

by superposing the results of parts (a) and (b). Also evaluate the voltage directly from its initial value and the initial value of its derivative.

22. (a) The switch in the circuit of Fig. 9–23 is closed at $t = 0$. Find $i(0^+)$, $di(0^+)/dt$, and $i(\infty)$. Match these values to a general step response of the form $i(t) = Ae^{-\alpha t} \cos(\omega_d t + \theta) + B$. (b) Find the voltage $e(t)$ across the capacitance in part (a) by integrating the current $i(t)$ and by matching the initial and final values.

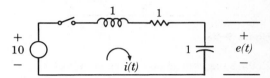

Figure 9–23

23. (a) The switch in the circuit of Fig. 9–24 is closed at $t = 0$. At this time there is no energy stored in the circuit. Find $i(0^+)$, $di(0^+)/dt$, and $i(\infty)$. Match the response to the general over-damped expression $i(t) = A_1 e^{p_1 t} + A_2 e^{p_2 t} + B$. (b) Find the voltage e_C on the capacitance in Fig. 9–24 by integrating the current and by matching the initial and final values.

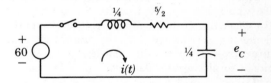

Figure 9–24

24. (a) The switch in the circuit of Fig. 9–25 is opened at $t = 0$. Find $e(0^+)$, $de(0^+)/dt$, and $e(\infty)$. Match these values to a step-function response of the form $e(t) = Ae^{-\alpha t} \cos(\omega_d t + \theta) + B$. (b) Find the current $i(t)$ in the inductance of Fig. 9–25 by integrating the voltage response and by matching directly to the initial and final values.

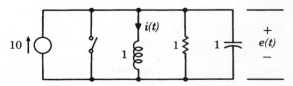

Figure 9–25

Problems

1. Find the current $i(t)$ in the circuit of Fig. 9–26 for $t > 0$.

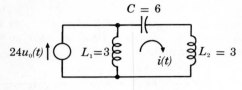

Figure 9–26

2. Find the voltage $e(t)$ in the circuit of Fig. 9–27 by superposition and by computing $e(0^+)$, $de(0^+)/dt$, and $e(\infty)$.

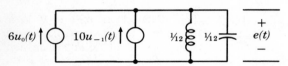

Figure 9–27

3. The elements in the circuit of Fig. 9–28 can be changed to produce critical damping. (a) Find the values of α, ω_0, and ω_d for the given circuit. (b) Change L in the original circuit to give critical damping. (c) Change C in the original circuit to give critical damping. (d) Change R in the original circuit to give critical damping. (e) Find the current which would flow in the circuit with the resistance adjusted to give critical damping.

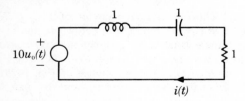

Figure 9–28

4. Compute ω_0 and α for the circuit of Fig. 9–29 and find the type of response which it must produce. If the initial voltage on the capacitance is 10 v, and the initial current in the inductance is 50 amp, what is the voltage $e(t)$ across the resistance?

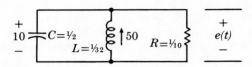

Figure 9–29

5. In the circuit of Fig. 9–30 the step voltage is applied at $t = 0$. At this time there is a current of 50 amp in the circuit and a voltage of 50 v on the capacitance. Find the voltage on C as a function of time, subsequent to this instant.

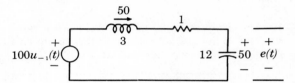

Figure 9–30

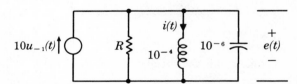

Figure 9–31

6. Adjust the value of R in the circuit of Fig. 9–31 to give critical damping, and find the voltage $e(t)$ which is obtained for this condition.

7. Sketch the natural frequencies in the p-plane and write a general expression for the transient response for each of the following: (a) a series R-L circuit with $R = 2$ ohms and $L = 4$ h excited by an impulse voltage source; (b) a series R-C circuit with $R = 3$ ohms and $C = 4$ f excited by an impulse voltage source; (c) a series L-C circuit with $L = 5$ h and $C = 20$ f excited by a voltage impulse; (d) a series R-L-C circuit with $R = 1$ ohm, $C = 1$ f, and $L = 1$ h excited by a voltage impulse; (e) a parallel R-C circuit with $R = 2$ ohms and $C = 3$ f excited by an impulse current source; (f) a par-

allel *R-L* circuit with $R = 6$ ohms and $L = 3$ h excited by an impulse current source; (g) a parallel *L-C* circuit with $L = \frac{1}{4}$ h and $C = \frac{1}{16}$ f excited by a current impulse; (h) a parallel *R-L-C* circuit with $R = 1$ ohm, $L = 1$ h, and $C = 1$ f excited by an impulse current.

8. The natural response frequency of a two-terminal circuit with an open circuit at the terminal-pair is

$p = -2$. With a short circuit across the terminal-pair it is $p = -3$. (a) Give the form of the response current when the circuit is driven by an impulse voltage. (b) Give the form of the response voltage when the circuit is driven by an impulse current. (c) How would the answers to parts (a) and (b) change if the sources were step functions instead of impulses?

CHAPTER **10**

SINE WAVES, PHASORS, AND THE FREQUENCY DOMAIN

Eternity is a pendulum whose balance wheel says unceasingly only the two words, in the silence of a tomb, "always! never! never! always!..."

JACQUES BRIDAINE

10–1 Introduction

The motion of a pendulum has exerted a fascination for human minds since the first savage watched the swaying of the first tree branch. The smooth sinusoidal motion, back and forth, seems to express some secret of the universe. Indeed nature "loves" the sinusoid. From the motions of the stars and the planets to the tides on earth, and from our heartbeats to our psychological states, we are surrounded by sinusoids. Most of the electric power systems in the world produce sinusoidal waveforms, and most of our communications systems rely on sinusoidal waves. We could justify special techniques for handling sinusoidal excitation on this basis alone. In addition, however, Fourier's theorem expresses arbitrary waveforms in terms of sinusoids and thereby extends the usefulness of the sinusoidal techniques.

These "frequency-domain" methods make use of complex algebra to reduce steady-state sinusoidal problems to essentially resistive networks. An ability to use this technique is the "bread and butter" tool of the electrical engineer.

In addition to the cogent arguments we have given for devoting our time to the steady-state sinusoid, the best is still the simplicity of the resulting analysis! Other waveforms can be used as building blocks, but none of these has the basic mathematical simplicity of the sine wave. The sums, differences, integrals, and derivatives of sine waves of a given frequency are themselves sine waves of the same frequency. No other waveform is preserved in this fashion.*

---

* Actually, the most general case is the exponentially damped sine wave. The constant-amplitude sine wave and the exponential curve are special cases.

In summary, our reasons for devoting a good deal of attention to the responses of networks to sinusoidal steady-state excitation are:

1. Sinusoids occur in many practical generators.

2. Fourier's theorem allows sinusoidal analysis to be extended to the general case.

3. Sinusoids are easily handled mathematically.

10–2 Phasors

We shall use the term "sinusoidal wave" to represent any waveform that can be expressed as a sine or a cosine. For analytical work we shall use the cosine as the basic form. The cosine is perfectly general, since the addition of a phase angle of $-90°$ converts it into the sine. Thus

$$|F| \cos (\omega t - 90°) = |F| \sin \omega t. \qquad (10\text{–}1)$$

Our basic waveform will have the trigonometric form

$$f(t) = |F| \cos (\omega t + \theta). \qquad (10\text{–}2)$$

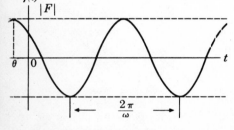

Figure 10–1. The sinusoidal waveform $f(t) = |F| \cos (\omega t + \theta)$.

A sketch of this waveform is shown in Fig. 10–1. The f is used to represent the time function, and the F is used to represent the maximum amplitude of the sinusoid. Magnitude bars are used to enclose F because later we shall use a complex number F to represent the amplitude and phase of the sinusoid.* If F is a real, positive number, the magnitude bars can be removed. The phase angle which we will use is the phase angle of a *cosine* wave. This is an arbitrary choice, but once we make the choice we must stick to it. The period of the wave of Eq. (10–2) is

$$T = \frac{2\pi}{\omega} \text{ sec}, \qquad (10\text{–}3)$$

and its frequency is

$$f = \frac{1}{T} = \frac{\omega}{2\pi} \text{ cycles/sec}, \qquad (10\text{–}4)$$

from which

$$\omega = 2\pi f \text{ rad/sec}.$$

For the 60-cycle frequency used in power systems, the value of ω is $2\pi \times 60 = 377 \text{ rad/sec}$.

The phasor representation of sine waves. The projection of a vector on the real axis is a cosine function of the angle which the vector

---

* In textbooks, vectors are frequently denoted by boldface letters. For the sake of simplicity in our notation, the vectors we shall study will be denoted by the customary capital italic letters.

makes with the axis. If the angle changes with time, the projection
on the axis also changes, and its length represents the cosine of the
angle. To represent the function of Eq. (10–2), the angle must be
equal to θ at $t = 0$ and increase linearly thereafter. The net result
is a vector which rotates about the origin, as a spoke rotates about
an axle. It is called a *rotating phasor*. The term *phasor*, alone, is
used for the stationary vector at $t = 0$. The phasor which represents
the sinusoid of Eq. (10–2) is shown in Fig. 10–2. It is a vector of
length $|F|$, standing at an angle of θ from the real axis. If the phasor
is made to rotate at an angular frequency of ω, its projection on the
real axis is the cosine function. The cosine graph is sketched below
the phasor, with time t increasing vertically downward. When the
quantity $(\omega t + \theta)$ is 90° the projection is zero; when the quantity
$(\omega t + \theta)$ is 180° the projection is $-|F|$; when the quantity $(\omega t + \theta)$
is 270° the projection is zero again, and so on.

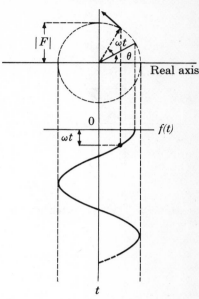

Figure 10–2. A rotating phasor and its
sinusoidal projection on the real axis.

In problems with only a single excitation function, all the sinusoidal functions will be of the same frequency, and thus all the rotating
vectors will have the same angular velocity, or frequency. A sort of
"merry-go-round" exists on which all the vectors are riding. The
merry-go-round is the *frequency domain*. Since all the phasors in
any given problem are on the same merry-go-round, they are stationary with respect to each other, and can be manipulated by the
ordinary rules of vector geometry or vector algebra. When the resultant vector, or phasor, has been obtained its projection on the
real axis is the time-function solution of the problem. Stepping on
the merry-go-round, where the vectors are stationary, is called
transforming the problem to the frequency domain. The resultant
vector is called the frequency-domain solution, and the process of
finding its projection on the real axis is called transforming the
resultant to the time domain. The method is akin to the use of
logarithms, in which we transform real numbers to the domain of
logarithms in order to perform multiplication by simply adding the
logarithms.

The complex-algebra representation of sine waves. The full advantage of phasors is not realized until they are expressed in algebraic form. The vector form is useful for visualizing relationships,
but the algebraic form is preferable for computations. There is, of
course, a one-to-one correspondence between a two-dimensional
vector, or phasor, and a complex number. The basis of the relationship is the equation (Euler's formula)

$$e^{\pm j\theta} = \cos \theta \pm j \sin \theta. \qquad (10\text{–}5)$$

In Eq. (10–5) the quantity $e^{j\theta}$ is a vector with a real part of $\cos \theta$

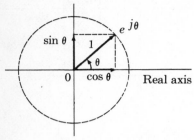

Figure 10–3. The unit vector or phasor $e^{j\theta} = \underline{/\theta}$.

and an imaginary part of $\sin \theta$.* The length of the vector is

$$\sqrt{\cos^2 \theta + \sin^2 \theta} = 1.$$

It is therefore a unit vector standing at an angle of θ from the real axis as shown in Fig. 10–3. If the vector has a length of $|F|$ its algebraic expression is

$$F = |F|e^{j\theta} = |F| \cos \theta + j|F| \sin \theta. \qquad (10\text{–}6)$$

In Eq. (10–6) the complex number F represents the phasor. To obtain the corresponding time function we must rotate the vector and take its projection on the real axis. Rotating the vector changes θ to $\theta + \omega t$, and the projection on the real axis is the real part of the complex number. [We shall use the notation $\text{Re}(F)$ to denote the real part of a complex number.] The time function therefore is

$$f(t) = |F| \cos (\omega t + \theta). \qquad (10\text{–}7)$$

In summary, the time-domain and frequency-domain expressions for a sinusoid are as follows:

Time-domain expression	*Frequency-domain expression*
$f(t) = |F| \cos (\omega t + \theta)$	$F = |F|e^{j\theta}$
	$= |F| \cos \theta + j|F| \sin \theta$

The transformation from the time domain to the frequency domain can also be discussed algebraically. We start with

$$f(t) = |F| \cos (\omega t + \theta), \qquad (10\text{–}8)$$

and using Euler's formula, we replace the cosine function to obtain

$$f(t) = |F| \text{ Re } [e^{j(\omega t + \theta)}].$$

Since $|F|$ is real it can be moved within the real-part sign, and thus

$$f(t) = \text{ Re } [|F|e^{j\theta}e^{j\omega t}]. \qquad (10\text{–}9)$$

To obtain the frequency-domain vector we drop the real-part sign and the $e^{j\omega t}$. The stationary vector is

$$F = |F|e^{j\theta}. \qquad (10\text{–}10)$$

To transform the frequency-domain phasor to the time function we

---

* The idea of considering the real part of a complex number as a value along the real axis and the imaginary part as a value along an axis at right angles to it is an arbitrary, but useful, concept.

reverse this process. We multiply by $e^{j\omega t}$ and take the real part. Thus

$$f(t) = \text{Re}\,[|F|e^{j\theta}e^{j\omega t}]$$
$$= |F|\cos(\omega t + \theta). \qquad (10\text{--}11)$$

When we multiply by $e^{j\omega t}$ we cause the vector to rotate with an angular velocity of ω rad/sec, and when we take the real part we are taking the projection on the real axis.

The transformations between the time and the frequency domains are used so frequently that it is customary to memorize the results. *The magnitude of the frequency-domain phasor is the same as the amplitude of the sinusoid, and the angle of the phasor with respect to the real axis is the phase angle of the sinusoid written in cosine form.* These two rules allow rapid transformations in either direction.

Phasor algebra. In the following sections we shall review some of the rules of complex algebra as they apply to phasors.

Polar and rectangular forms. A complex number can be expressed in terms of its magnitude and angle, or in terms of its projection on the two axes. A typical example of a phasor is shown in Fig. 10–4. It has a length of $|F|$, and it stands at an angle of θ with respect to the real axis. The *polar* form of the phasor is

$$F = |F|e^{j\theta} = |F|\,\underline{/\theta}. \qquad (10\text{--}12)$$

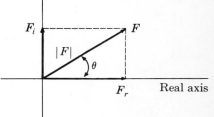

Figure 10–4. A phasor in rectangular and polar forms.

The second form in Eq. (10–12) is read "F magnitude at an angle of θ." It is in every way equivalent to the $e^{j\theta}$ notation and is actually the preferred form when the angle is in degrees rather than radians. The *rectangular* form of the same phasor is

$$F = F_r + jF_i, \qquad (10\text{--}13)$$

where F_r and F_i are the projections on the real and imaginary axes, respectively.

Polar to rectangular form. The conversion of a given phasor from polar to rectangular form can be accomplished by a formal manipulation of Eq. (10–12) or by resolving the vector geometrically along the two axes. Thus

$$F = |F|e^{j\theta} = |F|\cos\theta + j|F|\sin\theta,$$

and the real and imaginary components are

$$F_r = |F|\cos\theta, \qquad F_i = |F|\sin\theta. \qquad (10\text{--}14)$$

Rectangular to polar form. The conversion of a given phasor from rectangular to polar form is accomplished by applying the theorem of Pythagoras to the right triangle of Fig. 10–4. The length of the phasor is

$$|F| = \sqrt{F_r^2 + F_i^2}, \tag{10–15}$$

and the angle at which it stands is

$$\theta = \tan^{-1} \frac{F_i}{F_r}. \tag{10–16}$$

An alternative technique for obtaining the magnitude and angle is:

1. Take the ratio of F_i/F_r.
2. Obtain $\theta = \tan^{-1} F_i/F_r$.
3. Divide F_i by $\sin \theta$ to obtain $|F|$.

This method should be used for numerical work on a slide rule. Since the tangent scale runs only up to 45°, the complementary triangle should be solved whenever F_i is greater than F_r. The value of $|F|$ is unchanged, and the phasor angle is: 90° minus the angle obtained.

The sum or difference of two phasors. In order to add two phasors it is convenient to write them in rectangular form. Suppose the two phasors are

$$F_1 = F_{r1} + jF_{i1}, \qquad F_2 = F_{r2} + jF_{i2}.$$

The sum is obtained by adding separately the real and imaginary parts. Thus

$$F_1 + F_2 = (F_{r1} + F_{r2}) + j(F_{i1} + F_{i2}). \tag{10–17}$$

If the original phasors are given in polar form it is necessary to convert them to rectangular form before performing the addition.

The product of two phasors. In order to multiply two phasors it is convenient to write them in polar form. Suppose the two phasors are

$$F_1 = |F_1|e^{j\theta_1}, \qquad F_2 = |F_2|e^{j\theta_2}.$$

The product is obtained by multiplying the magnitudes and adding the angles. Thus

$$F_1 \times F_2 = |F_1|\,|F_2|e^{j(\theta_1 + \theta_2)}. \tag{10–18}$$

Since the product of two magnitudes is the magnitude of the product, Eq. (10–18) can also be written in the form

$$F_1 \times F_2 = |F_1 F_2|\,\underline{|\theta_1 + \theta_2}. \tag{10–19}$$

Although it is convenient to have the phasors in polar form for multiplication, it is not necessary. In rectangular form they are multiplied by the well-known rules of algebra. If the phasors are

$$F_1 = F_{r1} + jF_{i1}, \qquad F_2 = F_{r2} + jF_{i2},$$

the product is

$$F_1 \times F_2 = (F_{r1} + jF_{i1})(F_{r2} + jF_{i2})$$

$$= (F_{r1}F_{r2} - F_{i1}F_{i2}) + j(F_{r1}F_{i2} + F_{i1}F_{r2}). \qquad (10\text{–}20)$$

The quotient of two phasors. Let us suppose that we are dealing with the same two phasors which we considered for multiplication. If they are in polar form the quotient of F_1 divided by F_2 is

$$\frac{F_1}{F_2} = \frac{|F_1|e^{j\theta_1}}{|F_2|e^{j\theta_2}} = \frac{|F_1|}{|F_2|}\, e^{j(\theta_1 - \theta_2)}. \qquad (10\text{–}21)$$

Since the quotient of the magnitudes is the magnitude of the quotient, Eq. (10–21) can also be written in the form

$$\frac{F_1}{F_2} = \left|\frac{F_1}{F_2}\right| \underline{|\theta_1 - \theta_2}. \qquad (10\text{–}22)$$

If the two phasors are given in rectangular form the quotient can be obtained by rationalization. We multiply numerator and denominator by the conjugate of the denominator. (Conjugate phasors are defined in the following subsection.) Thus

$$\frac{F_1}{F_2} = \frac{F_{r1} + jF_{i1}}{F_{r2} + jF_{i2}} \times \frac{F_{r2} - jF_{i2}}{F_{r2} - jF_{i2}}$$

$$= \frac{F_{r1}F_{r2} + F_{i1}F_{i2} + j(-F_{r1}F_{i2} + F_{i1}F_{r2})}{F_{r2}^2 + F_{i2}^2}. \qquad (10\text{–}23)$$

Alternatively, of course, the phasors can be changed to polar form before the division is attempted. In general, the polar form is preferred for multiplication and division, and the rectangular form for addition and subtraction.

Conjugate phasors. A pair of conjugate phasors have the same magnitude and equal angles, each angle being the negative of the other. Thus, if

$$F = |F|e^{j\theta} = F_r + jF_i,$$

the conjugate phasor is

$$F^* = |F|e^{-j\theta} = F_r - jF_i. \qquad (10\text{–}24)$$

In order to extend Eq. (10–24) to the general case we note that the real part of the vector remains unchanged when the conjugate is taken, but that the imaginary part is reversed in sign. No matter how complicated the expression for a vector or phasor, the conjugate can be obtained merely by changing the sign of all the j's which occur in the expression.

Conjugate phasors are useful for several reasons. For example, the sum of a phasor and its conjugate is

$$F + F^* = F_r + jF_i + F_r - jF_i = 2F_r, \qquad (10\text{–}25)$$

and the difference is

$$F - F^* = F_r + jF_i - F_r + jF_i = 2jF_i. \qquad (10\text{–}26)$$

The product of a phasor and its conjugate is

$$F \times F^* = |F|e^{j\theta} \times |F|e^{-j\theta} = |F|^2, \qquad (10\text{–}27)$$

and the quotient is

$$\frac{F}{F^*} = \frac{|F|e^{j\theta}}{|F|e^{-j\theta}} = e^{j2\theta} = \underline{|2\theta}. \qquad (10\text{–}28)$$

Equations (10–25), (10–26), (10–27), and (10–28) give explicit expressions for the real part, the imaginary part, the magnitude, and the phase of a phasor in terms of the phasor and its conjugate.

Numerical examples. Because of the importance of the phasor operations we have just discussed, we shall illustrate them by means of numerical examples involving the two phasors

$$F_1 = 3 + j4 = 5\,\underline{|53°},$$
$$F_2 = 1 + j1.732 = 2\,\underline{|60°}.$$

(a) Polar to rectangular form:

$$\begin{aligned}
F_1 &= 5\,\underline{|53°}, \\
F_r + jF_i &= 5\cos 53° + j5\sin 53° \\
&= 5 \times 0.6 + j5 \times 0.8 \\
&= 3 + j4.
\end{aligned}$$

(b) Rectangular to polar form:

$$\begin{aligned}
F_2 &= 1 + j1.732 \\
|F_2|\,\underline{|\theta_2} &= \sqrt{1^2 + (1.732)^2}\,\underline{|\tan^{-1} 1.732} \\
&= 2\,\underline{|60°}.
\end{aligned}$$

(c) Sum and difference:

$$F_1 + F_2 = 3 + j4 + 1 + j1.732 = 4 + j5.73,$$
$$F_1 - F_2 = 3 + j4 - 1 - j1.732 = 2 + j2.27.$$

(d) Product in polar form:

$$F_1 \times F_2 = 5\,\underline{|53°} \times 2\,\underline{|60°} = 10\,\underline{|113°}.$$

(e) Product in rectangular form:

$$
\begin{aligned}
F_1 \times F_2 &= (3 + j4)(1 + j1.732) \\
&= (3 - 6.92) + j(4 + 5.19) \\
&= -3.92 + j9.19 \\
&= 10\,\underline{|113°}.
\end{aligned}
$$

(f) Quotient in polar form:

$$\frac{F_1}{F_2} = \frac{5\,\underline{|53°}}{2\,\underline{|60°}} = 2.5\,\underline{|-7°}.$$

(g) Quotient in rectangular form:

$$
\begin{aligned}
\frac{F_1}{F_2} &= \frac{3 + j4}{1 + j1.732} \times \frac{1 - j1.732}{1 - j1.732} \\
&= \frac{9.92 - j1.20}{4} \\
&= 2.48 - j0.30 \\
&= 2.5\,\underline{|-7°}.
\end{aligned}
$$

(h) Conjugates:

$$F_1^* = 3 - j4 = 5\,\underline{|-53°},$$
$$F_2^* = 1 - j1.732 = 2\,\underline{|-60°},$$
$$F_1 + F_1^* = 3 + j4 + 3 - j4 = 6,$$
$$F_1 - F_1^* = 3 + j4 - 3 + j4 = j8,$$
$$F_1 \times F_1^* = 5\,\underline{|53°} \times 5\,\underline{|-53°} = 25,$$
$$\frac{F_1}{F_1^*} = \frac{5\,\underline{|53°}}{5\,\underline{|-53°}} = \underline{|106°} = e^{j106°}.$$

10–3 The frequency domain

Many of the trigonometric operations upon single-frequency sinusoids can be carried out more easily in the frequency domain than in the time domain. There are three distinct steps in the frequency domain method:

1. The transformation of the sine waves to frequency-domain phasors.

2. The performance of the desired operations in the frequency domain.

3. The transformation of the resultant back to the time domain.

Addition and subtraction. The addition or subtraction of a pair of phasors in the frequency domain performs the equivalent operations on the corresponding sinusoidal waves in the time domain. Vector addition is required because both the angle and the magnitude are significant. For example, for the case of two sine waves of equal amplitude and a phase difference of 180°, the sum is zero.

As an example of the method let us consider the addition of the two sinusoids

$$i_1(t) = 10 \cos (377t + 60°),$$
$$i_2(t) = 10 \sin 377t = 10 \cos (377t - 90°).$$

Step 1. Translation to the frequency domain. The frequency-domain phasors which represent our time functions are

$$I_1 = 10 \,\underline{|60°},$$
$$I_2 = 10 \,\underline{|-90°}.$$

Step 2. Addition of the phasors. The sum of the two frequency-domain phasors is

$$
\begin{aligned}
I_1 + I_2 &= 10 \,\underline{|60°} + 10 \,\underline{|-90°} \\
&= 5 + j8.66 - j10 \\
&= 5 - 1.34j \\
&= 5.19 \,\underline{|-15°}.
\end{aligned}
$$

Step 3. Translation back to the time domain. The resulting wave in the time domain has a magnitude (amplitude) of 5.19 and a phase of −15°. Its analytical expression is

$$i_1(t) + i_2(t) = 5.19 \cos (377t - 15°).$$

Note that this result has been obtained with a great deal less effort than a trigonometric solution.

Trigonometric manipulation. Expressions in the time domain will sometimes be written in terms of cosine functions and sometimes in terms of sine functions. The phase angles must be obtained from cosine expressions. It is important therefore to be able to transform rapidly and accurately from sine expressions to cosine expressions. In this regard, four particularly useful phasors to remember are those for $\cos \omega t$, $\sin \omega t$, $-\cos \omega t$, and $-\sin \omega t$. The phasor for $\cos \omega t$ is a unit vector at angle zero; the phasor for $\sin \omega t$ is a unit vector at $-90°$; the phasor for $-\cos \omega t$ is a unit vector at $\pm 180°$; and the phasor for $-\sin \omega t$ is a unit vector at $90°$. A sketch of these phasors is shown in Fig. 10–5.

Figure 10–5 can be used to transform from sine functions to cosine functions and to obtain expressions for the time-domain equivalents of phasors. For example, phasor A in the illustration is 135° behind the cosine (the positive direction is the counterclockwise direction). Its time-domain expression is therefore

$$a(t) = |A| \cos (\omega t - 135°).$$

The phasor is 45° behind the positive sine function. Thus an equivalent time-domain expression is

$$a(t) = |A| \sin (\omega t - 45°).$$

The phasor is 45° ahead of the negative cosine. Hence

$$a(t) = -|A| \cos (\omega t + 45°).$$

Since the phasor is 135° ahead of the negative sine, we also obtain

$$a(t) = -|A| \sin (\omega t + 135°).$$

All four of these expressions are, of course, equivalent. The sine-cosine phasor diagram permits us to pass easily from one form to another. The use of this simple diagram is highly recommended, since it avoids the necessity of remembering formulas. The whole point of complex algebra and the frequency domain is to avoid the use of trigonometric formulas by replacing them with a few simple rules of algebra.

Differentiation and integration. Phasors are implied functions of time, since they are rotating at an angular velocity of ω rad/sec. The operations of differentiation and integration on the time functions have the effect of modifying the lengths of the phasors and advancing or retarding them by 90°. If the original time function is

$$f(t) = |F| \cos (\omega t + \theta), \tag{10–29}$$

its derivative is

$$f'(t) = |F| \omega \cos (\omega t + \theta + 90°).$$

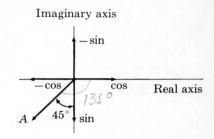

Figure 10–5. The phasors for sines and cosines.

Note here that the length of the phasor has been multiplied by ω and the phase has been advanced by 90°. The two phasors are shown as F and F' in Fig. 10–6.

As far as variations at the frequency ω are concerned, the integral of Eq. (10–29) is

$$f^{-1}(t) = \frac{|F|}{\omega} \cos (\omega t + \theta - 90°).$$

Here we note that integration divides the length of the phasor by ω and retards the phase by 90°. The phasor for the integral is shown as F^{-1} in Fig. 10–6.

As an example let us find the derivative of

$$i(t) = 10 \cos (6t + 120°).$$

Step 1. *Translation to the frequency domain.* The phasor is

$$I = 10 \,\underline{|120°}.$$

Step 2. *Phasor elongation and rotation.* Differentiation causes the phasor amplitude to be multiplied by 6 and the angle to be increased by 90°. Thus

$$I' = 60 \,\underline{|210°}.$$

Step 3. *Translation back to the time domain.* The time derivative is

$$i'(t) = 60 \cos (6t + 210°).$$

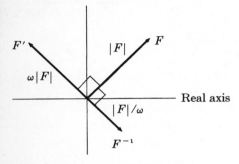

Imaginary axis

Real axis

Figure 10–6. Phasors for the derivatives and integrals of sinusoids.

10–4 Frequency-domain networks

Transformation of networks. The behavior of any network is completely determined by Kirchhoff's equations and the volt-ampere equations of the elements. We shall show how these equations transform to the frequency domain and therefore how networks are transformed to the frequency domain.

Kirchhoff's laws in the frequency domain. In the time domain the two Kirchhoff laws are

$$\sum e_n = 0, \qquad \sum i_n = 0. \tag{10–30}$$

In a steady-state sinusoidal problem, all the currents and all the voltages are sinusoids of a single frequency. If we write each sinusoid as a cosine with an arbitrary amplitude and an arbitrary phase, Kirchhoff's laws therefore become

$$\sum |E_n| \cos (\omega t + \theta_n) = 0, \qquad \sum |I_n| \cos (\omega t + \phi_n) = 0. \tag{10–31}$$

Each of the sinusoids in Eq. (10–31) can be represented in the frequency domain by a phasor with a length equal to the magnitude of the sinusoid, and an angle equal to the phase of the sinusoid. Equation (10–31) states that the sum of the projections of the phasors on the real axis must be zero as the phasors are rotated with an angular velocity of ω radians per second. The only phasor whose projection on the real axis would always be zero is that of zero length. Thus the resultant phasor in the frequency domain must be one of zero length. Kirchhoff's laws in the frequency domain therefore state that the sum of the voltage phasors around any closed path must be zero, and the sum of the current phasors at any junction point must be zero. Analytically,

$$\sum E_n = 0, \qquad \sum I_n = 0, \qquad (10\text{–}32)$$

where $E_n = |E_n| \underline{|\theta_n}$, and $I_n = |I_n| \underline{|\phi_n}$.

It is perhaps worth emphasizing that the summations indicated in Eqs. (10–32) are vector summations, and that the quantities to be added are vectors or complex numbers. Otherwise Kirchhoff's laws have the same form in the frequency domain as in the time domain.

The volt-ampere equations in the frequency domain. *Resistance.* A resistance in the time domain is shown in Fig. 10–7(a). The current is a sinusoid of the form

$$i = |I| \cos (\omega t + \theta). \qquad (10\text{–}33)$$

The volt-ampere equation for the resistance is

$$e = iR, \qquad (10\text{–}34)$$

and hence the voltage is

$$e = |I|R \cos (\omega t + \theta). \qquad (10\text{–}35)$$

The phasor representing the current of Eq. (10–33) is

$$I = |I| \underline{|\theta},$$

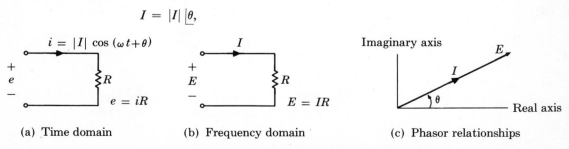

(a) Time domain   (b) Frequency domain   (c) Phasor relationships

Figure 10–7. The resistance element with sinusoidal excitation.

and the phasor representing the voltage in Eq. (10–35) is

$$E = |I|R \,\underline{|\theta}.$$

The relationship between the two phasors is simply

$$E = IR. \tag{10–36}$$

Equation (10–37) has the same form as Ohm's law, but it refers to two vectors, or two complex numbers, and not to a voltage and a current. The current and the voltage phasors are in the same straight line, and the length of the voltage phasor is R times the length of the current phasor. The frequency-domain diagram for the resistance element is shown in Fig. 10–7(b), and the relationship between the current and voltage phasors is shown in Fig. 10–7(c).

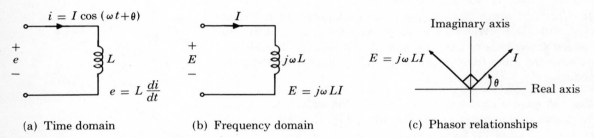

(a) Time domain   (b) Frequency domain   (c) Phasor relationships

Figure 10–8. The inductance element with sinusoidal excitation.

Inductance. An inductance in the time domain is shown in Fig. 10–8(a). The excitation is a current

$$i(t) = |I| \cos (\omega t + \theta). \tag{10–37}$$

The volt-ampere equation for the inductance is

$$e = L \frac{di}{dt}, \tag{10–38}$$

and hence the voltage is

$$e(t) = L|I| \frac{d}{dt} [\cos (\omega t + \theta)]$$

$$= \omega L|I| \cos (\omega t + \theta + 90°). \tag{10–39}$$

The phasor for the current of Eq. (10–37) is $I = |I| \,\underline{|\theta}$, and the phasor for the resulting voltage of Eq. (10–39) is

$$E = \omega L|I| \,\underline{|\theta + 90°}. \tag{10–40}$$

Equation (10–40) shows that the voltage phasor is equal to the current phasor multiplied by ωL in magnitude and shifted 90° ahead in phase. Thus

$$E = (\omega L \times I)\underline{|90°}$$
$$= (\omega L \times I)(\cos 90° + j \sin 90°)$$
$$= j\omega L \times I. \qquad (10\text{–}41)$$

The effect of the j factor in Eq. (10–41) is to advance the phase by 90°. The effect of the ωL is to multiply the magnitude of the phasor by a constant. This phasor equation is the volt-ampere relationship of the inductance in the frequency domain. If we reverse the roles of the stimulus and the response, we obtain

$$I = \frac{E}{j\omega L}. \qquad (10\text{–}42)$$

The quantity $j\omega L$ in Eqs. (10–41) and (10–42) is the complex "resistance" of the inductance in the frequency domain. It is given the name *impedance*, and the symbol Z. An inductance is transformed to the frequency domain by replacing it by a complex resistance, or impedance, of value $Z = j\omega L$. In the frequency domain, this impedance has the formal properties of a resistance. It satisfies an equation which is identical in form to Ohm's law. That is,

$$E = IZ, \qquad \text{with } Z \text{ in ohms.} \qquad (10\text{–}43)$$

In Eq. (10–43) both E and I are phasors, and Z is a complex number or operator which changes the magnitude and phase of one of the phasors until it is identical to the other. In the frequency-domain diagram the inductance is replaced by its impedance, $Z = j\omega L$, as shown in Fig. 10–8(b). The corresponding current and voltage phasors are shown in Fig. 10–8(c).

An heuristic method of keeping track of the phase relationships in an inductance is provided by recalling that the voltage must exist across an inductance first in order to force a current through it. The voltage phasor therefore leads the current phasor.

Capacitance. A capacitance in the time domain is shown in Fig. 10–9(a). The excitation is a voltage

$$e(t) = |E| \cos (\omega t + \theta). \qquad (10\text{–}44)$$

The volt-ampere equation for the capacitance is

$$i = C\frac{de}{dt}, \qquad (10\text{–}45)$$

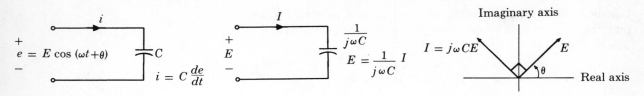

(a) Time domain   (b) Frequency domain   (c) Phasor relationships

Figure 10–9. The capacitance element with sinusoidal excitation.

and hence the current is

$$i(t) = C\frac{d}{dt}[|E|\cos(\omega t + \theta)]$$

$$= \omega C|E|\cos(\omega t + \theta + 90°). \qquad (10\text{–}46)$$

The voltage phasor, from Eq. (10–44), is

$$E = |E|\,\underline{|\theta}, \qquad (10\text{–}47)$$

and the resulting current phasor, from Eq. (10–46), is

$$I = \omega C|E|\,\underline{|\theta + 90°}. \qquad (10\text{–}48)$$

From Eqs. (10–47) and (10–48) it is apparent that the current and voltage phasors are related by the following equation:

$$I = (\omega C \times E)\,\underline{|90°} = j\omega CE. \qquad (10\text{–}49)$$

Equation (10–49) is the volt-ampere equation for the capacitance in the frequency domain. If we had applied a current and computed the resulting sinusoidal voltage, we would have obtained

$$E = \frac{I}{j\omega C}. \qquad (10\text{–}50)$$

Equations (10–49) and (10–50) have the general Ohm's-law form

$$E = IZ,$$

where the impedance of the capacitance in the frequency domain is

$$Z = \frac{1}{j\omega C}. \qquad (10\text{–}51)$$

Thus, it is seen that in the frequency domain the capacitance is replaced by a complex number, or phasor operator, $Z = 1/j\omega C$. The frequency-domain diagram is shown in Fig. 10–9(b). The corresponding phasor relationships are shown in Fig. 10–9(c). If the voltage phasor is given, the current phasor leads it by 90° and has a magnitude which is ωC times as large as the voltage phasor. If the current phasor is given, the voltage phasor lags it by 90° and has a magnitude which is $1/\omega C$ times the magnitude of the current phasor. These phase relationships can be easily recalled if the student will remember that current must charge a capacitance before a voltage appears. The current, therefore leads the voltage.

Solutions by phasor algebra. The solution of a steady-state sinusoidal problem by means of phasor algebra involves the following steps:

1. The problem is transformed to the frequency domain.
2. The phasor solution is obtained by the methods of resistive circuits.
3. The resulting phasor is transformed back to a time function.

By transforming from the time domain to the frequency domain we change from differential equations to algebraic equations, and all the methods which we have learned for resistive circuits can be applied. The fact that the "resistances" are really complex impedances does not change the methods of solution. It merely requires that complex algebra, rather than real algebra, be used to obtain the numerical results. As an example we will solve the circuit of Fig. 10–10(a).

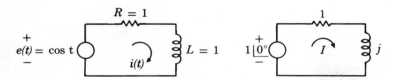

(a) A circuit excited by a   (b) Frequency-domain diagram   **Figure 10–10.** An example solved in the
       sinusoidal time function   frequency domain.

Step 1. Transformation to the frequency domain. The time-domain circuit is shown in Fig. 10–10(a) and the frequency-domain circuit in Fig. 10–10(b). The phasor representing the voltage source has an angle of zero and a magnitude of unity. The 1-ohm resistance transforms to the frequency domain as an impedance of 1 real ohm; the angular frequency is $\omega = 1$; and the inductance transforms to the frequency domain as an impedance of $Z = j1$, or one "imaginary" ohm.

Step 2. Solution in the frequency domain. The solution in the frequency domain is obtained by the same methods we used for resistive circuits. Thus the total impedance of the circuit is the sum of the two series impedances:

$$Z = 1 + j.$$

The current is the voltage divided by the impedance:

$$I = \frac{E}{Z} = \frac{1\,\underline{|0}}{1 + j} = 0.707\,\underline{|-45°}.$$

This current is a complex number or phasor, and the actual current as a function of time must be obtained by a transformation back to the time domain.

Step 3. *Transformation to the time domain.* The time function is a cosine wave with a frequency of $\omega = 1$, an amplitude equal to the amplitude of the current phasor, and a phase angle equal to the angle of the phasor. Thus

$$i(t) = 0.707 \cos (t - 45°). \tag{10–52}$$

Frequency-domain methods are the work horse of electrical engineering. We have introduced them in this chapter and have shown that they are closely related to the resistive methods which we have already developed. In the next two chapters we will pursue this theme further.

Summary

Methods of representing sinusoids

Time domain

(a) Graph

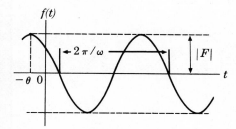

(b) Trigonometry

$$f(t) = |F| \cos(\omega t + \theta)$$

Frequency domain

(c) Phasor

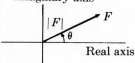

Imaginary axis

Real axis

(d) Complex algebra

$$F = |F|e^{j\theta} = |F| \cos\theta + j|F| \sin\theta$$

The rules of phasor algebra

1. Polar form

$$F = |F|e^{j\theta} = |F| \underline{|\theta}$$

2. Rectangular form

$$F = F_r + jF_i$$

3. Polar to rectangular

$$F_r = |F| \cos\theta$$
$$F_i = |F| \sin\theta$$

4. Rectangular to polar

$$|F| = \sqrt{F_r^2 + F_i^2}$$
$$\theta = \tan^{-1}(F_i/F_r)$$

5. Addition and subtraction

$$F_1 \pm F_2 = (F_2 \pm F_{r2}) + j(F_{i1} \pm F_{i2})$$

6. Multiplication

$$F_1 \times F_2 = |F_1|\,|F_2|\,\underline{|\theta_1 + \theta_2}$$

7. Division

$$F_1/F_2 = (|F_1|/|F_2|)\,\underline{|\theta_1 - \theta_2}$$

8. Conjugate

$$F^* = |F|e^{-j\theta} = F_r - jF_i$$

Frequency domain methods

1. Transform to the frequency domain

2. Operate on the phasors

3. Transform the result to the time domain

Sine-cosine phasors

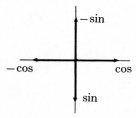

Frequency-domain networks

Time domain	Frequency domain
Variable	
$f = |F| \cos(\omega t + \theta)$	$F = |F|\,\underline{|\theta°}$
	$= |F|e^{j\theta}$

Time domain   *Frequency domain*   Capacitance

Resistance

                   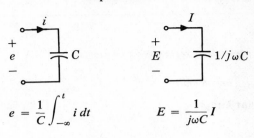

$$e = iR$$ $$E = IR$$ $$e = \frac{1}{C}\int_{-\infty}^{t} i\,dt \qquad E = \frac{1}{j\omega C}I$$

Inductance   Kirchhoff's laws

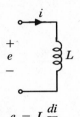   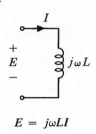

$$\begin{cases}\sum i = 0 \\ \sum e = 0\end{cases} \qquad \begin{array}{c}\sum I = 0 \\ \sum E = 0\end{array}$$

$$e = L\frac{di}{dt} \qquad E = j\omega LI$$

References

Alternating-current circuit theory is the "bread and butter" tool of electrical engineering. Phasor methods were first used by Lord Rayleigh in his *Theory of Sound*. They were introduced to electrical engineers by Oliver Heaviside and popularized in America by Kennelly and Steinmetz. Most standard electrical-engineering circuit books cover phasors in great detail. Of the references given here, the first four cite original sources; the remainder give a few selected present-day texts.

1. A. E. KENNELLY, "Impedance," *AIEE Trans.*, 1893 (175–216).

2. C. P. STEINMETZ, "Reactance," *AIEE Trans.*, 1894 (640–648).

3. LORD RAYLEIGH, *The Theory of Sound*, Vol. 1, Ch. 4 and 5, Macmillan and Co., London, Eng. 1894.

4. O. HEAVISIDE, "On Resistance and Conductance Operators," *Phil. Mag.*, **XXVI,** 1878 (479–502).

5. MIT EE Staff, *Electric Circuits*, John Wiley, New York, 1944. Chapter 4 gives an excellent introduction to the use of frequency-domain vectors to solve sinusoidal circuit problems.

6. E. A. GUILLEMIN, *Introductory Circuit Theory*, John Wiley, New York, 1953. Chapter 6 gives an introduction to sinusoidal analysis and explains the importance of the sine wave to electrical engineers. The time domain and the frequency domain are clearly distinguished.

7. KERCHNER and CORCORAN, *Alternating Current Circuits*, John Wiley, New York, 3rd ed., 1951. This book begins Chapter 1 with alternating-current waveforms and by Chapter 4 has developed the phasor method of solution for sinusoidal problems.

8. LEPAGE and SEELY, *General Network Analysis*, McGraw-Hill, New York, 1951. Chapter 1 discusses the use of complex numbers to represent sine waves. The phasors are related to the RMS (root-mean-square) values of the sinusoids, rather than to the peak values as in this text.

9. H. H. SKILLING, *Electrical Engineering Circuits*, John Wiley, New York, 1957. Skilling discusses sinusoids and the use of phasors very early in the text (Chapter 3). Here also, the phasors are related to RMS values.

10. M. E. VAN VALKENBURG, *Network Analysis*, Prentice-Hall, New Jersey, 1955. The approach used by Van Valkenburg is completely different from the ones discussed above. The general Laplace transform theory is developed first, and the sinusoidal steady-state analysis is treated as a special case.

Exercises

SECTION 10–2

1. Plot several cycles of the sinusoidal function

$$f(t) = 100 \cos (377t + 30°)$$

by means of the graphical technique in which the projection of the rotating vector on the real axis represents the sinusoid. Give the amplitude, phase, frequency and period of the waveform.

2. Draw the phasors (rotating vectors at $t = 0$) which represent the two functions

$$f_1(t) = 10 \cos 2\pi t, \qquad f_2(t) = 10 \sin 2\pi t,$$

and obtain the resultant phasor by vector addition. Obtain the time function for the sum of the two functions by causing the resultant vector to rotate and by finding the projection on the real axis. Verify your results by trigonometry.

3. Sketch the phasors which represent the following sinusoids.
   - (a) $10 \cos t$
   - (b) $5 \cos (377t + 45°)$
   - (c) $10 \sin t$
   - (d) $-5 \cos (377t - 45°)$
   - (e) $10 \cos (t + 135°)$

4. Write the time functions which correspond to the following phasors.
   - (a) $10 \angle 0° \qquad \omega = 1$
   - (b) $10 \angle 90° \qquad \omega = 377$
   - (c) $5 \angle -60° \qquad \omega = 1000$
   - (d) $5 \angle 53° \qquad \omega = 1$
   - (e) $2.82 \angle 135° \qquad \omega = 1/10$

5. Write the time functions which correspond to the frequency-domain complex numbers given below, and use the general angular frequency ω in each case:
   - (a) $1 + j$
   - (b) $3 - j4$
   - (c) $-2 - j2$
   - (d) $-3 + j4$
   - (e) j

6. Find the sum of the following phasors by vector geometry.
   - (a) $1 \angle 0° + 1 \angle 90°$
   - (b) $1 \angle \theta° + 1.732 \angle 90° + \theta°$

   - (c) $2 \angle -225° + 2 \angle 45°$
   - (d) $-3 \angle 215° + 6 \angle 35°$
   - (e) $3 \angle 70° + 4 \angle 160°$
   - (f) $5 \angle 0° + 5 \angle 180°$
   - (g) $10 \angle 0° + 10 \angle -120° + 10 \angle -240°$
   - (h) $5 \angle 30° + 5 \angle -30° + 8.66 \angle 120° + 8.66 \angle 240°$
   - (i) $5 \angle 0° + 7.07 \angle 45° + 10 \angle 60° - 15 \angle 0° - 13.66 \angle 90°$
   - (j) $5 \angle 16° + 5 \angle 32° + 5 \angle 106° + 5 \angle 152° + 5 \angle 196° + 5 \angle 272° + 5 \angle 286°$

7. (a) Change the following complex numbers from polar to rectangular form.
   - (i) $5 \angle 0°$
   - (ii) $10 \angle 45°$
   - (iii) $1.732 \angle -120°$
   - (iv) $10 \angle 1°$
   - (v) $10 \angle -89°$

   (b) Change the following complex numbers from polar to rectangular form.
   - (i) $10e^{j\pi}$
   - (ii) $5e^{j\pi/3}$
   - (iii) $10e^{-j0.6\pi}$
   - (iv) $0.4e^{j16\pi/3}$
   - (v) $-10e^{-j\pi/4}$

   (c) Change the following complex numbers from rectangular to polar form.
   - (i) $j6$
   - (ii) $1 - j2$
   - (iii) $-1 - j2$
   - (iv) $3 + j4$
   - (v) $-3 + j4$

   (d) Change the following complex numbers from rectangular to polar form.
   - (i) $0.345 + j0.216$
   - (ii) $0.123 - j0.794$
   - (iii) $-0.0134 + j0.637$
   - (iv) $343 + j$
   - (v) $-1.73 \times 10^6 - j3.12 \times 10^6$

   (e) Find the magnitudes of the following complex numbers.
   - (i) $2 + j3$
   - (ii) $2 - j3$
   - (iii) $\dfrac{1}{2 + j3}$
   - (iv) $(2 - j3)(2 + j3)$
   - (v) $e^{(1+j\pi/4)}$

(f) Find the real part of each of the following complex numbers.

(i) $j17$

(ii) $e^{j\pi/4}$

(iii) $(3 + j4)(2 - j)$

(iv) $\dfrac{1}{3 + j4}$

(v) $10\,\underline{|115°}$

(g) Write the polar form of the complex numbers which are complex-conjugate to the following:

(i) $7 - j13$

(ii) $(1 + j)(1 - j)$

(iii) $\dfrac{1}{1 + j}$

(iv) $4\,\underline{|60°} + 2\,\underline{|-83°}$

(v) $e^{(2+j\pi/2)}$

8. Evaluate the following expressions and write the answers in polar and rectangular form.

(a) $(3 + j4)(3 - j4)$

(b) $\dfrac{1}{3 + j4}$

(c) $3 + \dfrac{10}{1 + j}$

(d) $\dfrac{2 + j3}{3 + j2}$

(e) $\dfrac{3 - j2}{-2 + j3}$

(f) $3 + \dfrac{4 + j5}{6 + j7}$

(g) $\dfrac{1}{-1 - j} + \dfrac{1}{-4 + j5}$

(h) $3\,\underline{|-45°} + \dfrac{1 + j2}{4 - j3}$

(i) $\dfrac{(1 + j2)(4 + j3)}{(5 + j4)}$

(j) $\dfrac{10\,\underline{|53°} + 7\,\underline{|-13°}}{4\,\underline{|3°} - 10\,\underline{|120°}}$

SECTION 10–3

9. Translate the following two sinusoids to the frequency domain, add the phasors, and then translate the resulting phasor back to the time domain. Check your result by trigonometry.

$$e_1(t) = 100 \cos (\omega t - 30°),$$
$$e_2(t) = 100 \cos (\omega t + 60°).$$

10. Add the following three sinusoids by means of frequency-domain phasors.

$$e_1(t) = 100 \cos (377t),$$
$$e_2(t) = 100 \cos (377t + 120°),$$
$$e_3(t) = 100 \cos (377t + 240°).$$

11. Perform the following trigonometric operations using phasors in the frequency domain. Express the results as time functions.

(a) $4 \cos (t + 45°) - 3 \cos (t - 45°)$

(b) $5 \cos (t + 30°) + 5 \cos (t - 30°)$

(c) $8.66 \cos (t + 120°) - 8.66 \cos (t + 240°)$

(d) $7 \cos 13t + 4 \cos (13t + 70°)$

(e) $-\sin (3t + 45°) + \cos (3t + 45°) + \sin 3t$

12. Express the following waveforms as positive cosine functions with a phase angle. In the process make use of phasor diagrams.

(a) $100 \sin t$

(b) $-100 \cos t$

(c) $-100 \sin t$

(d) $100 \sin (t + \pi)$

(e) $-100 \cos (t + \pi/2)$

13. Give equivalent positive cosine functions for the following expressions.

(a) $4 \sin (377t + 45°)$ (b) $-6 \sin (t + 30°)$

(c) $-7 \cos (t - 135°)$ (d) $\sin (1000t + 7\pi/6)$

(e) $10 \sin 3(t - \pi/2)$

14. An alternating voltage is given by

$$e(t) = 100 \cos 377t.$$

By phasor methods find the sum

$$e(t) + \frac{e'(t)}{100}.$$

15. An alternating current is given by

$$i(t) = 100 \cos (1000t + 45°).$$

By phasor methods find the sum

$$\frac{i(t)}{10} + 100 \int_{-\infty}^{t} i(t)\, dt.$$

Assume that the value of the integral at $t = -\infty$ is zero.

16. An alternating voltage is given by

$$e(t) = 100 \cos (2t + 45°).$$

By phasor methods find the sum

$$e(t) + \frac{de}{dt} + 4 \int_{-\infty}^{t} e\, dt.$$

Assume that the value of the integral at $t = -\infty$ is zero.

SECTION 10–4

17. In a certain network the voltage drops around a mesh are given by

$$e_1(t) = 100 \cos t,$$

$$e_2(t) = -100 \sin t,$$

$$e_3(t) = -141 \cos (t + 45°).$$

(a) Show that the sum of the voltages is zero in the time domain. (b) Show that the sum of the voltage phasors is zero in the frequency domain.

18. In a certain network the currents leaving a node are given by

$$i_1(t) = 100 \cos 377t,$$

$$i_2(t) = 173 \sin 377t,$$

$$i_3(t) = -200 \cos (377t - 60°).$$

(a) Show that the sum of the currents is zero at all times in the time domain. (b) Show that the sum of the current phasors is zero in the frequency domain.

19. In the circuit of Fig. 10–11 find the current in the inductance (a) by using the time-domain volt-ampere relationship and (b) by using the frequency-domain phasors (neglect the value of the integral at $t = -\infty$).

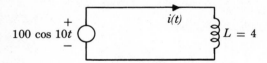

Figure 10–11

20. In the circuit of Fig. 10–12 find the current in the capacitance (a) by using the time-domain volt-ampere relationships and (b) by using the frequency-domain phasors.

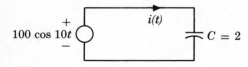

Figure 10–12

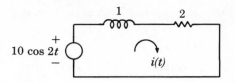

Figure 10–13

21. Solve for the current in the circuit of Fig. 10–13 by the following steps: (a) make a frequency-domain diagram, (b) find the current phasor, and (c) transform this phasor to the time domain.

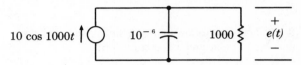

Figure 10–14

22. Find the voltage $e(t)$ in the circuit of Fig. 10–14 using the following steps: (a) make a frequency-domain diagram, (b) find the voltage phasor, and (c) transform this phasor to the time domain.

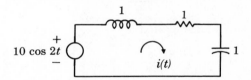

Figure 10–15

23. In the circuit of Fig. 10–15 find the current by means of frequency-domain methods.

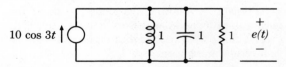

Figure 10–16

24. In the circuit of Fig. 10–16 find the voltage $e(t)$ by phasor methods.

Problems

1. (a) Find the square roots of unity by solving the equation

$$x^2 = 1 = e^{in\pi}, \qquad \text{where } n = 0, \pm2, \pm4, \ldots.$$

(b) Express the roots in phasor form and show that each one when multiplied by itself yields unity.
(c) Find the phasor sum of the two square roots of unity.

2. (a) Find the six sixth-roots of unity by solving the equation

$$x^6 = 1 = e^{in\pi}, \qquad \text{where } n = 0, \pm2, \pm4, \ldots.$$

(b) Express the roots as phasors and show that each one multiplied by itself six times yields unity.
(c) Find the phasor sum of the six sixth-roots of unity.

3. Two voltages $e_1(t)$ and $e_2(t)$ are given below. By phasor methods find their sum, $e_1(t) + e_2(t)$, and also find their difference, $e_1(t) - e_2(t)$.

$$e_1(t) = 10 + 5 \sin \omega t + 3 \sin (3\omega t + 45),$$

$$e_2(t) = 5 + 5 \cos \omega t + 2 \cos (3\omega t - 45).$$

4. Show that sinusoids can be represented as the instantaneous sum of two vectors rotating in opposite directions. Give the pairs of vectors at $t = 0$ which represent the following sinusoids.

    (a) $10 \cos t$ (b) $5 \cos (t + 45°)$
    (c) $2 \sin t$ (d) $-10 \sin (t + 45°)$
    (e) $2 \cos (t + 225°)$

5. Transform the circuit of Fig. 10–17 to the frequency domain, write the mesh equations, and solve for the current phasor I_2. Transform this phasor back to the time domain in order to obtain $i_2(t)$.

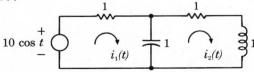

Figure 10–17

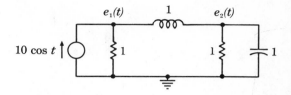

Figure 10–18

6. Transform the circuit of Fig. 10–18 to the frequency domain, write the node equations, and solve for the voltage phasor E_2. Transform this phasor to the time domain in order to obtain $e_2(t)$.

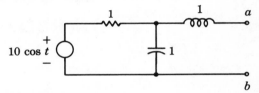

Figure 10–19

7. (a) Transform the circuit of Fig. 10–19 to the frequency domain and obtain the Thévenin equivalent circuit at terminal-pair a-b, in the form of a single voltage in series with a single impedance.
(b) If a short circuit is placed across terminal-pair a-b, what current flows in it?

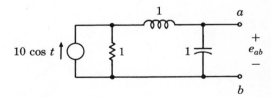

Figure 10–20

8. (a) Transform the circuit of Fig. 10–20 to the frequency domain and obtain the Norton equivalent circuit at terminal-pair a-b, in the form of a single current source in parallel with a single impedance.
(b) If the terminals are left open-circuited, what voltage appears across them?

CHAPTER **11**

FREQUENCY-DOMAIN CIRCUITS AND DRIVING-POINT IMPEDANCES

. . . for thou shalt learn
The wisdom early to discern
True beauty in utility.

LONGFELLOW

11–1 Introduction

Frequency-domain networks are certainly useful. They are the work horse of electrical engineering. And yet they are not without their beauty. Perhaps it lies in their utility, as Longfellow suggests, or perhaps in the internal consistency which allows us to treat steady-state sinusoidal networks, resistive networks, transient excitation, and arbitrary excitation by the same general techniques. Indeed, sinusoidal methods are so appealing that they are used in many fields remote from electrical engineering. Sinusoidal response functions have been obtained for human operators and for the economic system.

In the frequency domain the effect of the circuit on the input phasor is most easily obtained by the use of phasor algebra. The procedures are identical with those which we used for resistive networks, except that the algebra is complex instead of real. There is a one-to-one correspondence, of course, between phasor algebra and the corresponding operations by means of phasor geometry. The geometrical diagram provides a picture from which the operation of a circuit may often be visualized. We will discuss both the algebraic and the geometric method of solving a circuit problem, with perhaps slightly more emphasis on the algebraic method because of its generality.

A resistive one-terminal-pair network is completely characterized by a single real number, its equivalent input resistance. At a particular frequency a frequency-domain network with one-terminal-pair is similarly characterized by a single number, except that the number is now complex, an "impedance" instead of a resistance. It is a simple extension to the concept of an impedance as an algebraic function of frequency, characterizing the network for all frequencies. Alternatively, curves of the magnitude and the phase of the impedance can be plotted as functions of frequency.

11–2 Frequency-domain networks at a single frequency

The solution of steady-state problems by means of phasors involves three distinct steps:

1. The problem is transformed to the frequency domain.
2. The frequency domain problem is solved by means of complex algebra.
3. The resultant phasor is transformed into the time domain.

All of the methods which we have developed for direct-current circuits apply to frequency-domain networks. As examples we will solve problems by mesh currents, node voltages, and Thévenin's theorem.

Example 1. A problem which can be solved by means of mesh currents is shown in Fig. 11–1. The time domain diagram is shown in Fig. 11–1(a), and the corresponding frequency domain diagram in Fig. 11–1(b). The two resistances remain 1 ohm each. The source frequency is $\omega = 2$, and so the impedance of the inductance is $j2$ ohms, and the impedance of the capacitance is $1/j2$ ohm. The mesh currents i_1 and i_2 in the time domain transform to mesh-current phasors I_1 and I_2 in the frequency domain. The source voltage is a phasor with a magnitude of 10 and an angle of $0°$.

The mesh-current equations in the frequency domain are

$$I_1(1 + 2j) - I_2 = 10 \underline{|0°},$$

$$-I_1 + I_2\left(2 + \frac{1}{2j}\right) = 0. \tag{11–1}$$

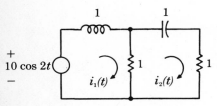

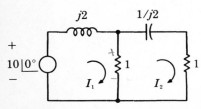

(a) Time-domain circuit

(b) Frequency-domain circuit

Figure 11–1. A mesh-current problem in the frequency domain.

The solutions for the currents are

$$I_1 = \frac{\begin{vmatrix} 10 & -1 \\ 0 & 2 - \frac{1}{2}j \end{vmatrix}}{\begin{vmatrix} 1 + 2j & -1 \\ -1 & 2 - \frac{1}{2}j \end{vmatrix}} = -5.13 \underline{|105.8°},$$

$$\tag{11–2}$$

$$I_2 = \frac{\begin{vmatrix} 1 + 2j & 10 \\ -1 & 0 \end{vmatrix}}{\begin{vmatrix} 1 + 2j & -1 \\ -1 & 2 - \frac{1}{2}j \end{vmatrix}} = 2.48 \underline{|-60.2°}.$$

As a final step the current phasors given by Eqs. (11–2) are transformed to the time domain. The resulting expressions are

$$i_1(t) = -5.13 \cos (2t + 105.8°),$$

$$i_2(t) = 2.48 \cos (2t - 60.2°). \tag{11–3}$$

Example 2. As a second example we will solve the problems of Fig. 11–2 by means of node-voltage equations. The time-domain network is shown in Fig. 11–2(a), and the corresponding frequency-domain network in Fig. 11–2(b).

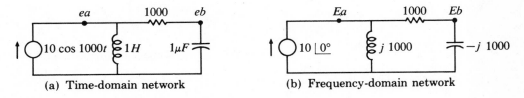

(a) Time-domain network   (b) Frequency-domain network

Figure 11–2. A node-voltage problem in the frequency domain.

The transformation to the frequency domain leaves the resistance unchanged. The source frequency is $\omega = 1000$, the impedance of the inductance is $j1000$ and the impedance of the capacitance is

$$\frac{1}{j10^{-3}} = -j1000.$$

The node voltages e_a and e_b transform to the node-voltage phasors E_a and E_b. The source has a magnitude of 10 and an angle of 0°. (If there is only one source it can usually be taken at a reference angle of 0°.)

The node-voltage equations are

$$E_a \left(\frac{1}{1000} + \frac{1}{j1000} \right) - E_b \frac{1}{1000} = 10 \underline{|0},$$

$$-E_a \left(\frac{1}{1000} \right) + E_b \left(\frac{1}{1000} - \frac{1}{j1000} \right) = 0,$$

or

$$E_a(1 - j) - E_b = 10^4,$$
$$-E_a + E_b(1 + j) = 0, \qquad (11\text{--}4)$$

from which

$$E_a = \frac{\begin{vmatrix} 10^4 & -1 \\ 0 & 1 + j \end{vmatrix}}{\begin{vmatrix} (1 - j) & -1 \\ -1 & (1 + j) \end{vmatrix}} = 1.41 \times 10^4 \underline{|45°},$$

and

$$E_b = \frac{\begin{vmatrix} 1 - j & 10^4 \\ -1 & 0 \end{vmatrix}}{\begin{vmatrix} (1 - j) & -1 \\ -1 & 1 + j \end{vmatrix}} = 10^4 \underline{|0}.$$

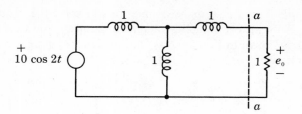

(a) Time-domain circuit

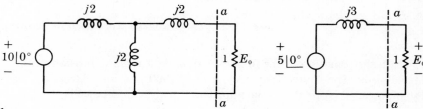

Figure 11–3. A sinusoidal problem solved by Thévenin's theorem.

(b) Frequency-domain circuit   (c) Thévenin equivalent

As a final step the time functions corresponding to the phasors E_a and E_b are

$$e_a = 14100 \cos (1000t + 45°),$$

$$e_b = 10000 \cos 1000t. \qquad (11\text{–}5)$$

Example 3. An example which can be conveniently treated by means of Thévenin's theorem is shown in Fig. 11–3(a), in the time domain. The first step in the solution is the transformation of the network to the frequency domain, as shown in Fig. 11–3(b). Since the source frequency is $\omega = 2$, the impedance of each of the inductances is $j2$ ohms. The source has a magnitude of 10 and an angle of zero.

The frequency-domain circuit is easily treated by means of Thévenin's theorem. The open-circuit voltage at terminals a–a is

$$E_{\text{oc}} = \frac{j2}{j2 + j2} \times 10 \,\big|\underline{0°} = 5 \,\big|\underline{0°}.$$

The "dead" network consists of an impedance $j2$ in series with a parallel combination of two $j2$ impedances. The net impedance is therefore

$$Z = 2j + \frac{2j \times 2j}{2j + 2j} = 3j.$$

The equivalent Thévenin circuit is shown in Fig. 11–3(c). The output voltage, E_0, of this circuit, is

$$E_0 = \frac{1}{1 + 3j} \times 5 \,\underline{|0°} = 1.57 \,\underline{|-71.6°}.$$

Translated back to the time domain, this voltage becomes

$$e_0(t) = 1.57 \cos (2t - 71.6°).$$

Frequency scaling. The frequency variable can appear in a circuit associated only with an inductance or a capacitance in an impedance expression of the form $j\omega L$ or $1/j\omega C$. The impedance in ohms will remain unchanged if the products ωL and ωC remain unchanged. Thus, if we wish to increase the frequency by some factor we can decrease inductances and capacitances by the same factor, and the branch impedances in ohms will be unchanged. The phasor currents and voltages are the same as they were, and the time-domain currents and voltages have the same magnitudes and phases but, of course, a new frequency.

The sort of frequency normalization we have just discussed is important from several points of view. In the first place, it lets us consider circuits with normalized values of inductance and capacitance in the vicinity of 1 henry and 1 farad. Such values are most convenient for calculations, although they are not convenient sizes to obtain physically. In the second place, normalized circuits provide a common ground for comparing the behavior of similar circuits, such as series resonant circuits, parallel resonant circuits, and double-tuned circuits. One frequency-domain model covers a whole class of time-domain circuits.

As an example of frequency normalization, consider the circuit of Fig. 11–4(a). In the time domain the original circuit is driven by

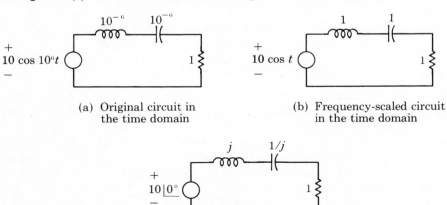

(a) Original circuit in
the time domain

(b) Frequency-scaled circuit
in the time domain

(c) Frequency-domain circuit

Figure 11–4. Frequency scaling and the frequency domain.

a frequency of $\omega = 10^6$ rad/sec, and has physically realizable sizes of inductance and capacitance. A normalized time-domain circuit in which the frequency has been reduced by 10^6 and the inductance and capacitance have been increased by 10^6 is shown in Fig. 11–4(b). Both these circuits are represented in the frequency domain by the same network. The voltage source is a phasor of $10\ \underline{|0°}$, the inductance is an impedance of j ohms, and the capacitance is an impedance of $1/j$ ohms, as shown in Fig. 11–4(c). The problem can be solved in the frequency domain, and the answer can be transformed to either the time domain or the normalized time domain. For example, the current in the frequency domain is

$$I = \frac{10}{1 + j + 1/j} = 10\ \underline{|0°}. \tag{11–6}$$

The corresponding current in the time domain is

$$i(t) = 10 \cos 10^6 t, \tag{11–7}$$

while in the normalized time domain, it is

$$i(t) = 10 \cos t. \tag{11–8}$$

Magnitude normalization in the frequency domain is also possible. If all of the impedances are multiplied by a constant, and if the voltage is multiplied by the same constant, the currents will be unchanged. If all of the impedances are multiplied by a constant and an applied current is divided by this constant, the voltages everywhere will remain unchanged. The name "impedance leveling" is given to this process. In summary, to multiply the impedance level of a circuit by K:

1. All the R's are multiplied by K.
2. All the L's are multiplied by K.
3. All the C's are divided by K.

The capacitance element is treated differently from the inductance and resistance elements because it occurs in the denominator of an impedance expression.

Finally we can combine amplitude and frequency scaling. A normalized time-domain circuit is shown in Fig. 11–5(a). It is desired to increase the frequency of this circuit by the factor 10^6, and to increase the impedance level by the factor 10^3. In effect, the resonant frequency is to be moved from $\omega = 1$ to $\omega = 10^6$ rad/sec, and the impedance at resonance is to be increased from 1 to 10^3 ohms.

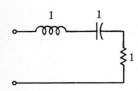

(a) Original circuit

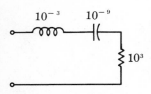

(b) Scaled version: frequency by 10^6 and impedance by 10^3

Figure 11–5. Combined frequency and magnitude scaling.

The new circuit values will be

$$R = 1 \times 10^3 \qquad\qquad = 10^3 \text{ ohms},$$
$$L = 1 \times 10^3 \times 10^{-6} \quad = 10^{-3} \text{ henry},$$
$$C = 1 \times 10^{-3} \times 10^{-6} = 10^{-9} \text{ farad}.$$

The scaled circuit is shown in Fig. 11–5(b). It is almost magical that the normalized 1-ohm, 1-henry, 1-farad, and 1-rad/sec values result in practical element values when scaled both in frequency and impedance level!

11–3 Driving-point impedances as functions of frequency

A one-terminal-pair resistive network can be reduced to a single equivalent resistance. This equivalent resistance determines the response which will be obtained from any possible stimulus function. A one-terminal-pair network in the sinusoidal steady-state can be reduced to one equivalent impedance, called a *driving-point imped-ance*, in the frequency domain.

If the input excitation is a single-frequency sine wave, the driving-point impedance reduces to two terms, the real and imaginary parts of a complex number. *An equivalent network* can always be found which will represent this impedance in the form of a resistance and either an inductance or a capacitance, depending on the sign of the imaginary part of the impedance. This equivalent network, however, gives the response only to a sinusoid of a particular frequency, and the equivalent network at any other frequency will be very different.

We can obtain a driving-point impedance which is applicable for all possible input frequencies. The frequency ω is merely left as an unknown variable. The real part of the impedance is then a function of frequency and so is the imaginary part. To visualize the impedance function, we can plot its real and imaginary parts, or its magnitude and phase, as functions of frequency. *There is no simple equivalent network which will represent the original network at all frequencies.* We are forced to represent the network by an analytical impedance function.

The driving-point impedance. The driving-point impedance of a one-terminal-pair network is the ratio of the voltage phasor applied to it divided by the resulting current phasor. Thus

$$Z = \frac{E}{I}, \qquad \text{with } Z \text{ measured in ohms.} \qquad (11\text{–}9)$$

Equation (11–9) is of the same form as Ohm's law, but the resulting impedance is a complex number rather than a constant. If we break the impedance up into its real and imaginary parts, we obtain

$$Z = R + jX. \tag{11-10}$$

In Eq. (11-10) the real part of the impedance is called *resistance*, and the coefficient of the imaginary part is called *reactance*. Both resistance and reactance are measured in ohms. The resistance is positive, but the reactance can have either sign.

The reciprocal of a resistance is a conductance, and it is measured in mhos. The reciprocal of an impedance also has a name. It is called *admittance*, and it has the symbol Y. Thus

$$Y = \frac{1}{Z}, \qquad \text{with } Y \text{ measured in mhos.} \tag{11-11}$$

The admittance, like the impedance, is a complex number and it can be separated into a real and an imaginary part:

$$Y = G + jB. \tag{11-12}$$

In Eq. (11-12) the real part of the admittance is called *conductance*, and the coefficient of the imaginary part is called *susceptance*. Both conductance and susceptance are measured in mhos. Conductance, like resistance, is positive, but susceptance can have either sign.

Example of driving-point impedance. A simple circuit consisting of a resistance in parallel with an inductance is shown in Fig. 11-6(a). The driving-source frequency is $\omega = 1$, and the frequency-domain diagram is shown in Fig. 11-6(b). The impedance is obtained by treating the branch impedances as if they were resistances. Thus

$$Z = \frac{1 \times j}{1 + j} = \frac{1}{2} + j\frac{1}{2}. \tag{11-13}$$

At this particular frequency the impedance has a resistive part of $\frac{1}{2}$ ohm and a reactive part of $\frac{1}{2}$ ohm. An equivalent circuit which gives the same impedance is a $\frac{1}{2}$-ohm resistance in series with a $\frac{1}{2}$-henry inductance, as shown in Fig. 11-6(c). The equivalent circuit holds only at $\omega = 1$.

In order to obtain a driving-point impedance which is characteristic of the circuit for all frequencies we use the frequency-domain diagram of Fig. 11-7. The impedance of the 1-henry inductance is written as $j\omega$. For this diagram, the input impedance is

$$Z = \frac{1 \times j\omega}{1 + j\omega} = \frac{j\omega(1 - j\omega)}{1 + \omega^2} \tag{11-14}$$

$$= \frac{\omega^2}{1 + \omega^2} + j\frac{\omega}{1 + \omega^2}. \tag{11-15}$$

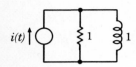

(a) Time domain ($\omega = 1$)

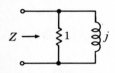

(b) Frequency-domain impedance

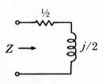

(c) Equivalent impedance at $\omega = 1$

Figure 11-6. Equivalent impedances at a single frequency.

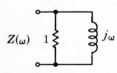

Figure 11-7. The impedance of Fig. 11-6 for any value of ω.

In Eq. (11-15) both the resistance and the reactance are functions of frequency. There is no simple equivalent circuit. We can plot the two terms as functions of frequency, but more often the magnitude and phase of Z are plotted. The polar form of Z is

$$Z = \frac{\omega}{\sqrt{1 + \omega^2}} \; \underline{|\tan^{-1} 1/\omega}. \qquad (11\text{-}16)$$

The polar form is preferred to the rectangular form principally because it is easier to measure the magnitude and the phase in the laboratory.

The equivalent admittance of the circuit of Fig. 11-7 is

$$Y = \frac{1}{Z} = 1 + \frac{1}{j\omega} = 1 - j\omega. \qquad (11\text{-}17)$$

The real part of Eq. (11-17) is the conductance, and the imaginary part is the susceptance. The student should note that the whole impedance expression must be inverted to obtain the admittance, that conductance is *not* the reciprocal of resistance, and that susceptance is *not* the reciprocal of reactance.

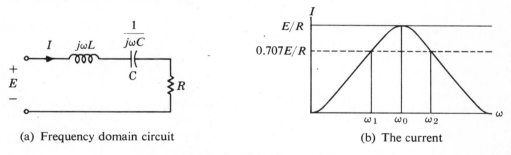

(a) Frequency domain circuit   (b) The current

Figure 11-8.   A series resonant circuit.

Series resonant circuit. Everyone has experienced the phenomenon of resonance. Many physical systems have approximately sinusoidal transient response functions and if they are excited by steady-state sinusoids of the same frequency they respond with great enthusiasm. Swings, pendulums, musical instruments, and many vibrating systems are examples. An electrical example is the series resonant circuit shown in Fig. 11-8(a) in the frequency domain. The impedance of the circuit of Fig. 11-8 is

$$Z = R + j\omega L + \frac{1}{j\omega C}$$

$$= R + j\left(\omega L - \frac{1}{\omega C}\right). \qquad (11\text{-}18)$$

If we consider frequency as the variable in Eq. (11–18) it is apparent that the impedance approaches infinity for small values of ω and for large values of ω and that it has minimum value of $Z = R$ when

$$\omega L = \frac{1}{\omega C}$$

or

$$\omega = \frac{1}{\sqrt{LC}}. \tag{11–19}$$

This value of ω is the resonant frequency, ω_0. If the circuit is driven by a voltage, the current which flows at this frequency has a maximum value of

$$I\,(\text{max}) = \frac{E}{R}. \tag{11–20}$$

When the current decreases to 0.707 of its maximum value on either side of ω_0, the power in the circuit has decreased to $\frac{1}{2}$ of its maximum value. The corresponding frequencies ω_1 and ω_2 shown in Fig. 11–8(b) are called the lower and upper half-power frequencies. They occur when the impedance increases to $\sqrt{2}\,R$ and at this point the phase angle is 45° and

$$\omega L - \frac{1}{\omega C} = \pm R, \tag{11–21}$$

from which

$$\omega = \pm\,\frac{R}{2L} \pm \sqrt{\frac{R}{2L}^2 + \frac{1}{LC}}.$$

If we pick the positive values of ω and if $R/2L$ is small compared with $1/LC$ (as it must be for a pronounced resonance), then

$$\omega_1 = \omega_0 - \frac{R}{2L}, \tag{11–22}$$

and

$$\omega_2 = \omega_0 + \frac{R}{2L}.$$

The frequency spread between ω_1 and ω_2 is called the bandwidth B, and is

$$B = \frac{R}{L}. \tag{11–23}$$

The sharpness of the resonance peak depends on the ratio of the resonant frequency to the bandwidth, which ratio is called the Q of the circuit. In general,

$$Q = \omega_0/B, \tag{11–24}$$

and for the series resonant circuit,

$$Q = \omega_0 L/R. \tag{11–25}$$

Parallel resonant circuit. The parallel resonant circuit shown in Fig. 11–9 is the dual of the series resonant circuit. The admittance is

$$Y = \frac{1}{R} + j\left(\omega C - \frac{1}{\omega L}\right). \qquad (11\text{–}26)$$

The resonant frequency is again

$$\omega_0 = \frac{1}{\sqrt{LC}}. \qquad (11\text{–}27)$$

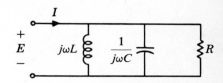

Figure 11–9. A parallel resonant circuit.

If the circuit is driven by a current the voltage produced at this frequency has the maximum value,

$$E_{\max} = IR. \qquad (11\text{–}28)$$

The lower and upper half-power points are

$$\omega_1 = \omega_0 - \frac{1}{2RC}, \qquad (11\text{–}29)$$

and

$$\omega_2 = \omega_0 + \frac{1}{2RC}. $$

The bandwidth is

$$B = \frac{1}{RC}, \qquad (11\text{–}30)$$

and the Q is

$$Q = \omega_0 RC. \qquad (11\text{–}31)$$

11–4 Three phase circuits

Most commercial electric power systems are three phase. The sources are arranged in a symmetrical fashion resulting in a smooth and economical distribution of power and at the same time a simple and convenient method of analysis. The symmetry is based on the phase relationships of the sources and is more conveniently visualized in terms of phasor diagrams than in terms of phasor algebra. The waveforms of three-phase circuits are produced by generators, such as the one shown in Fig. 11–10.

In Fig. 11–10(a) a magnet is shown rotating past three sets of stationary windings A–A', B–B', and C–C'. As it does so, it induces an approximately sinusoidal voltage in each winding in turn. The reference polarities for the three generated voltages are shown in Fig. 11–10(b). The double subscript notation is convenient for keeping track of the voltages in an analytical fashion. Thus $V_{AA'}$ represents the voltage drop from A to A', and so on.

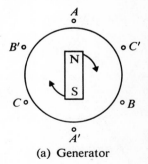

(a) Generator

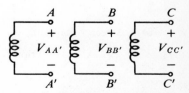

(b) Winding reference polarities

Figure 11–10. A three-phase generator

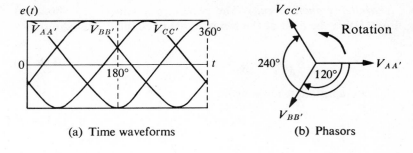

Figure 11–11. A set of three-phase voltages.

(a) Time waveforms   (b) Phasors

A sketch of the voltage waveforms as they would appear on an oscilloscope is shown in Fig. 11–11(a).

The voltage $V_{BB'}$ lags the voltage $V_{AA'}$ by one third of a complete cycle or 120° and the voltage $V_{CC'}$ lags $V_{AA'}$ by 240°. The analytical expressions for the voltages (assuming $t = 0$ at the peak value of $v_{AA'}$) are

$$v_{AA'} = |E| \cos \omega t,$$
$$v_{BB'} = |E| \cos (\omega t - 120°), \qquad (11\text{–}32)$$
$$v_{CC'} = |E| \cos (\omega t - 240°).$$

The frequency is usually 60 cps, and ω is therefore 377 rad/sec. The corresponding phasors are shown in Fig. 11–11(b) and given analytically as

$$V_{AA'} = |E| \underline{|0},$$
$$V_{BB'} = |E| \underline{|-120°}, \qquad (11\text{–}33)$$
$$V_{CC'} = |E| \underline{|-240°}.$$

The phase sequence of the phasors in Eq. (11–33) is positive. As the phasors rotate they come past the zero line in the order $V_{AA'}$, $V_{BB'}$, $V_{CC'}$. A negative sequence can be obtained by interchanging any two of the phasors. Analytically, a negative sequence can be obtained by changing the signs of the phase angles.

The coils AA', BB', and CC' of Fig. 11–10(b) can be connected in two ways to make a balanced three phase system. The Δ-connection is shown in Fig. 11–12(a) and the corresponding phasor diagram in Fig. 11–12(b). The net voltage around the loop is zero, since the sum of three vectors of equal magnitude and 120° apart in phase is zero.

A Y-connection is shown in Fig. 11–13(a), and the corresponding phasor diagram in Fig. 11–13(b). The line-to-line voltages in the Y-connected case are greater than the coil voltages (phase voltages).

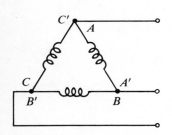

(a) The Δ-circuit

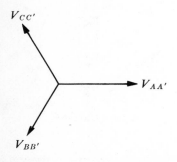

(b) A Δ-vector diagram

Figure 11–12. A Δ-connection.

The line-to-line voltage V_{AB} is

$$V_{AB} = V_{AA'} + V_{B'B} = V_{AA'} - V_{BB'} = |E|\underline{|0} - |E|\underline{|-120}$$

$$= |E|\left[1 - \left(-\frac{1}{2} - j\frac{\sqrt{3}}{2}\right)\right] = E\left(\frac{3}{2} + j\frac{\sqrt{3}}{2}\right)$$

$$= \sqrt{3}\,E\,\underline{|30°}. \tag{11-34}$$

Similarly

$$V_{BC} = \sqrt{3}\,E\,\underline{|-90°} = \sqrt{3}\,E\,\underline{|30 - 120°},$$

$$V_{CA} = \sqrt{3}\,E\,\underline{|-210°} = \sqrt{3}\,E\,\underline{|30 - 240}.$$

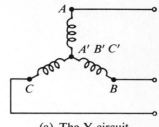

(a) The Y-circuit

The line-to-line voltages have magnitudes that are $\sqrt{3}$ times the magnitudes of the voltages from the lines to the common or neutral point. Furthermore the line-to-line voltages are 120° apart in phase. They also form a balanced three-phase set of voltages. They are perhaps more easily obtained by means of a phasor diagram as shown in Fig. 11-13(b). To obtain V_{AB}, the phasor $V_{BB'}$ is reversed and added to the phasor $V_{AA'}$. The angle of the resulting phasor is 30° and the length is clearly $\sqrt{3}$ times the magnitude of the phase voltage.

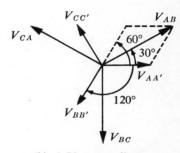

(b) A Y-vector diagram

Figure 11-13. A Y-connection.

Balanced Δ-circuits. The load as well as the source can be connected in Y or Δ. If the load is in Δ and the line-to-line voltages are known, the currents in each branch (phase) can be obtained easily. The line currents are then obtained by vector addition. Consider the example of Fig. 11-14. The current from A' to B' is

$$I_{A'B'} = \frac{V_{A'B'}}{R_{A'B'}} = \frac{100\,\underline{|0}}{10} = 10\,\underline{|0}.$$

Similarly

$$I_{B'C'} = \frac{V_{B'C'}}{R_{B'C'}} = \frac{100\,\underline{|-120}}{10} = 10\,\underline{|-120},$$

and

$$I_{C'A'} = \frac{V_{C'A'}}{V_{A'C'}} = \frac{100\,\underline{|-240}}{10} = 10\,\underline{|-240}.$$

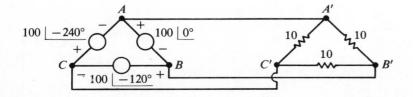

Figure 11-14. A Δ-Δ problem.

From these values the line currents can be found:

$$I_{AA'} = I_{A'B'} + I_{A'C'} = I_{A'B'} - I_{C'A'}$$

$$= 10\,\underline{|0} - 10\,\underline{|-240} = 10\sqrt{3}\,\underline{|-30°}.$$

Similarly

$$I_{BB'} = 10\sqrt{3}\,\underline{|-150°},$$

and

$$I_{CC'} = 10\sqrt{3}\,\underline{|90}.$$

A vector diagram showing the various voltages and currents is shown in Fig. 11–15. In some cases it is easier to perform the analysis by means of the vector diagram rather than by algebra. The steps can be followed in Fig. 11–15.

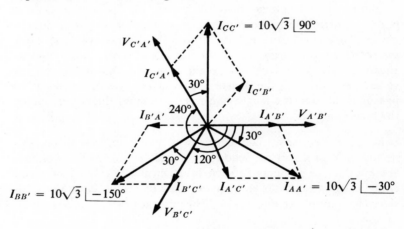

Figure 11–15. Vector diagram for the circuit of Fig. 11–14.

Balanced Y-circuits. A balanced Y-source feeding a balanced Y-load is again a symmetrical combination that can be solved easily. The neutral point O' at the centre of the generator and the neutral point at the centre of the load are at the same potential and can be joined by a short circuit. The most direct proof of this fact is obtained by inserting the short circuit and computing the current in it, as in Fig. 11–16. The current in the short-circuit $I_{O'O}$ is made up of three components: $I_{AA'O'O}$, $I_{BB'O'O}$, and $I_{CC'O'O}$. They can be computed separately, as follows:

$$I_{AA'O'O} = \frac{E}{Z} = I,$$

$$I_{BB'O'O} = \frac{E}{Z}\,\underline{|-120} = I\,\underline{|-120}, \qquad (11\text{–}35)$$

$$I_{CC'O'O} = \frac{E}{Z}\,\underline{|-240} = I\,\underline{|-240}.$$

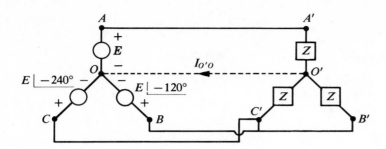

Figure 11–16. A Y–Y circuit.

The total current is

$$I_{O'O} = I_{AA'O'O} + I_{BB'O'O} + I_{CC'O'O}$$

$$= I + I\underline{|-120} + I\underline{|-240}$$

$$= I[1 + (-\tfrac{1}{2} - j0.866) = (-\tfrac{1}{2} + j0.866)] \qquad (11\text{–}36)$$

$$= 0.$$

Since no current flows in the short-circuit $I_{O'O}$, the voltages at the two neutral points must be equal and the addition of the short circuit has no effect on the currents and voltages. The presence of the short circuit, however, reduces the problem to three single-phase problems that can be solved by the simple approach of Eq. (11–35).

Y–Δ and Δ–Y circuits. When the generator and the load have different connections it is usually simplest to transform one or the other so that they will agree in form. The usual Y–Δ and Δ–Y formulas hold. In a balanced circuit, the Δ-impedances are simply three times the Y-impedances, and the Y-impedances are one-third of the Δ-impedances. A typical example is shown in Fig. 11–17. The Y-impedance in Fig. 11–17(b) is obtained from Fig. 11–17(a) as

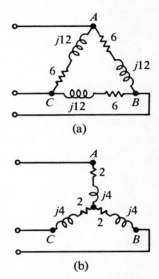

Figure 11–17. Y–Δ transformations of balanced circuits.

$$Z_Y = \frac{Z_\Delta}{3} = \frac{6 + j12}{3} = 2 + j4.$$

The transformation of sources from Y to Δ and from Δ to Y is slightly more complicated and is best accomplished by means of a "topological" vector diagram. The voltages in Fig. 11–18 are shown with double subscripts. Thus, the voltage V_{AB} is the voltage drop from point A to point B. The topological significance is obtained by considering the tail of the phasor V_{AB} to *be* the point A and the head to *be* the point B. Phasors carry direction and magnitude information but not position, and it is usually necessary to move them around in the plane in order to obtain a phasor diagram with topological significance. An example of the reasoning involved is shown in Fig. 11–19. The vectors in Fig. 11–19(a) have magnitude

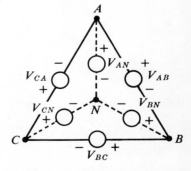

Figure 11–18. Y–Δ generator system.

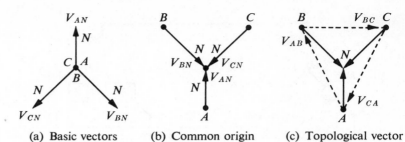

Figure 11–19. Y–Δ and Δ–Y topological vector diagrams.

(a) Basic vectors　　　(b) Common origin　　　(c) Topological vector diagram

and direction but not position. The vector diagram of Fig. 11–19(b) is identical in information but the vectors have a topological meaning. There is a common point N and the three tails of the vectors represent the three points A, B, and C relative to this neutral point. The voltages V_{BC}, V_{CA}, and V_{AB} can be obtained quickly from the phasor diagram of Fig. 11–19(b) by joining the appropriate points. The final topological phasor diagram with all the phasors marked is shown in Fig. 11–19(c). This diagram can be used for transferring from Y to Δ or from Δ to Y. For example, if the Y-voltages are

$$V_{AN} = 100\ \underline{|90},$$

$$V_{BN} = 100\ \underline{|-30},$$

$$V_{CN} = 100\ \underline{|-150},$$

then the Δ-voltages are

$$V_{AB} = 173\ \underline{|120},$$

$$V_{BC} = 173\ \underline{|0},$$

$$V_{CA} = 173\ \underline{|-120}.$$

The special methods which we have discussed for taking advantage of the symmetry in three-phase problems do not apply to unbalanced circuits. Such circuits can be handled readily enough by mesh or node equations although the amount of algebra may be considerable.

Summary

Frequency-domain networks

All methods of dc circuits apply

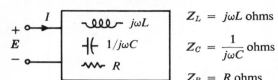

$Z_L = j\omega L$ ohms

$Z_C = \dfrac{1}{j\omega C}$ ohms

$Z_R = R$ ohms

Z = impedance (ohms)
R = resistance (ohms)
X = reactance (ohms)
Y = admittance (mhos)
G = conductance (mhos)
B = susceptance (mhos)

Frequency scaling

Z_L is unchanged if ω is multiplied by K_1 and L is divided by K_1.

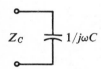

Z_C is unchanged if ω is multiplied by K_1 and C is divided by K_1.

Magnitude scaling

Multiply R by a constant.
Multiply L by the same constant.
Divide C by the same constant.
All impedances are multiplied by the constant.

Driving-point impedance

General network

$$Z(\omega) = \frac{E}{I} = Z\underline{|\theta} = R(\omega) + jX(\omega)$$

$$Y(\omega) = \frac{1}{Z(\omega)} = G(\omega) + jB(\omega)$$

Series resonance

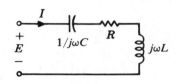

$$Z = R + j\left(\omega L - \frac{1}{\omega C}\right)$$

Resonant frequency $\qquad \omega_0 = \dfrac{1}{\sqrt{LC}}$

Bandwidth $\qquad B = \dfrac{R}{L}$

Quality factor $\qquad Q = \dfrac{\omega_0}{B} = \dfrac{\omega_0 L}{R}$

Parallel resonance

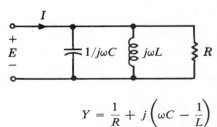

$$Y = \frac{1}{R} + j\left(\omega C - \frac{1}{L}\right)$$

$$\omega_0 = \frac{1}{\sqrt{LC}}$$

$$B = \frac{1}{RC} \qquad Q = \omega_0 RC$$

Three-phase waveforms

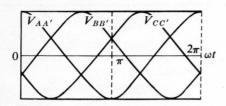

$$v_{AA'} = |E| \cos \omega t$$
$$v_{BB'} = |E| \cos (\omega t - 120°)$$
$$v_{CC'} = |E| \cos (\omega t - 240°)$$

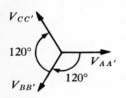

$$V_{AA'} = |E| \underline{|0°}$$
$$V_{BB'} = |E| \underline{|-120°}$$
$$V_{CC'} = |E| \underline{|-240°}$$

Δ- and Y-voltages

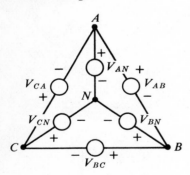

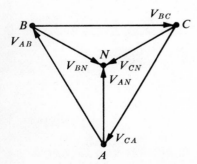

Balanced Δ-problems

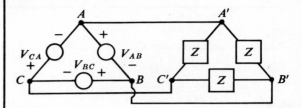

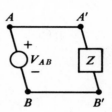

Equivalent single phase

Balanced Y-problems

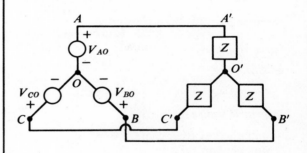

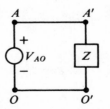

Equivalent single phase

Balanced Y-Δ transformation

$$Z_Y = \frac{Z_\Delta}{3}$$

References

The sharp distinction which we have made between time-domain networks and frequency-domain networks is not followed in some of the standard texts. A few selected references are given below.

1. MIT EE Staff, *Electric Circuits*, John Wiley, New York, 1943. Chapter 4 introduces steady-state circuits. The discussion of resonant circuits is particularly good.

2. E. A. GUILLEMIN, *Introductory Circuit Theory*, John Wiley, New York, 1953. In Chapter 6 Guillemin gives an excellent discussion of sinusoids, time- and frequency-domain networks, phasor diagrams, and resonance. The complex frequency "*s*" is introduced at the outset.

3. H. H. SKILLING, *Electrical Engineering Circuits*, John Wiley, New York, 1957. Skilling's book is primarily concerned with frequency-domain networks, which he calls transform networks. They are introduced in Chapter 2 and used throughout the book.

4. BRENNER and JAVID, *Analysis of Electric Circuits*, McGraw-Hill, New York, 1959. Brenner and Javid introduce the steady-state sinusoidal response as a special case of the general operational response to exponentials.

5. M. E. VAN VALKENBURG, *Network Analysis*, Prentice-Hall, New Jersey, 1955. In this text the steady-state response is introduced as a special case of the general Laplace transform theory. This approach has the advantage of clearly separating the time and frequency domains.

6. M. B. REED, *Alternating-Current Circuit Theory*, Harper, New York, 1956. Reed distinguishes the time and the frequency domains by using the *R-L-C* elements in the time domain and square boxes for impedances in the frequency domain.

7. KERCHNER and CORCORAN, *Alternating Current Circuits*, 3rd ed., John Wiley, New York, 1951. This book is devoted to frequency-domain methods. The last two chapters return to the time domain, with a discussion of some simple differential equations.

Exercises

SECTION 11–2

1. Write and solve the mesh equations for the frequency-domain circuit of Fig. 11–20.

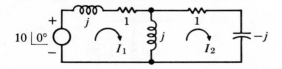

Figure 11–20

2. (a) Write and solve the node equations for the frequency domain circuit of Fig. 11–21. (b) What

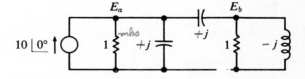

Figure 11–21

is the relationship between the circuits of Exercises 1 and 2?

3. (a) Find the Thévenin equivalent for the frequency-domain circuit shown in Fig. 11–22 at the terminal-pair *a–a*. (b) What are the magnitude and

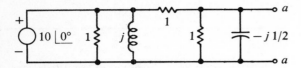

Figure 11-22

the phase of current which would flow in a short circuit placed across terminals *a–a*?

4. (a) Find the Norton equivalent circuit for the frequency domain circuit of Fig. 11–23 at the terminal-pair *a–a*. (b) Give the voltage phasor which would occur across *a–a* if an impedance of $Z = -j$ were placed across it.

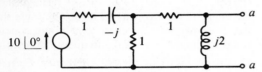

Figure 11-23

5. The frequency-domain diagram of Fig. 11–24 has the units of ohms. (a) Give the corresponding time-domain diagram if the frequency is 1 rad/sec. (b) Give the time-domain diagram if the frequency is $\omega = 10^3$ rps. (c) Give the time-domain diagram if the frequency is $\omega = 10^6$ rps.

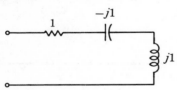

Figure 11-24

6. In the frequency-domain circuit of Fig. 11–25 the units are ohms. (a) Find the voltage phasor *E*. (b) If the frequency is $\omega = 1$, give the time-domain diagram and the voltage $e(t)$. (c) If the frequency is $\omega = 10^6$, give the time-domain diagram and the voltage $e(t)$.

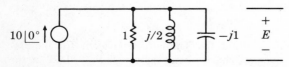

Figure 11-25

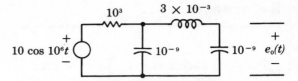

Figure 11-26

7. (a) Translate the circuit of Fig. 11–26 to the frequency domain and scale to an impedance level which gives a 1-ohm resistance. (b) Solve the normalized circuit for the phasor E_0. (c) Write the time function for the original voltage $e_0(t)$.

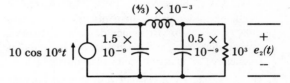

Figure 11-27

8. (a) Translate the circuit of Fig. 11–27 to the frequency domain and normalize the impedance level so that the resistance assumes a value of 1 ohm. (b) Solve for the normalized voltage phasor E_2. (c) Write the original time function $e_2(t)$.

SECTION 11-3

9. For the circuit of Fig. 11–28: (a) Draw a frequency-domain diagram if the excitation frequency is $\omega = 1$ rad/sec. (b) Find the input impedance of the circuit at $\omega = 1$. (c) What equivalent series circuit will have the same impedance at $\omega = 1$. (d) Find the input impedance of the original circuit as a function of a general ω. (e) Give the real and imaginary parts of the input impedance as functions of frequency, and sketch graphs for them. (f) Why is there no equivalent circuit in the general case?

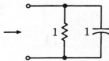

Figure 11-28

10. For the circuit of Fig. 11–29: (a) Make a frequency-domain circuit if $\omega = 1$. (b) Find the input

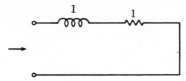

Figure 11–29

admittance. (c) Give an equivalent parallel circuit with the same admittance at $\omega = 1$. (d) Find the input admittance as a function of ω. (e) Separate the admittance into its real and imaginary parts and sketch them. (f) Why is there no parallel equivalent circuit in the general case?

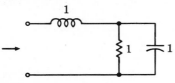

Figure 11–30

11. For the circuit of Fig. 11–30: (a) Find the input impedance at $\omega = 1$. (b) Give the equivalent two-element series circuit at $\omega = 1$. (c) Give the equivalent two-element parallel circuit at $\omega = 1$. (d) Find the impedance as a function of frequency and separate it into its real and imaginary parts.

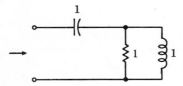

Figure 11–31

12. For the circuit of Fig. 11–31: (a) Find the input impedance at $\omega = 1$. (b) Give the equivalent two-element series circuit at $\omega = 1$. (c) Give the equivalent two-element parallel circuit at $\omega = 1$. (d) Find the input impedance as a function of ω and separate it into its real and imaginary parts.

13. A series R-L-C circuit is excited by the voltage source $e(t) = 100 \cos \omega t$. The element values are $R = 1$ ohm, $L = 10^{-2}$ h, and $C = 10^{-6}$ f. The frequency of the source is a variable. Assume a current and draw a phasor diagram. Find the frequency at which a maximum current will flow (the resonant

frequency). At this frequency find the ratio of the voltage phasor across the inductance to the voltage phasor across the resistance. (The magnitude of this ratio is the Q of the circuit.)

14. A parallel R-L-C circuit is excited by the current source

$$i(t) = 100 \cos 10^6 t.$$

The value of R is 100 ohms; the value of L is 10^{-4} h. What value of C will result in a maximum magnitude of the voltage? At this value of C what is the ratio of the magnitude of the current phasor in the capacitance to the magnitude of the current phasor in the resistance? (The circuit is in parallel resonance, and this ratio is the Q.)

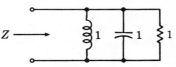

Figure 11–32

15. (a) Write the impedance of the circuit of Fig. 11–32 as a function of ω. (b) Scale the circuit so that the impedance magnitude will be increased by a factor of 1000, and write the new impedance. (c) Scale the circuit so that the resonant frequency will be increased from $\omega = 1$ to $\omega = 10^6$, and again write the impedance. Include also the magnitude scaling of part (b). (d) Sketch the magnitude of the impedances in parts (a) and (c) as functions of frequency.

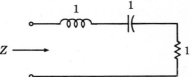

Figure 11–33

16. (a) Write the impedance of the circuit of Fig. 11–33 as a function of ω. (b) Scale the circuit so that it will have an impedance 1000 times as great as the original circuit, and write the impedance. (c) Scale the network of part (b) so that its resonant frequency will be increased from $\omega = 1$ to $\omega = 10^6$, and write the impedance. (d) Sketch the magnitudes of the impedances in parts (a) and (c) as functions of frequency.

SECTION 11–4

17. Sketch the waveforms, give the time-domain expressions, and write and sketch the frequency-domain phasors for 60-cps 110-volt-peak sinusoidal voltages which form (a) a balanced three-phase positive sequence set, (b) a balanced three-phase negative sequence set, (c) a balanced six-phase positive sequence set. (Assume the reference phases at zero angle.)

18. A set of three-phase voltages are given by the phasors

$$E_a = 100 \underline{|0,}$$
$$E_b = 100 \underline{|-120,}$$
$$E_c = 100 \underline{|-240.}$$

Find the line-to-line voltages E_{xy}, E_{yz}, and E_{zx} for the connections of Fig. 11–34, and sketch the vector diagrams.

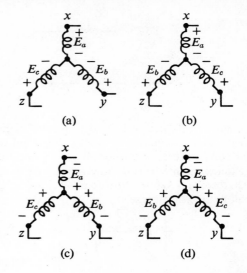

Figure 11–34

19. Find the line currents $I_{aa'}$, $I_{bb'}$, and $I_{cc'}$ in the circuit of Fig. 11–35.

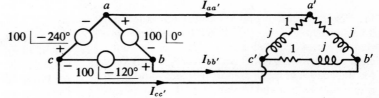

Figure 11–35

20. Find the line currents $I_{aa'}$, $I_{bb'}$, and $I_{cc'}$ in the circuit of Fig. 11–36.

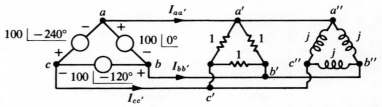

Figure 11–36

21. Find the line currents $I_{aa'}$, $I_{bb'}$, and $I_{cc'}$ in the circuit of Fig. 11–37.

Figure 11–37

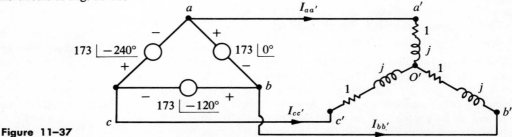

22. Find the line currents $I_{aa'}$, $I_{bb'}$, and $I_{cc'}$ in the circuit of Fig. 11–38.

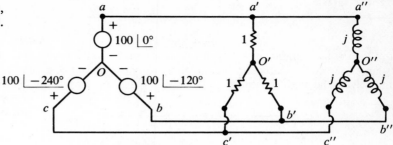

Figure 11–38

23. Find the line currents $I_{aa'}$, $I_{bb'}$, and $I_{cc'}$ in the circuit of Fig. 11–39 and the line-to-line load voltages.

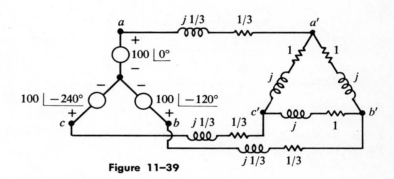

Figure 11–39

24. The line-to-neutral voltage in the "a"-phase of a balanced, Y-connected, three-phase generator is given by

$$e_{an} = 100 \cos \omega t + 50 \cos (3\omega t + 30°)$$
$$+ 50 \cos (5\omega t + 60°).$$

(a) Given that the phase sequence is positive, write the expression for e_{bn} and $e_{\cdot n}$. (b) Make phasor diagrams for each of the harmonics and find the line-to-line voltages. (c) Write the time expressions for the line-to-line voltages.

Problems

1. Find the line currents $I_{aa'}$, $I_{bb'}$, and $I_{cc'}$ in the un-balanced three-phase circuit in Fig. 11–40 by writing and solving the mesh equations.

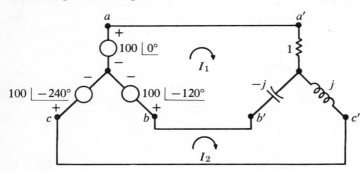

Figure 11–40

2. Find the input impedance of the circuit shown in Fig. 11–41.

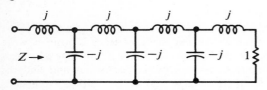

Figure 11–41

3. If the voltage is the excitation and the current is the response, the circuit of Fig. 11–42 is a low-pass filter. (a) Write the impedance Z as a function of frequency. (b) Scale the circuit so that the impedance is multiplied by 10^3. (c) Make a time-domain diagram for a circuit in which the response is down to 0.707 of its zero frequency value at a frequency of $\omega = 10^6$. (d) Write the impedance of the circuit of Fig. 11–43 as a function of frequency. (e) Scale

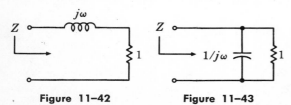

Figure 11–42   **Figure 11–43**

the circuit in the time domain so that the impedance will be multiplied by 1000. (f) Make a time-domain diagram in which the impedance is scaled as in part (b) and the response is down to 0.707 of its zero frequency value at $\omega = 10^6$.

4. (a) A series R-L circuit has a fixed reactance of 1 ohm and a fixed source voltage of $10\ \underline{|0°}$. The resistance value is varied from zero to infinity. From a phasor diagram sketch the locus of the tip of the phasor representing the voltage across the resistance. (b) A parallel R-L circuit has a fixed resistance of 1 ohm and has a fixed source current of $10\ \underline{|0°}$. The reactance is varied from zero to infinity. Find the locus of the tip of the phasor representing the current through the inductance.

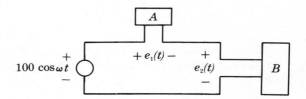

Figure 11–44

5. In the circuit of Fig. 11–44 all three voltages have magnitudes of 100 v, and the source is taken at the reference angle of zero degrees. The circuit in box B is known to be of an inductive nature. Draw the phasor diagram and write time expressions for $e_1(t)$ and $e_2(t)$, including their phase angles.

6. (a) A series R-L-C circuit is excited by the voltage source $e(t) = 100 \cos t$. The element values are $R = 1$ ohm, $L = 1$ h, and $C = 1$ f. Obtain the current by means of a phasor diagram only. Start with an assumed value of current, compute the voltage, and then scale. (b) A parallel R-L-C circuit is excited by the current source $i(t) = 100 \cos t$. The element values are $R = 1$ ohm, $L = 1$ h, and $C = 1$ f. Find the voltage by means of a phasor

diagram only. Start with an assumed value of the voltage, compute the current, and then scale.

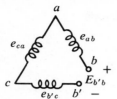

Figure 11–45

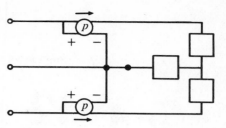

Figure 11–46

7. A three-phase generator has odd harmonics up to the fifth. The windings are connected in positive sequences as shown in Fig. 11–45. Write general expressions for the voltages e_{ab}, $e_{b'c}$, e_{ca}, and $e_{b'b}$. What happens if b and b' are connected?

8. Show that the algebraic sum of the two-watt meter readings in the circuit of Fig. 11–46 will give the correct instantaneous power absorbed by the three-phase load.

CHAPTER 12

FREQUENCY-DOMAIN CIRCUITS: TRANSFER IMPEDANCES

The inevitable comes to pass by effort.

OLIVER WENDELL HOLMES

12–1 Introduction

A one-terminal-pair network is described by a single impedance or admittance parameter. A two-terminal-pair network requires three parameters which may be impedances, admittances, or hybrids. Because of the superposition theorem each of these parameters can be considered by itself and each of them is a complex function of frequency. A typical example is the transfer impedance, the ratio of an output phasor voltage at some point to an input phasor current at another. Transfer impedances, like driving-point impedances, are described by curves of amplitude and phase as functions of frequency.

Mutual inductance and transformers represent particularly important examples of two-terminal-pair devices. A mutual inductance exists between two coils when they are linked by a common magnetic flux so that a changing current in one induces a changing voltage in the other. Coupled coils can also be viewed as "transformers" which pass energy from one coil to the other and change the energy level in the process.

The transformer is similar to the lever in mechanics. The lever transforms a small motion and a large force into a large motion and a small force. A gear train provides the same function for rotary motions. As the speed is increased the torque is decreased.

In mechanics ideal gears have no losses of energy, no inertia, and can therefore respond instantly to changes in torque level. Similarly, in electric circuits *ideal transformers* change the voltage and the current by fixed ratios, and do not introduce resistance or inductance in the circuit. Ideal transformers are not physically realizable, but within limits practical transformers can be treated as ideal transformers. A *unity-coupled* coil is a practical transformer in which all the magnetic-field flux produced by one coil links the other coil. To obtain this effect many transformers are wound on iron cores which offer an easy path for the magnetic flux and channel it from one core to the other. Although an iron core transformer is itself a nonlinear device, its equivalent circuit is linear. The resistances are largely the resistances of the windings, and the inductances arise from "leakage" flux which exists in the air around the coils and does not link them. The equivalent circuit as a transformer is therefore linear, although the self and mutual inductances of the coils are very nonlinear.

12–2 Transfer impedances as functions of frequency

Parameters for two-terminal-pair networks. The impedances which describe a two-terminal-pair frequency-domain network are similar to the driving-point and transfer resistances which we used previously to describe a two-terminal-pair resistive network. For example, the phasor relationships for the general two-terminal-pair network of Fig. 12–1 are

$$E_1 = z_{11}I_1 + z_{12}I_2,$$
$$E_2 = z_{12}I_1 + z_{22}I_2. \qquad (12\text{–}1)$$

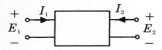

Figure 12–1. General two-terminal-pair network in the frequency domain.

For these equations the definitions of the z's are similar to the definitions of the r's in the resistive case. That is, z_{11} is the input impedance with the output terminals open-circuited, z_{22} is the impedance at the output terminals with the input terminals open-circuited, and z_{12} is the output voltage which is produced by an input current of $1\ \underline{/0^\circ}$. By analogy with the g-parameters we can also write

$$I_1 = y_{11}E_1 + y_{12}E_2,$$
$$I_2 = y_{12}E_1 + y_{22}E_2. \qquad (12\text{–}2)$$

The y's are admittance parameters. Thus, y_{11} is the input admittance with a short circuit on the output terminals, y_{22} is the admittance at the output terminals with a short circuit on the input terminals, and y_{12} is the current which flows in a short circuit at the output terminals when a voltage of $1\ \underline{/0^\circ}$ is applied to the input terminals.

If the z-parameters of Eqs. (12–1) and the y-parameters of Eqs. (12–2) are computed *at a single frequency*, it is possible to find an *equivalent* T- or *π-circuit* in terms of three resistances and three reactances. If we wish the z-parameters or the y-parameters to describe the behavior of a network for any input frequency, however, we must compute them as functions of frequency. The general functions must be used in algebraic form or plotted as magnitude and phase curves *vs.* frequency.

As an example of the three-impedance equivalent circuit which can be obtained at a single frequency, consider the network of Fig. 12–2(a). The input frequency is $\omega = 1$; the frequency-domain network is shown in Fig. 12–2(b). For this network,

$$z_{11} = \frac{(-2j)(-j)}{-3j} = -\tfrac{2}{3}j = z_{22},$$

$$z_{12} = \frac{(-2j)(-2j)}{-3j} = -\tfrac{4}{3}j.$$

The equivalent T-circuit has the general form shown in Fig. 12–2(c). The mutual element is z_{12} and the two arms are $(z_{11} - z_{12})$ and $(z_{22} - z_{12})$. For this particular case the reactances of the arms have the values shown in Fig. 12–2(d). The mutual arm is a negative reactance, and hence a capacitance; the series arms are positive reactances, and hence inductances.

The frequency-domain diagram for the same circuit driven at an arbitrary frequency ω is shown in Fig. 12–3. The three impedances obtained from this circuit are

$$z_{22} = z_{11} = \frac{2/j\omega \times (j\omega + 2/j\omega)}{j\omega + 4/j\omega} = \frac{2}{j\omega}\frac{(-\omega^2 + 2)}{(-\omega^2 + 4)},$$

$$z_{12} = \frac{2/j\omega \times 2/j\omega}{j\omega + 4/j\omega} = \frac{2}{j\omega}\frac{2}{(-\omega^2 + 4)}. \qquad (12\text{–}3)$$

The three functions represented in Eqs. (12–3) completely describe the given network for all possible frequencies of excitation.

The hybrid parameters, which we used with resistive circuits, can also be applied in the frequency domain. Thus

$$E_1 = h_{11}I_1 + h_{12}E_2,$$

$$I_2 = h_{21}I_1 + h_{22}E_2. \qquad (12\text{–}4)$$

In Eq. 12–4 the parameter h_{11} is the impedance E_1/I_1 with a short circuit at E_2, h_{12}, is the reverse voltage ration E_1/E_2 with an open circuit at I_1, h_{21} is the forward current ratio with a short at E_2, and h_{22} is the admittance I_2/E_2 with an open circuit at I_1.

Often we are concerned not with the complete representation of a two-terminal-pair network, but only with a single stimulus-response relationship. If the stimulus and response occur at the same terminal-pair the relationship is called a *driving-point function;* if they occur at different terminal-pairs, it is called a *transfer function.* Both driving-point and transfer relationships are complex functions of frequency. They can be expressed algebraically or by means of magnitude and phase curves.

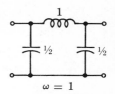

(a) Time-domain diagram

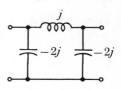

(b) Frequency-domain diagram

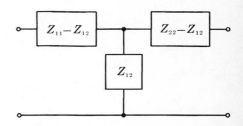

(c) Equivalent T in general

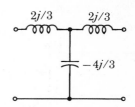

(d) Equivalent T for network of (b)

Figure 12–2. Equivalent single-frequency, two-terminal-pair networks.

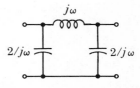

Figure 12–3. The network of Fig. 12–2 driven by an arbitrary frequency.

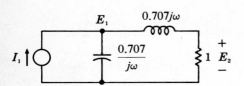

Figure 12-4. A transfer impedance.

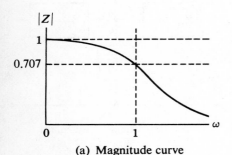

(a) **Magnitude curve**

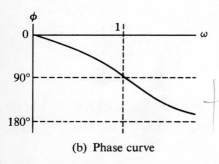

(b) **Phase curve**

Figure 12-5. Magnitude and phase for the transfer function of Fig. 12-4.

As an example of a transfer function we will compute the transfer impedance E_2/I_1 for the circuit of Fig. 12-4.

The node voltage equations for Fig. 12-4 are

$$E_1 \left(1.41 j\omega + \frac{1.41}{j\omega}\right) - E_2 \frac{(1.41)}{j\omega} = I_1$$

$$E_1 \left(\frac{1.41}{j\omega}\right) + E_2 \left(\frac{1.41}{j\omega} + 1\right) = 0$$

from which $\qquad\qquad\qquad\qquad\qquad\qquad$ (12-5)

$$\frac{E_2}{I_1} = \frac{\begin{vmatrix} \left(1.41 j\omega + \dfrac{1.41}{j\omega}\right) & I \\[2ex] \dfrac{1.41}{j\omega} & 0 \end{vmatrix}}{\begin{vmatrix} \left(1.41 j\omega + \dfrac{1.41}{j\omega}\right) & \dfrac{1.41}{j\omega} \\[2ex] \dfrac{1.41}{j\omega} & \left(\dfrac{1.41}{j\omega} + 1\right) \end{vmatrix}}$$

$$= \frac{1}{(1 - \omega^2) + j1.41\omega}$$

$$= \frac{1}{1 + \omega^4} \left| -\tan^{-1} \frac{1.41\omega}{1 - \omega^2}\right.$$

A sketch of the magnitude is shown in Fig. 12-5(a) and a sketch of the phase in Fig. 12-5(b). For small values the magnitude is unity; for large values it is zero; for $\omega = 1$ it is 0.707. At small values the phase is zero; at large values it is $-180°$; at $\omega = 1$ it is $-90°$. This particular transfer function represents a low-pass filter.

12-3 Mutual inductance

Mutual inductance was discovered by Michael Faraday in 1831. He found that when the current in one wire was varied a voltage would appear in a second wire close to, but not touching, the first wire. He attributed the effect to the magnetic field produced by the current in the first wire. In Faraday's view the magnetic field consisted of lines of flux, behaving somewhat like "elastic bands." When the current increases the elastic bands spread out from the wire, and when the current decreases the elastic bands collapse back into the wire. As they do so they give up their energy to the current in the wire in the form of an induced voltage. Any other wire in the magnetic field is also cut by the changing lines of flux, and has a similar voltage induced in it. By showing that a physical motion of a magnetic field would cause the same sort of voltage to be produced, Faraday convinced himself that it was the motion of the lines of flux that produced the voltage.

Mutually coupled coils have two external terminal-pairs, and the volt-ampere equations which describe them must relate the input current and voltage to the output current and voltage. An additional unique feature of mutual coupling between coils is the arbitrariness of the sign of the mutual inductance. By changing the direction of the winding of the coils relative to each other, the manufacturer can change the polarity of the mutually induced voltages in the windings. Since the actual windings are usually hidden from view, the relative polarities are marked with dots on the case. The dots are placed so that if current enters at a dot in one winding it will induce a voltage in the other winding which is positive at the dot. The symbols used for two coupled coils in the time domain are shown in Fig. 12–6(a), and the equations which define them are

$$e_1 = L_1 \frac{di_1}{dt} + M \frac{di_2}{dt},$$

$$e_2 = M \frac{di_1}{dt} + L_2 \frac{di_2}{dt}.$$

(12–6)

The signs of the mutually induced voltages of Eqs. (12–6) are obtained from the marked dots and the assumed positive directions of the currents and voltages in the two windings. When the current i_1 enters the dotted end of the L_1 inductance, it induces a voltage in the L_2 inductance which has the value $M \, di_1/dt$ and a polarity which is positive at the dotted end of L_2. This voltage adds a positive component to e_2 of Eq. (12–6). Similarly, the current i_2 enters L_2 at the dot, and produces a voltage $M \, di_2/dt$ which is positive at the dotted end of L_1 and therefore appears as a positive voltage in Eq. (12–6). Reversing the dots, or reversing the assumed directions of the currents or voltages in either winding, will change the sign of the mutual terms in Eq. (12–6).*

Mutual inductance transforms to the frequency domain in much the same fashion as self-inductance. The induced voltage, like the voltage across an inductance, leads the current producing it by 90°. In the frequency domain, Eqs. (12–6) become

$$E_1 = j\omega L_1 I_1 + j\omega M I_2,$$

$$E_2 = j\omega M I_1 + j\omega L_2 I_2.$$

(12–7)

_____

* It is also possible to define the currents in terms of the voltages by means of "reciprocal" inductances, but this is seldom done.

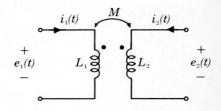

(a) Time-domain circuit

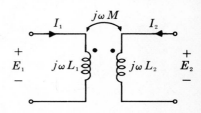

(b) Frequency-domain circuit

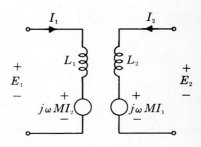

(c) Mutual inductance as voltage generators

Figure 12–6. The forms of mutual inductance.

Equations (12–7) relate the phasor currents and phasor voltages of the coupled coils. The effect of the mutual inductance is to introduce a mutual reactance X_m, or a mutual impedance Z_m, expressed as

$$Z_m = jX_m = j\omega M. \qquad (12\text{–}8)$$

A frequency-domain diagram is shown in Fig. 12–6(b). Note that the sign convention and meaning of the dot notation are not changed by the transformation to the frequency domain.

Each of Eqs. (12–7) consists of two terms, one of which is the voltage drop produced in the winding by the current which flows in the winding, and the other of which is the voltage generated or induced in the winding by the current in the other winding. It is possible to draw the induced voltages as separate voltage generators, with the correct polarities assigned to them, as shown in Fig. 12–6(c).

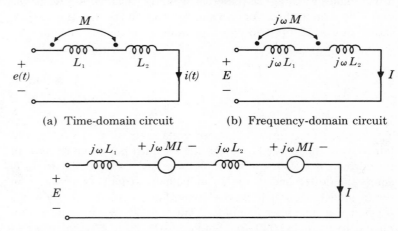

(a) Time-domain circuit   (b) Frequency-domain circuit

(c) Circuit with mutual- inductance voltage generators

Figure 12–7. Two inductors in series.

As an example, consider the two series inductances shown in Fig. 12–7(a). The equivalent frequency-domain diagram is shown in Fig. 12–7(b). The variable assumed is the mesh current $i(t)$, which has a frequency-domain value of I. This current flows through both L_1 and L_2 and produces voltage drops in them. In addition, there is a voltage generator in each coil produced by the flow of current in the other coil. The voltage generators are shown in Fig. 12–7(c). Because of the polarity of the dots, they both appear as voltage drops in the circuit. The voltage-law equation for the loop is

$$I(j\omega L_1 + j\omega L_2) + 2j\omega MI = E$$

or $\qquad\qquad\qquad\qquad\qquad\qquad\qquad\qquad\qquad\qquad$ (12–9)

$$I = \frac{E}{j\omega(L_1 + L_2 + 2M)}.$$

If the dot on one coil were reversed, the sign of the mutual term in Eq. (12–9) would be minus. From this equation it is easy to verify that the equivalent inductance of two mutually coupled coils connected in series is

$$L_{\text{eq}} = L_1 + L_2 \pm 2M. \qquad (12\text{–}10)$$

Since the net inductance must be positive,*

$$L_1 + L_2 \geq 2M. \qquad (12\text{–}11)$$

The inductances in parallel are shown in Fig. 12–8(a) in the time domain, and in Fig. 12–8(b) in the frequency domain. The net current entering at the dotted end of L_1 is $I_1 - I_2$, and the net current entering at the dotted end of L_2 is I_2. These currents drive the generators in the two-generator equivalent circuit of Fig. 12–8(c). The mesh equations for this circuit are

$$I_1 j\omega L_1 - I_2 j\omega L_1 + j\omega M I_2 = E,$$

$$-I_1 j\omega L_1 + j\omega M I_1 + I_2 j\omega L_1 + I_2 j\omega L_2 - 2I_2 j\omega M = 0. \qquad (12\text{–}12)$$

A solution for I_1 is

$$I_1 = \frac{\begin{vmatrix} E & -j\omega L_1 + j\omega M \\ 0 & j\omega L_1 + j\omega L_2 - 2j\omega M \end{vmatrix}}{\begin{vmatrix} j\omega L_1 & -j\omega L_1 + j\omega M \\ -j\omega L_1 + j\omega M & j\omega L_1 + j\omega L_2 - 2j\omega M \end{vmatrix}}$$

$$= \frac{E(L_1 + L_2 - 2M)}{j\omega(L_1 L_2 - M^2)}. \qquad (12\text{–}13)$$

The equivalent inductance of the parallel combination is therefore

$$L_{\text{eq}} = \frac{L_1 L_2 - M^2}{L_1 + L_2 - 2M}. \qquad (12\text{–}14)$$

We have established that the expression in the denominator is positive. Since the over-all inductance must be positive,

$$L_1 L_2 - M^2 \geq 0. \qquad (12\text{–}15)$$

Equation (12–11) states that the mutual inductance must be less than the arithmetic mean, while Eq. (12–15) states that the mutual inductance must be less than the geometric mean. The geometric mean is less than the arithmetic mean except when the two induct-

---

* A negative inductance would supply infinite amounts of energy to a source of positively increasing current.

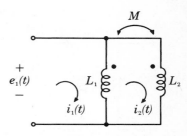

(a) Time-domain circuit

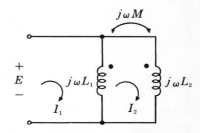

(b) Frequency-domain circuit

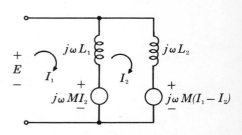

(c) Circuit with mutual- inductance voltage generators

Figure 12–8. Two inductors in parallel.

ances are equal. Hence the maximum value of the mutual inductance is

$$M_{\max} = \sqrt{L_1 L_2}. \tag{12–16}$$

The ratio of the actual mutual inductance to the maximum value
which it can have is called the *coefficient of coupling*, K, and is
given by

$$K = \frac{M}{\sqrt{L_1 L_2}}. \tag{12–17}$$

The coefficient of coupling K ranges from zero when there is no
mutual inductance between the two coils to a value of unity when
all the flux produced by the current in one of the coils links the other.
The coefficients of coupling of the iron-core transformers used in
power distribution systems are very nearly unity. Much lower values
occur in the air-core coils used in radio and television receivers. In
general, when the coefficient of coupling is low it is convenient to
view coupled coils in terms of self and mutual inductances, and
when it is high it is convenient to view the coupled coils as a transformer.

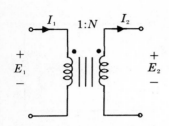

(a) An ideal transformer

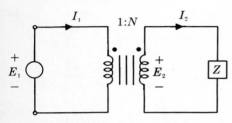

(b) An ideal transformer with a load

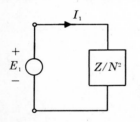

(c) Equivalent primary circuit

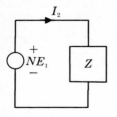

(d) Equivalent secondary circuit

Figure 12–9. The properties of an ideal
transformer.

12–4 Transformers

In mechanics a lever can transform a force applied at one place
to a much larger force applied at another place. There is no net
gain in energy, however, since the larger force acts through a pro-
portionately smaller distance. Similarly, a gear train can transform
a high-speed rotation to a slower-speed rotation and at the same
time increase the torque which is available. In electric circuits the
analog of the lever and the gear is the transformer. The ideal transformer has two pairs of terminals. The input pair is called the
primary and the output pair, the secondary. The voltage across the
primary and the voltage across the secondary are related by a constant. In step-up transformers the secondary voltage is higher than
the primary voltage; in step-down transformers the secondary voltage is less than the primary voltage. Whenever the voltage is stepped
up, the current is stepped down by the same ratio in order to have
the power, or energy, remain unchanged.

Ideal transformers. The symbol for an ideal transformer is shown
in Fig. 12–9(a). It is similar to a pair of coupled coils except for the
bars between the coils and the ratio $1:N$ which is marked on the
coils to show whether the transformer is a step-up or a step-down
type. The following equations define an ideal transformer:

$$E_2 = NE_1, \qquad I_2 = \frac{1}{N}I_1, \tag{12–18}$$

where N is called the "turns-ratio" of the transformer. The input power and the output power are the same; that is,

$$E_1 I_1 = E_2 I_2. \tag{12–19}$$

There is no power lost in the transformer itself, and there is no energy stored.

The effective impedance in the primary circuit is modified by the presence of the transformer. In the circuit of Fig. 12–9(b), a load impedance Z is connected in the secondary circuit, and a voltage is applied to the primary circuit. To obtain the effective primary impedance we note that

$$E_2 = I_2 Z. \tag{12–20}$$

If the definitions of E_1 and I_1, from Eqs. (12–18), are substituted in Eq. (12–20) the result is

$$NE_1 = \frac{I_1}{N} Z$$

or

$$\frac{E_1}{I_1} = \frac{1}{N^2} Z. \tag{12–21}$$

The ratio of the primary voltage to the primary current is the effective primary impedance, Z_1. Thus

$$Z_1 = \frac{1}{N^2} Z. \tag{12–22}$$

The equivalent primary circuit is shown in Fig. 12–9(c). The secondary impedance has been divided by the square of the turns-ratio of the transformer. It is convenient for the student to note that *the impedance is modified by the square of the turns-ratio*, and *that the high impedance occurs on the side with the larger number of turns.*

It is also possible to transform current and voltage sources from one side of a transformer to another. A voltage source is multiplied by the turns-ratio in the direction in which it is moved, and a current source by the reciprocal of this number. For example, in Fig. 12–9(a) if the source is moved to the right, through the transformer, it must be multiplied by the turns-ratio N. The equivalent secondary circuit is shown in Fig. 12–9(d). Both impedances and sources can be moved through ideal transformers at will. The sources are altered by the turns-ratio to the first power, and the impedances by the square of the turns-ratio.

A numerical example of a problem involving an ideal transformer is shown in Fig. 12–10(a). We will first solve the problem by means of mesh currents. In addition to the usual mesh equations, we must

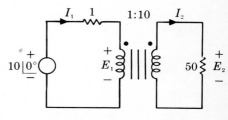

(a) The original circuit

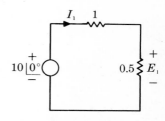

(b) The equivalent primary circuit

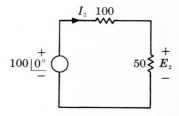

(c) The equivalent secondary circuit

Figure 12–10. An example involving an ideal transformer.

write the two constraint equations which define the transformer. The mesh equations are

$$I_1(1) = E - E_1,$$

$$I_2(50) = E_2.$$

The constraint equations are

$$E_2 = 10E_1,$$

$$I_2 = \frac{I_1}{10}.$$

From these equations we obtain

$$\begin{aligned}
E_2 = 10E_1 &= 10E - 10I_1 \\
&= 100 - 100I_2 \\
&= 100 - \tfrac{100}{50}E_2
\end{aligned}$$

or

$$E_2 = 33.3 \text{ volts.}$$

Our second solution for the problem of Fig. 12–10(a) will be in terms of the equivalent primary circuit shown in Fig. 12–10(b). From this diagram the primary voltage E_1 can be easily obtained:

$$E_1 = \frac{0.5}{1 + 0.5} \times 10 = 3.33 \text{ volts.}$$

The secondary voltage is the turns-ratio multiplied by this value:

$$E_2 = 10 \times 3.33 = 33.3 \text{ volts.}$$

A third solution will be obtained for the equivalent secondary circuit of Fig. 12–10(c). The primary resistance is multiplied by 10^2 as it is moved through the transformer, and the primary voltage is multiplied by 10. The voltage E_2 is obtained directly from the equivalent secondary circuit, and is

$$E_2 = \frac{50}{50 + 100} \times 100 = 33.3 \text{ volts.}$$

Unity-coupled coils. A unity-coupled coil, as shown in Fig. 12–11(a), is equivalent to an ideal transformer with a parallel inductance, as shown in Figs. 12–11(b) and 12–11(c). The mesh equations for the coils of Fig. 12–11(a) are

$$\begin{aligned}
E_1 &= j\omega L_1 I_1 + j\omega M I_2, \\
E_2 &= j\omega M I_1 + j\omega L_2 I_2.
\end{aligned} \qquad (12\text{–}23)$$

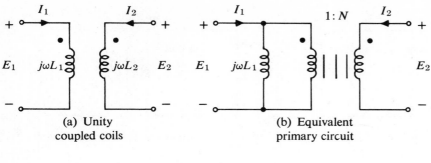

(a) Unity
coupled coils

(b) Equivalent
primary circuit

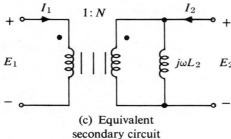

(c) Equivalent
secondary circuit

Figure 12–11. The equivalence of unity-coupled coils and transformers.

The condition for unity coupling, $L_1L_2 = M^2$, can be written as

$$\frac{M}{L_1} = \frac{L_2}{M} = N = \sqrt{\frac{L_2}{L_1}}, \qquad (12\text{–}24)$$

where N is an arbitrary constant called the turns-ratio of the coils (because inductance is proportional to the square of the number of turns if the flux is constant). A combination of Eqs. (12–23) and (12–24) yields

$$E_1 = j\omega L_1[I_1 + (M/L_1)I_2] = j\omega L_1(I_1 + NI_2),$$
$$E_2 = j\omega M[I_1 + (L_2/M)I_2] = j\omega M(I_1 + NI_2), \qquad (12\text{–}25)$$

from which

$$\frac{E_2}{E_1} = \frac{M}{L_1} = N. \qquad (12\text{–}26)$$

From the first equation of (12–23),

$$I_1 = \frac{E_1}{j\omega L_1} - I_2\frac{M}{L_1} = \frac{E_1}{j\omega L_1} - NI_2. \qquad (12\text{–}27)$$

Equations (12–26) and (12–27) represent the equivalent circuit of Fig. 12–11(b). From the second equation of (12–23),

$$I_2 = \frac{E_2}{j\omega L_2} - I_1\frac{M}{L_2} = \frac{E_2}{j\omega L_2} - \frac{I_1}{N}. \qquad (12\text{–}28)$$

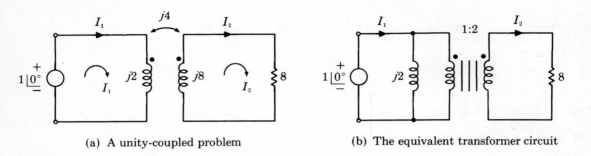

(a) A unity-coupled problem   (b) The equivalent transformer circuit

Figure 12-12. The solution of a problem with unity coupling.

Equations (12-26) and (12-28) represent the equivalent circuit of Fig. 12-11(c).

An example of a unity-coupled problem is shown in Fig. 12-12(a). The primary reactance is 2 ohms, the secondary reactance is 8 ohms, and the mutual reactance is 4 ohms. The coefficient of coupling is

$$K = \frac{M}{\sqrt{L_1 L_2}} = \frac{4}{\sqrt{16}} = 1.$$

The equivalent transformer-type circuit is shown in Fig. 12-12(b). The primary shunt reactance is $j2$ ohms. The turns-ratio of the ideal transformer is

$$N = \sqrt{\frac{L_2}{L_1}} = \sqrt{\frac{8}{2}} = 2.$$

The impedance reflected into the primary through the ideal transformer is

$$Z_f = \frac{Z}{N^2} = \frac{8}{4} = 2 \text{ ohms.}$$

The current drawn from the source is thus $1/j2$ amp through the shunt inductance and $\frac{1}{2}$ amp through the reflected load impedance. The total current is therefore

$$I_1 = \tfrac{1}{2} - j\tfrac{1}{2} \text{ amp.}$$

The output voltage in the secondary is the turns-ratio times the primary voltage:

$$E_2 = 1 \times 2 = 2 \text{ volts.}$$

Nonideal transformers. When the coefficient of coupling is less than unity, the mutual inductance is smaller than the square root of the product of the two self inductances. Effectively, the self inductances are too large to form a unity-coupled coil. We can remedy this situation by subtracting series inductances from each of the windings until the remaining inductances form a unity-coupled coil with the given mutual inductance. The inductances which must be subtracted are called the *leakage inductances* of the windings. They represent the magnetic effects which belong to the individual coils and which are not associated with the mutual flux which links them.

For an iron-core inductance the leakage flux is mostly in the air surrounding the inductor and is therefore essentially linear. After the leakage inductances are removed, the remainder of the transformer consists of a unity-coupled coil, and the unity-coupled coil can be replaced by an ideal transformer with a shunt inductance. For an iron-core transformer the shunt inductance is nonlinear because of the nonlinear properties of the iron, but it is a large inductance which draws very little current and has very little effect on the operation of the transformer. The iron-core transformer is therefore almost linear in its operation, and is usually treated by linear circuit theory.

Two coupled coils with arbitrary values of L_1, L_2, and M are shown in Fig. 12–13(a). Leakage inductances of L_a and L_b are sub-

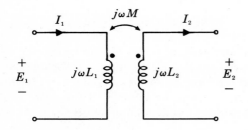

(a) Two coils with arbitrary L_1, L_2, and M

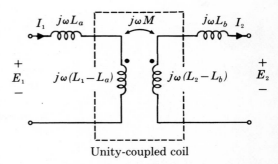

(b) Subtraction of leakage inductances to leave a unity-coupled coil

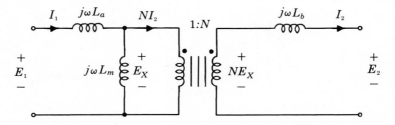

(c) The transformer-type equivalent circuit with leakage inductances and magnetizing inductance

Figure 12–13. The transformer-type equivalent circuit for coils with arbitrary coupling.

tracted from the primary and secondary inductances respectively in order to leave a unity-coupled coil, as shown in Fig. 12–13(b). We then replace it by an ideal transformer with a turns-ratio of N and a shunt reactance $j\omega L_m$, as shown in Fig. 12–13(c). If the two circuits of Figs. 12–13(a) and 12–13(c) are to be equivalent, they must satisfy the same equations relating the terminal currents and voltages. The equations for the circuit of Fig. 12–13(a) are

$$E_1 = j\omega L_1 I_1 - j\omega M I_2,$$
$$-E_2 = -j\omega M I_1 + j\omega L_2 I_2, \tag{12–29}$$

and the equations for the circuit of Fig. 12–13(c) are

$$E_1 = j\omega L_a I_1 + E_x = (j\omega L_a + j\omega L_m)I_1 - j\omega L_m N I_2, \tag{12–30}$$
$$-E_2 = -NE_x + j\omega L_b I_2 = -j\omega L_m N I_1 + (j\omega L_m N^2 + j\omega L_b)I_2.$$

If Eqs. (12–29) and (12–30) are to be identical, the corresponding coefficients must be identical. Thus

$$L_1 = L_a + L_m,$$
$$NL_m = M, \tag{12–31}$$
$$L_2 = N^2 L_m + L_b.$$

The quantities L_1, L_2, and M in Eqs. (12–31) can be considered to be known, with the quantities L_a, L_b, L_m, and N to be determined from them. Since there are four unknowns and only three equations, one of the unknowns can be picked arbitrarily. If we select a value for N and solve for the other three constants we obtain

$$L_a = L_1 - \frac{M}{N},$$
$$L_m = \frac{M}{N}, \tag{12–32}$$
$$L_b = L_2 - MN.$$

Algebraically, Eqs. (12–32) are true for all values of N. However, if we wish to have the leakage inductances positive we must make N greater than M/L_1 and smaller than L_2/M. Any value of N in this range will be satisfactory. Thus

$$\frac{M}{L_1} \leq N \leq \frac{L_2}{M}.$$

If we choose

$$N = \sqrt{\frac{L_2}{L_1}}, \tag{12–33}$$

it agrees with the turns-ratio which we used for the unity-coupled coils. The name "turns-ratio" strictly speaking applies only to unity-coupled coils. In a practical transformer the turns-ratio is usually obtained by measuring the inductances rather than by counting the turns. An interesting corollary of the definition of N given by Eq. (12–32) is that the leakage inductances referred to the same side of the transformer are equal, since

$$L_b = N^2 L_a. \tag{12–34}$$

Let us now consider a numerical example in which the transformer-type of circuit is developed from self and mutual inductances. Two coupled coils are shown in Fig. 12–14(a). They have the parameters

$$L_1 = 2 \text{ henrys}, \qquad L_2 = 50 \text{ henrys}, \qquad M = 3 \text{ henrys}.$$

The equivalent turns-ratio is

$$N = \sqrt{\frac{L_2}{L_1}} = \sqrt{25} = 5.$$

The primary leakage inductance is

$$L_a = L_1 - \frac{M}{N} = 2 - \tfrac{3}{5} = \tfrac{7}{5} \text{ henrys}.$$

The secondary leakage inductance is

$$L_b = L_2 - MN = 50 - 3 \times 5 = 35 \text{ henrys}.$$

The shunt inductance (also called the magnetizing inductance) is

$$L_m = \frac{M}{N} = \tfrac{3}{5} \text{ henrys}.$$

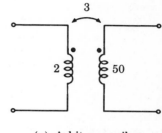

(a) Arbitrary coils

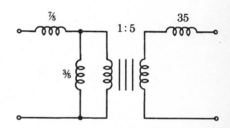

(b) Equivalent transformer circuit

Figure 12–14. An example of a general transformer-type equivalent circuit.

The equivalent transformer circuit is shown in Fig. 12–14(b). The coefficient of coupling of the coils is low (0.3), and therefore the leakage inductances are large. This example is given to emphasize the fact that the transformer-type of equivalent circuit is not restricted to iron-core coils, but can be found for any pair of coupled coils.

The subject of iron-core transformers is beyond the scope of this text, since it involves the nonlinear properties of iron cores and the practical problems of size, weight, materials, cost, and cooling. In this chapter we have attempted merely to relate the coupled-circuit theory, which is used for air-core coils, and the transformer theory, which is used for iron-core coils.

Summary

Two-terminal-pair networks

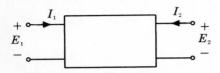

z-parameters

$$E_1 = z_{11}I_1 + z_{12}I_2$$

$$E_2 = z_{12}I_1 + z_{22}I_2$$

$$z_{11} = \frac{E_1}{I_1}\bigg|_{I_2=0}, \qquad z_{12} = \frac{E_2}{I_1}\bigg|_{I_2=0},$$

$$z_{22} = \frac{E_2}{I_2}\bigg|_{I_1=0}$$

y-parameters

$$I_1 = y_{11}E_1 + y_{12}E_2$$

$$I_2 = y_{12}E_1 + y_{22}E_2$$

$$y_{11} = \frac{I_1}{E_1}\bigg|_{E_2=0}, \qquad y_{12} = \frac{I_2}{E_1}\bigg|_{E_2=0},$$

$$y_{22} = \frac{I_2}{E_2}\bigg|_{E_1=0}$$

h-parameters

$$E_1 = h_{11}I_1 + h_{12}E_2$$

$$I_2 = h_{21}I_1 + h_{22}E_2$$

$$h_{11} = \frac{E_1}{I_1}\bigg|_{E_2=0}, \qquad h_{21} = \frac{I_2}{I_1}\bigg|_{E_2=0},$$

$$h_{12} = \frac{E_1}{E_2}\bigg|_{I_1=0}, \qquad h_{22} = \frac{I_2}{E_2}\bigg|_{I_1=0}$$

Magnitude and phase plots

$$T(j\omega) = \frac{1}{1 + j\omega T}$$

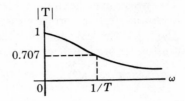

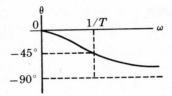

$$T(j\omega) = \frac{1}{1 + 2\zeta j\omega T + (j\omega T)^2}$$

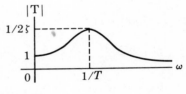

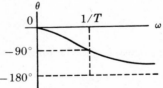

Mutual inductance

Time domain

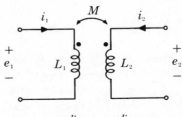

$$e_1 = L_1\frac{di_1}{dt} + M\frac{di_2}{dt} \qquad e_2 = M\frac{di_1}{dt} + L_2\frac{di_2}{dt}$$

Frequency domain

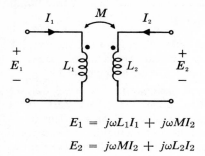

$$E_1 = j\omega L_1 I_1 + j\omega M I_2$$

$$E_2 = j\omega M I_2 + j\omega L_2 I_2$$

Coefficient of coupling

$$K = \frac{M}{\sqrt{L_1 L_2}} \qquad 0 \le K \le 1$$

Ideal transformer

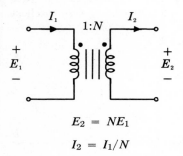

$$E_2 = N E_1$$

$$I_2 = I_1 / N$$

Unity-coupled coils $(L_1 L_2 - M^2 = 0)$

$$N = \sqrt{\frac{L_2}{L_1}} = \frac{M}{L_1} = \frac{L_2}{M}$$

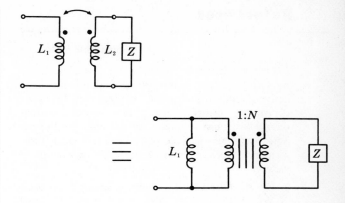

Real transformer

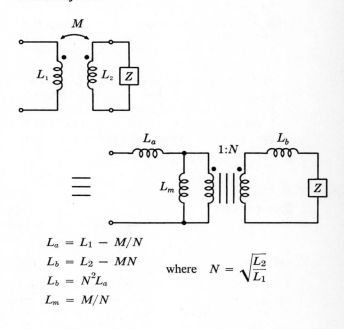

$$L_a = L_1 - M/N$$

$$L_b = L_2 - MN$$

$$L_b = N^2 L_a$$

$$L_m = M/N$$

$$\text{where} \quad N = \sqrt{\frac{L_2}{L_1}}$$

References

Two-terminal-pair networks are treated in many modern texts, particularly those dealing with linear active circuits. Two points of view will be found concerning transformers. The communications theory texts use self and mutual inductances; the power texts use leakage reactances and ideal transformers. We have tried to relate the two points of view.

1. E. A. GUILLEMIN, *Communications Networks*, Vol. 2, John Wiley, New York, 1935. This text is the best reference on the various parameters for two-terminal-pair networks.

2. E. J. ANGELO, *Electronic Circuits*, McGraw-Hill, New York, 1958. A typic text devoted to active circuits and using *z*-parameters, *y*-parameters, and *h*-parameters.

3. MIT EE Staff, *Magnetic Circuits and Transformers*, John Wiley, New York, 1943. This text is a very complete reference for the presentation of leakage reactances and ideal transformers. The equivalent circuits are derived from com-

ponent fluxes rather than from self and mutual inductances. Practical problems of materials, heating, size, and cost are also included.

4. KERCHNER and CORCORAN, *Alternating Current Circuits*, 3rd ed., John Wiley, New York, 1951. Kerchner and Corcoran give an excellent treatment of the self- and mutual-inductance point of view. In addition to a general treatment of the dot convention they discuss a variety of practical tuned-transformer problems.

5. BRENNER and JAVID, *Analysis of Electrical Circuits*, McGraw-Hill, New York, 1959. Brenner and Javid give both points of view and explain the arbitrary choice of the turns-ratio in the general case.

6. FITZGERALD and HIGGINBOTHAM, *Basic Electrical Engineering*, 2nd ed., McGraw-Hill, New York, 1957. Chapters 8 and 9 give an excellent and somewhat simplified summary of the material of Reference 3.

Exercises

SECTION 12–2

1. (a) Find the open-circuit impedance parameters z_{11}, z_{12}, and z_{22} for the circuit of Fig. 12–15 when the excitation frequency is $\omega = 1$. (b) Give the equivalent T-network at $\omega = 1$. (c) Find z_{11}, z_{12}, and z_{22} as functions of ω. (d) Discuss the T-network reduction in the general case.

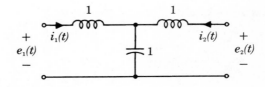

Figure 12–16

2. (a) Find the short-circuit admittance parameters y_{11}, y_{12}, and y_{22} for the circuit of Fig. 12–16 when the excitation frequency is $\omega = 1$. (b) Give the equivalent π-circuit for $\omega = 1$. (c) Find y_{11}, y_{12}, and y_{22} as functions of ω. (d) Discuss the π-network in the general case. (e) Repeat part (c) for a capacitance of $C = 2$.

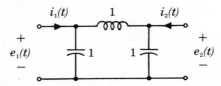

Figure 12–15

3. (a) Find the hybrid parameters for the circuit of Fig. 12–17 at a frequency of $\omega = 1$. (b) Draw the hybrid equivalent circuit. (c) Find h_{11}, h_{12}, h_{21}, and h_{22} as functions of frequency. (d) Discuss the equivalent circuit in the general case.

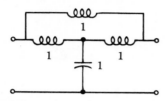

Figure 12–17

4. (a) Find the z-parameters of the two-terminal-pair network in Fig. 12–18. (b) Find the y-parameters of the network.

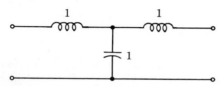

Figure 12–18

5. (a) For the network of Fig. 12–19 find the ratio E_2/E_1 as a function of ω. (b) Sketch the magnitude of the ratio in part (a) as a function of frequency. (c) Sketch the phase of the ratio in part (a) as a function of frequency. (d) Scale the network values to give a half-power frequency of 10 kc and a resistance of 100 kohms.

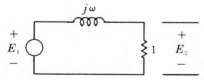

Figure 12–19

6. A transfer function is given by

$$T(j\omega) = \frac{1}{4 - \omega^2 + 5j\omega}.$$

(a) Sketch the magnitude-versus-frequency curve.
(b) Sketch the phase-versus-frequency curve.
(c) Give the values of the curves at $\omega = 1$ and $\omega = 4$ rad.

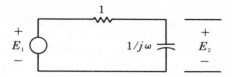

Figure 12–20

7. (a) Find the ratio E_2/E_1 for the network of Fig. 12–20. (b) Sketch magnitude and phase curves as functions of frequency. (c) Scale the network values to give a half-power frequency of $10^6/2\pi$ cps and a resistance of 10 kohms.

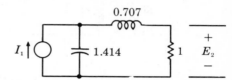

Figure 12–21

8. (a) A low-pass filter with two energy storage elements is shown in Fig. 12–21. Find the ratio E_2/I_1. (b) Sketch magnitude and phase curves for this ratio. (c) Scale the network to give a half-power frequency of $100/2\pi$ cps and a resistance of 1 kohm.

SECTION 12–3

9. Two coils have self inductances of $L_1 = 8$ h and $L_2 = 6$ h. The mutual inductance between them is 2 h. Find all the possible values of inductance which can be obtained by connecting them in various ways.

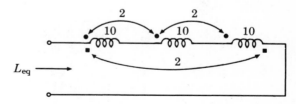

Figure 12–22

10. Find the net inductance of the three series-connected coils shown in Fig. 12–22. Note that the polarity dots on the three coils are not consistent and therefore must be represented by separate symbols.

11. Two coils have a primary inductance of 1 h and a secondary inductance of $\frac{1}{4}$ h. The coefficient of coupling between them is $\frac{1}{2}$. A sinusoidal current $i(t) = 10 \cos t$ is flowing in the primary circuit and the secondary is open-circuited. (a) Give the voltage across the primary coil. (b) Give the voltage across the secondary coil.

12. Write the mesh-current equations fot the circuit of Fig. 12–23 and find the magnitude and phase of the output voltage E_2.

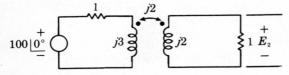

Figure 12–23

13. In the circuit of Fig. 12–24 the coefficient of coupling between the coils is $K = \frac{1}{2}$. Find the output voltage E_2 in magnitude and phase.

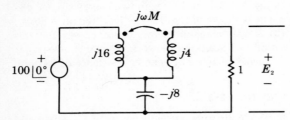

Figure 12–24

14. Find the input impedance Z of the circuit in Fig. 12–25.

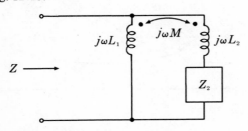

Figure 12–25

15. Find the input impedance Z of the circuit in Fig. 12–26.

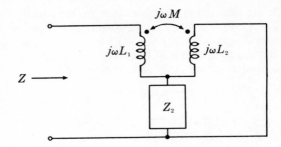

Figure 12–26

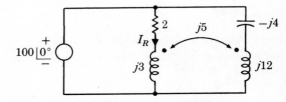

Figure 12–27

16. By means of mesh-current equations find the current I_R in the circuit of Fig. 12–27, in the form of a magnitude and a phase angle.

SECTION 12–4

17. The transformer in the circuit of Fig. 12–28 is "ideal." Solve for the voltage E_3 (a) by writing two mesh equations and two constraint equations and (b) by using an equivalent circuit referred to the output side of the transformer.

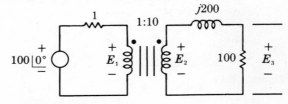

Figure 12–28

18. Find the input voltage E_1 in the circuit of Fig. 12–29 (a) by writing two node equations and two constraint equations and (b) by using an equivalent circuit referred to the input side of the ideal transformer.

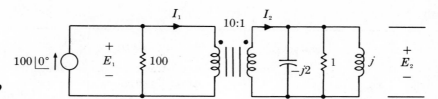

Figure 12-29

19. In the circuit of Fig. 12–30 the transformer is ideal. Find the current I_1 drawn from the source.

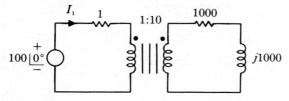

Figure 12-30

20. The transformer in the circuit of Fig. 12–31 is ideal. Find the current I_1 from the source.

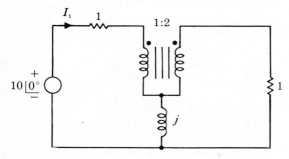

Figure 12-31

21. The primary winding of a transformer has a reactance X_1 of 100 ohms and a resistance R_1 of 10 ohms. The secondary winding has a reactance X_2 of 25 ohms and a resistance R_2 of 2 ohms. The coefficient of coupling is $\frac{1}{2}$. (a) Find an equivalent circuit involving an ideal transformer and having all the elements referred to the primary side. (b) Find an equivalent circuit involving an ideal transformer and having all the elements referred to the secondary side.

22. The coils in the circuit of Fig. 12–32 are unity-coupled. (a) Solve for the voltage E_2 by making an equivalent primary circuit. (b) Solve for the voltage E_2 by making an equivalent secondary circuit.

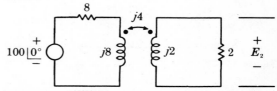

Figure 12-32

23. Convert the circuit of Fig. 12–33 to one involving self- and mutual-reactances.

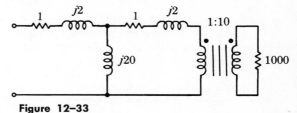

Figure 12-33

24. (a) Find the voltage E_2 in the circuit of Fig. 12–34 by writing mesh equations. (b) Convert the circuit to the transformer-type equivalent and again solve for E_2.

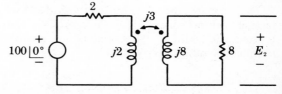

Figure 12-34

Problems

1. (a) A low-pass filter with three energy storages is shown in Fig. 12–35. Find the ratio E_2/I_1. (b) Sketch magnitude and phase curves for this ratio. (c) Scale the element values to give a half-power frequency of $1000/2\pi$ cps and an impedance of 1000 ohms at dc.

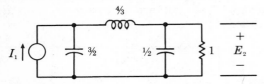

Figure 12–35

2. The transfer function of a resistance-capacitance coupled vacuum-tube amplifier is given by

$$\frac{E_2(j\omega)}{E_1(j\omega)} = \frac{100}{(1 + 100/j\omega)(1 + j\omega/10)}.$$

(a) Sketch the magnitude-versus-frequency curve. (b) Give the lower and the upper half-power frequencies. (c) What is the mid-band gain? (d) Sketch the phase-versus-frequency curve.

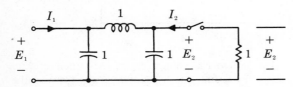

Figure 12–36

3. (a) Compute the z-parameters for the two-terminal-pair network of Fig. 12–36. (b) If a 1-ohm resistance is added to the output of the network compute the ratio $E_2/I_1 = Z_{12}$.

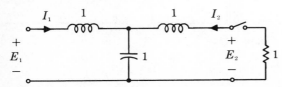

Figure 12–37

4. (a) Compute the y-parameters for the two-terminal-pair circuit of Fig. 12–37. (b) If a 1-ohm resistance is added to the output terminals, what is the transfer ratio $Y_{12} = I_2/E_1$.

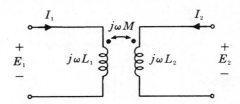

Figure 12–38

5. It is possible to represent a pair of coupled coils, like those of Fig. 12–38, by a set of inverse inductance parameters. These parameters are defined by the following equations:

$$I_1 = \frac{\Gamma_1}{j\omega} E_1 + \frac{\Gamma_m}{j\omega} E_2,$$

$$I_2 = \frac{\Gamma_m}{j\omega} E_1 + \frac{\Gamma_2}{j\omega} E_2.$$

Find the values of the inverse inductances (gamma's) in terms of the self- and mutual-inductances of the coils.

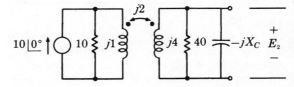

Figure 12–39

6. (a) In the circuit of Fig. 12–39, find the reactance X_C which will result in parallel resonance. (b) Compute the voltage E_2 with and without this reactance in place.

7. The circuit of Fig. 12–40 is called an "auto-transformer." (a) Find the input admittance Y of the circuit, considering that the two coils are unity-coupled. (b) Find the voltage ratio E_2/E_1.

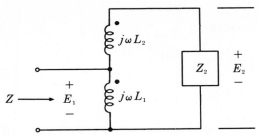

Figure 12–40

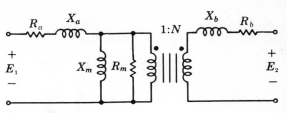

Figure 12–41

(c) Make an equivalent circuit for the auto-transformer, which includes an ideal transformer.

8. The circuit of Fig. 12–41 represents the equivalent circuit for a transformer. It includes the winding resistances and an extra resistance R_m to account for the energy lost in the iron core. The values of X_m and R_m are much larger than the other elements in the circuit. (a) Find the input impedance when the output is short-circuited. Obtain an approximate value which utilizes the conditions stated above. (b) Find the input impedance with the output open-circuited. Again use reasonable approximations. (c) A 10-KVA, 60-cps, 2300/230-volt distribution transformer is tested with the secondary open and with the secondary shorted. The data are as follows:

Open-circuit data
  Input voltage: 2300 v (rated voltage)
  Input current: $\frac{1}{10}$ amp
  Phase angle: 45° lagging current.

Short-circuit data
  Input voltage: 100 v
  Input current: 100 amp (rated current)
  Phase angle: 45° lagging current.

Assume that the leakage reactances and the winding resistances are equal when referred to the same side of the transformer. Obtain an equivalent circuit for the transformer referred to the high-voltage winding.

CHAPTER 13

POWER AND ENERGY

Do not underestimate the power of poetry. Poets are the unacknowledged legislators of the world.

PERCY BYSSHE SHELLEY

13–1 Introduction

The power of poetry lies in its ability to sway the minds of man. The importance of electricity also lies in what it can do for man. Electricity is useful because of the energy which it carries. In previous chapters we have dealt with the concepts of current and voltage. We did so because we were interested in the "quality" of the energy as well as its quantity. The underlying concept is still energy, however, and in this chapter we return to it.

Pure resistance circuits are capable only of dissipating energy. They can transmit energy from one place to another and convert it to some other form (usually heat), but they can not store it. Circuits with capacitance or circuits with inductance can store energy. Whenever the circuit is changed from one energy state to another, transient currents flow and energy is lost.

The expressions for the instantaneous power and energy in an ac circuit are complex functions of time. Usually, we are not interested in instantaneous power and energy, but only in the average values. A real simplification occurs here, for the average power and the average energy can be computed from frequency-domain phasors. There is no a priori reason why phasors should contain information about the power and energy in the circuit, since they were defined for linear operations, and power is a nonlinear quantity. It is a happy *coincidence* that the product of a current phasor and a voltage phasor gives the average power in a circuit.

13–2 Basic power and energy relationships

Current is a measure of the rate at which electric charge flows through a device. Voltage is a measure of the amount of energy associated with each unit of charge. Thus the product of voltage and current gives the rate at which energy is being absorbed or given

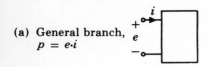

(a) General branch,
p = e·i

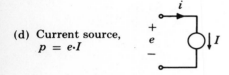

(b) Resistance,
p = i²R = e²/R

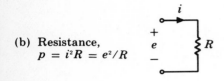

(c) Voltage source,
p = E·i

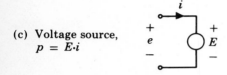

(d) Current source,
p = e·I

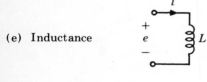

(e) Inductance

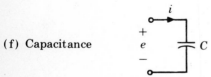

(f) Capacitance

Figure 13-1. The sign conventions for power absorbed.

off by the device. Current is measured in coulombs per second and voltage in joules per coulomb, and the product of the two is the power in joules per second, or watts. Thus the power, p, is

$$p = e \times i. \tag{13-1}$$

A second equation which is often useful expresses the algebraic requirement that the total power generated by the sources in a network must be equal to the total power absorbed by the passive elements. Since most of the elements are passive, we will take the power lost in a passive element to be positive and the power supplied by a source to be negative. Then

$$\sum p = 0. \tag{13-2}$$

Positive power is dissipated in the element if the voltage and the current have the signs shown in Fig. 13-1(a). The application of the formula to a resistive branch is shown in Fig. 13-1(b). The power is positive and has a value given by

$$p_R = e \times i = i^2 R = \frac{e^2}{R}. \tag{13-3}$$

The power associated with the voltage source of Fig. 13-1(c) is

$$p_V = e \times i = E \times i. \tag{13-4}$$

If the source is supplying energy the current will be negative and the power absorbed will also be negative. The power associated with the current source of Fig. 13-1(d) is

$$p_I = e \times i = e \times I. \tag{13-5}$$

If the source is supplying energy the voltage will be negative and the power absorbed by the source will also be negative. The power drawn by an inductance as in Fig. 13-1(e) is

$$p_L = e \times i = L \frac{di}{dt} \times i. \tag{13-6}$$

The energy stored in the inductance is

$$W_L(t) = \int_0^t (e \times i) \, dt = \int_0^t \left(L \frac{di}{dt} \times i \right) dt. \tag{13-7}$$

We can change the variable in Eq. (13-7) from time to current. The integration then occurs from the current at $t = 0$, which is taken to be zero, to the current at $t = t$, which is taken to be i, and

$$W_L(i) = \int_0^i Li \, di = \tfrac{1}{2}Li^2. \qquad (13\text{--}8)$$

The energy given by Eq. (13–8) is a function only of the current through the inductance. The power which flows into a capacitance as in Fig. 13–1(f) is

$$p_C = e \times i = C\frac{de}{dt} \times e. \qquad (13\text{--}9)$$

The total energy stored at any instant is

$$W_C(t) = \int_0^t (e \times i) \, dt = \int_0^t \left(C\frac{de}{dt} \times e\right) dt. \qquad (13\text{--}10)$$

If we change the variable in Eq. (13–10) from time to voltage, the lower limit is the voltage at $t = 0$, which we take to be zero, and the upper limit is the voltage at $t = t$, which we simply call e. The total energy then is

$$W_C(e) = \int_0^e (C \times e) \, de = \tfrac{1}{2}Ce^2. \qquad (13\text{--}11)$$

The energy in the capacitance, as given by Eq. (13–11), depends only on the voltage across it.

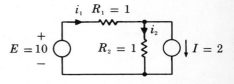

Figure 13–2. Power computations by means of branch currents.

Examples. For the first example we shall use the circuit of Fig. 13–2. The currents and the voltages in each branch can be computed by means of the superposition theorem. They are

$$i_1 = 5 + 1 = 6 \text{ amp,}$$
$$i_2 = 5 - 1 = 4 \text{ amp,}$$
$$e_1 = i_1R_1 \quad = 6 \text{ volts,}$$
$$e_2 = i_2R_2 \quad = 4 \text{ volts.}$$

The powers dissipated in the two resistances are

and
$$p_{R_1} = i_1^2R_1 = 6^2 \times 1 = 36 \text{ watts,}$$
$$p_{R_2} = i_2^2R_2 = 4^2 \times 1 = 16 \text{ watts.}$$

The total power lost in the two resistances is 52 watts. The power dissipated in the two sources is $p_V + p_1$, where

$$p_V = E \times i_1 = 10 \times -6 = -60 \text{ watts,}$$
$$p_I = e_2 \times I = 2 \times \quad 4 = \quad\; 8 \text{ watts.}$$

The net power absorbed by the sources is thus -52 watts, or the power supplied by the sources is $+52$ watts. The total algebraic power is

$$\sum p = 52 - 52 = 0.$$

In this example the two resistances and the current source are absorbing power, and the voltage source is supplying all the power. *The sign conventions must be observed carefully, because a source does not always supply power!*

As a second example we shall find the power and energy as functions of time for the circuit of Fig. 13–3. The current in this circuit is

$$i(t) = \frac{1}{L} u_{-2}(t) = \frac{t}{L} \quad \text{for} \quad t > 0. \quad (13\text{–}12)$$

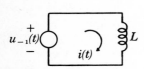

Figure 13–3. Power and energy relationships in an inductance.

The power is the product of the voltage and current:

$$p = \frac{u_{-2}(t) \times u_{-1}(t)}{L} = \frac{t}{L} \quad \text{for} \quad t > 0. \quad (13\text{–}13)$$

The energy is the integral of the power:

$$W = \int_0^t \frac{t}{L} \, dt = \frac{t^2}{2L}. \quad (13\text{–}14)$$

Equation (13–13) shows that the power absorbed by the inductance increases linearly with time. At the same time the total energy is increasing along a square-law curve. Alternatively, Eq. (13–14) can be obtained from the instantaneous current in the inductance, since

$$W = \tfrac{1}{2} L i^2 = \frac{L}{2} \times \frac{t^2}{L^2} = \frac{t^2}{2L}. \quad (13\text{–}15)$$

Root-mean-square (rms) values. When a sinusoidal current is passed through a resistance, the instantaneous power dissipated is a complex function of the time. For most applications we are interested only in the average power, which is a constant so long as the amplitude of the current is a constant. As an example we will compute the power in the resistance of Fig. 13–4. The current is

$$i(t) = |I| \cos \omega t,$$

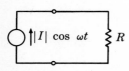

Figure 13–4. A resistance excited by an alternating current.

and the power as a function of time is

$$p = e \cdot i = i^2 R = |I|^2 R \cos^2 \omega t$$

$$= \frac{|I|^2 R}{2} (1 + \cos 2\omega t). \quad (13\text{–}16)$$

The instantaneous power of Eq. (13–16) is plotted in Fig. 13–5.*
It varies from a peak of $|I|^2R$ to a minimum of zero. The average
value, denoted by P, is

$$P = \frac{|I|^2R}{2}.$$ (13–17)

In order to make Eq. (13–17) agree in form with the expression for
power in a dc circuit, it is customary to write

$$P = I_{\mathrm{rms}}^2 R,$$ (13–18)

where

$$I_{\mathrm{rms}} = 0.707\,|I|;$$ (13–19)

I_{rms} is the equivalent heating value. Let us observe the process by
which it was obtained. The first step was to square the waveform,
as in Eq. (13–16). The second step was to take the average value
of the squared function, as in Eq. (13–17). The third step was to
take the root of this squared value, as in Eq. (13–19). What we
have done is to take the root of the mean of the squared function.
The abbreviation rms is thus a description of the process by which
the equivalent heating value is obtained.

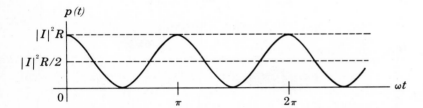

Figure 13–5. The instantaneous power
in the resistance of Fig. 13–4.

It is also clear that the rms property is a function of the wave-
shape and can be found for voltages as well as for currents. The
formula which expresses these operations is

$$F_{\mathrm{rms}} = \sqrt{\frac{1}{T}\int_0^T f^2(t)\,dt}.$$ (13–20)

As an example of the use of Eq. (13–20) we will obtain the rms value
of the waveform shown in Fig. 13–6. The function is defined by

$$f(t) = \begin{cases} t & 0 < t < 1, \\ 0 & 1 < t < 2. \end{cases}$$ (13–21)

---

* The student should observe for future reference that the average value
of the square of any sinusoidal wave is one-half the peak value of the
squared wave.

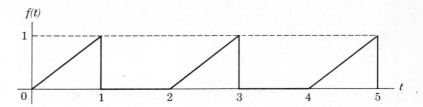

Figure 13-6. A function whose rms value is obtained analytically.

The period is $T = 2$, and the rms value is

$$F_{rms} = \sqrt{\tfrac{1}{2}\int_0^1 t^2\, dt}$$

$$= \sqrt{\tfrac{1}{2} \times \tfrac{1}{3}}$$

$$= 0.408.$$

A second rms example is the addition of two waves of different frequencies. The time expression for the sum of two sine waves is complex in form, and we are often glad to settle for the equivalent heating effect. Suppose the two sine waves are

$$i_1(t) = |I_1| \cos (\omega_1 t + \theta_1),$$

$$i_2(t) = |I_2| \cos (\omega_2 t + \theta_2).$$
(13-22)

The sum of the waves is

$$i(t) = |I_1| \cos (\omega_1 t + \theta_1) + |I_2| \cos (\omega_2 t + \theta_2). \qquad (13-23)$$

The square of Eq. (13-23) is

$$i^2(t) = |I_1|^2 \cos^2 (\omega_1 t + \theta_1) + |I_2|^2 \cos^2 (\omega_2 t + \theta_2)$$

$$+ 2|I_1|\,|I_2| \cos (\omega_1 t + \theta_1) \cos (\omega_2 t + \theta_2). \qquad (13-24)$$

The average value of each of the cosine-squared terms in Eq. (13-24) is $\tfrac{1}{2}$. The average value of the product term is zero.* If we denote the average value by a bar, we can write

$$\overline{i^2(t)} = \frac{|I_1|^2}{2} + \frac{|I_2|^2}{2},$$

and

$$I_{rms} = \sqrt{I_{1\,rms}^2 + I_{2\,rms}^2}. \qquad (13-25)$$

---

* The sum of the two cosine waves exhibits the phenomenon of beats. The envelope of the sum has a maximum when the waves are in phase and a minimum when they are out of phase. The average must extend over a beat period (1/difference frequency), and therefore the case of two equal frequencies is ruled out.

Equation (13–25) shows that the heating effect of the sum of two sinusoids is the root of the sum of the squares of the separate rms values; rms addition of this sort is used only for sine waves with different frequencies. Two direct-current values, or two identical waveforms of any kind, are added by *arithmetic addition*. Two sinusoids of the same frequency are added by *vector addition*. Arithmetic addition gives the complete resultant waveform; vector addition gives the resultant phasor; and rms addition gives only the equivalent heating effect. Not only is rms addition less informative than the other two, but also it is *wrong* for waveforms which can be treated by the other methods. For example, two equal and opposite sinusoids with a resultant of zero would have an apparent rms sum of 1.414 times the value of either one of them!

The rms values are commonly used for the computation of power and energy in the sinusoidal steady-state. Most meters for use on 60-cps systems are calibrated to read rms values. Indeed, if a 60-cps voltage or current is stated without any qualifications, it is safe to assume that it is an rms value. The 110-volt ac service for household lighting is 110 volts rms. The peak value of the voltage is about 155 volts.

13–3 Power and energy in the time domain

When we have several elements in a circuit, the energy is distributed among them as a function of the time. A general relationship which applies is

$$\text{Energy lost} + \text{Energy stored} = \text{Energy supplied,} \qquad (13\text{–}26)$$

or its derivative:

$$\text{Power lost} + \frac{d}{dt}(\text{Energy stored}) = \text{Power supplied.} \qquad (13\text{–}27)$$

The energy supplied must be either stored or dissipated. Similarly the power supplied is absorbed by the resistances, or increases the energy stored. The application of these general relationships can be illustrated by the following examples.

In Fig. 13–7 a step voltage is applied to a resistance, and an inductance in series. The current is

$$i(t) = \frac{E}{R}(1 - e^{-t/T}) \qquad \text{for} \quad t > 0, \qquad (13\text{–}28)$$

where $T = L/R$. We will verify the power relationship first. The

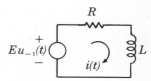

Figure 13–7. Power and energy relationships in an *R-L* circuit.

power lost in the resistance as a function of time is

$$p_R = i^2 R = \frac{E^2}{R}(1 - 2e^{-t/T} + e^{-2t/T}). \qquad (13\text{--}29)$$

The energy stored in the inductance as a function of time is

$$W_L = \tfrac{1}{2}Li^2 = \frac{LE^2}{2R^2}(1 - 2e^{-t/T} + e^{-2t/T}), \qquad (13\text{--}30)$$

and the power flowing into it is

$$\begin{aligned}
p_L = \frac{dW_L}{dt} &= \frac{LE^2}{2R^2}\left(\frac{2}{T}e^{-t/T} - \frac{2}{T}e^{-2t/T}\right) \\
&= \frac{E^2}{R}e^{-t/T}(1 - e^{-t/T}). \qquad (13\text{--}31)
\end{aligned}$$

The power supplied by the source is

$$p_S = e \times i = E \times \frac{E}{R}(1 - e^{-t/T}) = \frac{E^2}{R}(1 - e^{-t/T}). \qquad (13\text{--}32)$$

The sum of Eq. (13–29), or the power lost in the resistance, and Eq. (13–31), or the power entering the inductance, is

$$p_R + p_L = \frac{E^2}{R}(1 - e^{-t/T}). \qquad (13\text{--}33)$$

Equation (13–33), which gives the total power absorbed by the circuit, agrees with Eq. (13–32), which gives the power supplied by the source. Hence the power-balance equation is satisfied.

To verify the energy-balance equation we need to compute the energy lost in the resistance as a function of time and the energy supplied by the source. In Eq. (13–30) we have an expression for the energy stored in the inductance as a function of time. The energy lost in the resistance is

$$\begin{aligned}
W_R = \int_0^t i^2 R\, dt &= \int_0^t \frac{E^2}{R}(1 - 2e^{-t/T} + e^{-2t/T})\, dt \\
&= \frac{E^2}{R}\left[t - 2T(1 - e^{-t/T}) + \frac{T}{2}(1 - e^{-2t/T})\right]. \qquad (13\text{--}34)
\end{aligned}$$

The energy supplied by the source is

$$\begin{aligned}
W_S = \int_0^t (e \times i)\, dt &= \int_0^t \frac{E^2}{R}(1 - e^{-t/T})\, dt \\
&= \frac{E^2}{R}[t - T(1 - e^{-t/T})]. \qquad (13\text{--}35)
\end{aligned}$$

The sum of the energy lost in the resistance, Eq. (13–34), and the energy stored in the inductance, Eq. (13–35), is

$$W_R + W_L = \frac{E^2}{R}\left[t - 2T(1 - e^{-t/T}) + \frac{T}{2}(1 - e^{-2t/T})\right]$$
$$+ \frac{E^2}{R}\left(\frac{T}{2} - Te^{-t/T} + \frac{T}{2}e^{-2t/T}\right)$$
$$= \frac{E^2}{R}[t - T(1 - e^{-t/T})]. \qquad (13\text{–}36)$$

The sum of the energy lost in the resistance up to time t and the energy stored in the inductance at time t, Eq. (13–36), is equal to the energy supplied by the source between $t = 0$ and $t = t$, Eq. (13–35). The energy-balance equation is therefore satisfied. If we are interested in the energy at a particular instant the desired value of t has only to be substituted in the above equations.

A second circuit in which the energy method of analysis is useful is shown in Fig. 13–8. We assume here that the switch K is moved to position 1 for one second, then moved to position 2 for one second, and finally placed in the neutral position. The problem is to find the voltage on the capacitance after the switching operation. After the first second the current in the inductance is

$$i_L = \int_0^1 E\,dt = E[t]_0^1 = E \text{ amp.}$$

The energy stored is

$$W_L = \tfrac{1}{2}Li^2 = \tfrac{1}{2}LE^2 \text{ joules.}$$

The frequency of the oscillation, if it were allowed to continue after $t = 1$, would be

$$f = \frac{\omega}{2\pi} = \frac{1}{2\pi\sqrt{LC}} = \tfrac{1}{4} \text{ cps,}$$

and the corresponding period is

$$T = \frac{1}{f} = 4 \text{ sec.}$$

The switch is left in position 2 for one second, or one-quarter of a period. In one-quarter of a period all the energy which was stored in the inductance moves to the capacitance. The voltage on the capacitance can be obtained from the energy relationship

$$\tfrac{1}{2}Ce_{max}^2 = \tfrac{1}{2}Li_{max}^2 = \tfrac{1}{2}LE^2,$$

from which

$$\frac{e_{max}}{E} = \sqrt{L/C}. \qquad (13\text{–}37)$$

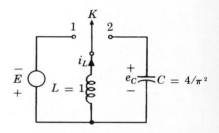

Figure 13–8. The transference of energy from inductance to capacitance.

Equation (13–37) shows that the voltage on the capacitance can be made very large if the ratio of inductance to capacitance is large. This principle is used in vibrator power supplies to obtain high direct voltages from low direct voltages.

Active and reactive power in the time domain. In alternating-current circuits the direction of power flow is important, since on one half-cycle a source may be delivering power to a circuit, and on the other half-cycle it may be receiving power from the circuit. A typical situation is diagrammed in Fig. 13–9. The energy flow to the resistance is always in one direction. The flow is not a constant, however, but pulsates from zero to a maximum value twice during each cycle. The energy flow to the energy-storage elements reverses twice during each cycle. The energy flows into the energy-storage element, and then it flows back to the source again. Energy is also interchanged between capacitive and inductive energy-storage elements within the network.

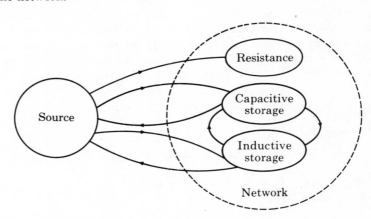

Figure 13–9. An energy flow chart for a general ac network.

A power company must supply generating capacity and transmission facilities for the power loaned to the network, as well as for the power absorbed by the network. Furthermore, the fluctuating currents produce losses in the generating and transmitting system, and somebody must pay for them! Thus a power company is forced to keep track not only of the *real power* which it is supplying but also of the energy which is "swapped" back and forth. The name *reactive-power*, or *imaginary power*, is given to the power associated with this energy interchange.

Consider a general branch in which resistance and reactance are combined, as shown in Fig. 13–10(a). The voltage is

$$e(t) = |E| \cos (\omega t),$$

and the current is

$$i(t) = |I| \cos (\omega t - \theta).$$

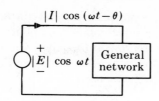

(a) A general network branch excited by an a-c voltage

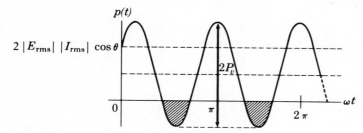

(b) The instantaneous power $p(t)$ and the vector power P_v

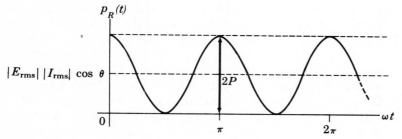

(c) The real power $p_R(t)$ and its average value P

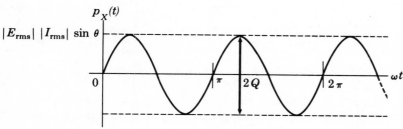

(d) The reactive power $p_X(t)$ and its peak value Q

Figure 13–10. Definition of real and reactive power in the time domain.

Since the current lags the voltage for an inductive load, a positive value of θ corresponds to an inductive load. The instantaneous power is

$$p = e \cdot i = |E|\,|I| \cos \omega t \cos (\omega t - \theta)$$

$$= \frac{|E|\,|I|}{2} \cos \theta + \frac{|E|\,|I|}{2} \cos (2\omega t - \theta)$$

$$= \underbrace{|E_{\mathrm{rms}}|\,|I_{\mathrm{rms}}| \cos \theta + |E_{\mathrm{rms}}|\,|I_{\mathrm{rms}}| \cos \theta \cos 2\omega t}_{\text{Real power}}$$

(13–38)

$$+ \underbrace{|E_{\mathrm{rms}}|\,|I_{\mathrm{rms}}| \sin \theta \sin 2\omega t}_{\text{Reactive power}}.$$

Equation (13–38) is plotted in Fig. 13–10(b). The power flow has both positive and negative components, but there is a net average positive value which represents the power absorbed in the resistance. The first two terms in Eq. (13–38), plotted in Fig. 13–10(c), represent the real power which fluctuates from zero to a maximum of

$$2E_{rms}I_{rms} \cos \theta.$$

The third term represents the reactive power which is surging back and forth, and which has no net average value. The peak value of the reactive power in the circuit is $E_{rms}I_{rms} \sin \theta$, as shown in Fig. 13–10(d). From this resolution we see that

$$P = |E_{rms}| \, |I_{rms}| \cos \theta,$$
$$Q = |E_{rms}| \, |I_{rms}| \sin \theta, \qquad (13\text{–}39)$$

where P represents the real power absorbed by the circuit, and Q represents the peak value of the reactive component, which is surging back and forth. The sign of Q is automatically taken care of by the sign of $\sin \theta$, with the assumption that θ is positive for an inductive load and negative for a capacitive load.* The factor $\cos \theta$ is called the *power factor*, and the factor $\sin \theta$ is called the *reactive factor*, since these factors modify the volt-amperes in each case.

Since power is a scalar quantity, Eq. (13–38) can be applied to each branch in a network, and the total power can be obtained as the arithmetic sum of the branch powers. The three terms remain separate, and hence

$$P_{total} = \text{Sum of the branch powers,} \qquad (13\text{–}40)$$

$$Q_{total} = \text{Sum of the branch reactive powers.} \qquad (13\text{–}41)$$

Equation (13–40) is simply the law of energy conservation, but Eq. (13–41) is more remarkable. It states in effect that a capacitance added at any point in a network can be used to cancel the effects of an inductance added at any other point, and that the cancellation will be complete provided that they both draw the same amounts of reactive power. The phenomenon is one of resonance, but it is a good deal more general than series or parallel resonance. As a practical matter, of course, if the problem is to supply negative reactive power to cancel some undesirable positive reactive power, the capacitance should be as close to the inductance as possible in order to minimize circuit losses produced in the intervening resistances.

---

* The choice of the sign of reactive power is arbitrary. Common usage in the USA assigns the positive sign to inductive reactive power.

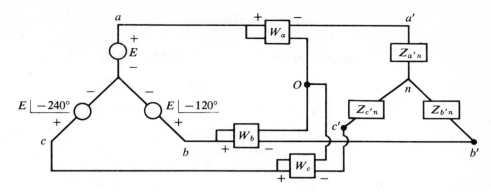

Figure 13–11. Three-phase power and reactive power.

Three-phase power. An interesting application of the above concepts occurs in three-phase circuits where it is possible to measure the real or the reactive power from three sources by means of only two meters. Consider the circuit of Fig. 13–11. The instantaneous power delivered to the three loads is

$$P = e_{a'n}i_{aa'} + e_{b'n}i_{bb'} + e_{c'n}i_{cc'}, \qquad (13\text{–}42)$$

but

$$e_{a'o} = e_{a'n} - e_{on},$$

$$e_{b'o} = e_{b'n} - e_{on},$$

$$e_{c'o} = e_{c'n} - e_{on}.$$

Hence

$$p = e_{a'o}i_{aa'} + e_{b'o}i_{bb'} + e_{c'o}i_{cc'} + e_{on}(i_{aa'} + i_{bb'} + i_{cc'});$$

and since

$$i_{aa'} + i_{bb'} + i_{cc'} = 0,$$

we find

$$p = e_{a'o}i_{aa'} + e_{b'o}i_{bb'} + e_{c'o}i_{cc'}. \qquad (13\text{–}43)$$

The meters in Fig. 13–11 are connected so that they individually give the terms of Eq. (13–43) and their sum therefore gives the total power. Since the equation holds for the instantaneous power it includes both the real power and reactive power as special cases. Since the point *o* is an arbitrary one we can pick it on one of the lines and thus eliminate the need for one of the meters. Thus three-phase power can be measured by means of two watt-meters, and similarly, three-phase reactive power can be measured by means of 2 var-meters. These arguments apply equally well to balanced or unbalanced loads and to *Y*- or Δ-connections.

13–4 Power and energy in the frequency domain

In the previous section we developed expressions for the real, or active, power P, and the imaginary, or reactive, power Q:

$$P = |E_{\text{rms}}|\,|I_{\text{rms}}|\cos\theta,$$

$$Q = |E_{\text{rms}}|\,|I_{\text{rms}}|\sin\theta,$$

where $|E_{\text{rms}}|$ and $|I_{\text{rms}}|$ are the rms values of the magnitudes of the voltage and the current waveforms, and θ is the angle between the current and the voltage. First we will change our frequency-domain vectors to rms values by dividing their lengths by 1.414. Suppose

$$E_{\text{rms}} = |E_{\text{rms}}|\,\underline{|\phi_1},$$

$$I_{\text{rms}} = |I_{\text{rms}}|\,\underline{|\phi_2},$$

as shown in Fig. 13–12. Then we take the conjugate vector for I_{rms}:

$$I_{\text{rms}}^* = |I_{\text{rms}}|\,\underline{|-\phi_2},$$

and multiply it by the rms voltage phasor:

$$E_{\text{rms}}I_{\text{rms}}^* = |E_{\text{rms}}|\,|I_{\text{rms}}|\,\underline{|\phi_1 - \phi_2} = |E_{\text{rms}}|\,|I_{\text{rms}}|\,\underline{|\theta}, \qquad (13\text{–}44)$$

in which θ is the angle between the voltage and the current phasors. The expansion of Eq. (13–44) is

$$E_{\text{rms}}I_{\text{rms}}^* = |E_{\text{rms}}|\,|I_{\text{rms}}|\cos\theta + j|E_{\text{rms}}|\,|I_{\text{rms}}|\sin\theta$$

$$= P + jQ. \qquad (13\text{–}45)$$

The phasor defined by Eq. (13–45) is called the *vector (or phasor) power* and is designated by P_v. Thus

$$P_v = E_{\text{rms}}I_{\text{rms}}^* = P + jQ. \qquad (13\text{–}46)$$

Equation (13–46) is the basic formula for computing power in the frequency domain. The three quantities P, Q, and P_v are all products of voltage and current and have the dimensions of volt-amperes. In order to distinguish them, the real power P is measured in *watts*, the reactive power Q is measured in *reactive volt-amperes, or vars*, and the vector power is measured in *volt-amperes, or va*. The corresponding time expressions are at a frequency of $2\omega t$, as shown in Eq. (13–38).

A common problem which occurs is the computation of the input power to a network from a source. A typical network is shown in Fig. 13–13, and the corresponding impedance triangle is plotted in

Imaginary axis

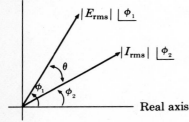

Figure 13–12. The rms vectors.

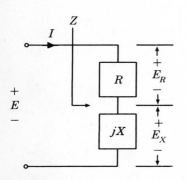

Figure 13–13. A general impedance branch.

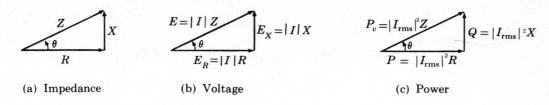

    (a) Impedance   (b) Voltage   (c) Power

Figure 13–14. The impedance-voltage-power triangle.

Fig. 13–14(a). If the impedance is multiplied by $|I|$, we obtain

$$|I|Z = |I|R + j|I|X,$$

or   (13–47)

$$E = E_R + jE_X.$$

 As a second step, let us multiply the impedance by $|I_{rms}|^2$. We then get

$$\begin{aligned}
|I_{rms}|^2 Z &= |I_{rms}|^2 R + j|I_{rms}|^2 X \\
&= |I_{rms}|^2 |Z| \cos\theta + j|I_{rms}|^2 |Z| \sin\theta \\
&= |I_{rms}| |E_{rms}| \cos\theta + j|I_{rms}| |E_{rms}| \sin\theta,
\end{aligned}$$

or

$$P_v = P + jQ.   (13–48)$$

The voltage vector diagram and the power vector diagram are shown in Figs. 13–14(b) and 13–14(c). The impedance diagram becomes voltage or power just by a change in scale!

 As a numerical example of the computation of vector power, real power, and reactive power, consider the circuit of Fig. 13–15. For this circuit, the impedance is

$$Z = 1 + j \text{ ohms.}$$

The current is

$$I_{rms} = \frac{1\ \underline{|0°}}{1 + j} = 0.707\ \underline{|-45°} \text{ amp,}$$

for an input voltage of

$$E_{rms} = 1\ \underline{|0°} \text{ volts.}$$

Vector power. The basic formula for the vector power is

$$P_v = E_{rms} I_{rms}^* = (1\ \underline{|0°})(0.707\ \underline{|45°}) = 0.5 + j0.5 \text{ va.}$$

An alternative method from the power triangle is

$$P_v = |I_{rms}|^2 (R + jX) = 0.5(1 + j) = 0.5 + j0.5 \text{ va.}$$

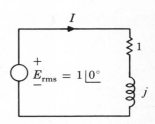

Figure 13–15. A simple example for the calculation of power quantities.

Real power. The real power can be obtained from the vector power. Thus

$$P = \text{Re} (E_{\text{rms}} I_{\text{rms}}^*) = |E_{\text{rms}}| \, |I_{\text{rms}}| \cos \theta = 0.5 \text{ watt.}$$

It can also be obtained from the power triangle, in the form

$$P = |I_{\text{rms}}|^2 R = 0.5(1) = 0.5 \text{ watt.}$$

Reactive power. The reactive power can be obtained from the vector power:

$$Q = \text{Im} (E_{\text{rms}} I_{\text{rms}}^*) = |E_{\text{rms}}| \, |I_{\text{rms}}| \sin \theta = 0.5 \text{ var.}$$

It can also be obtained from the power triangle, in the form

$$Q = |I_{\text{rms}}|^2 X = 0.5(1) = 0.5 \text{ var.}$$

Power factor. Sometimes an explicit statement of the power factor is desired. The basic definition is

$$\text{pf} = \cos \theta = \cos 45° = 0.707.$$

It can also be obtained from the power triangle.

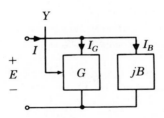

(a) Admittance circuit

(b) Admittance triangle

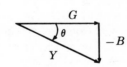

$I_G = |E| G$

$-I_B = -EB$

$I = |E| Y$

(c) Current triangle

$P = |E_{\text{rms}}|^2 G$

$Q = -|E_{\text{rms}}|^2 B$

$P_v = |E_{\text{rms}}|^2 Y^*$

(d) Power triangle

Figure 13-16. The admittance-current-power triangle.

It is also possible to replace the network by its equivalent admittance, as shown in Fig. 13-16(a). The admittance triangle is plotted in Fig. 13-16(b). The susceptance is plotted in the negative direction, because it is negative for an inductive circuit. If we multiply each side of the admittance triangle by $|E|$, we obtain the current triangle of Fig. 13–16(c), since

$$|E|Y = |E|G + j|E|B$$

is the same as

$$I = I_G + jI_B.$$

If we multiply each side of the admittance triangle by $|E_{\mathrm{rms}}|^2$, we obtain the power triangle of Fig. 13–16(d), since

$$|E_{\mathrm{rms}}|^2 Y = |E_{\mathrm{rms}}|^2 G + j|E_{\mathrm{rms}}|^2 B$$

is the same as

$$P_v^* = P - jQ. \qquad (13\text{–}49)$$

Note that when the sides of the admittance triangle are multiplied by $|E_{\mathrm{rms}}|^2$, it becomes a triangle for the conjugate of the vector power. The student can keep track of the sign of the reactive power by always making sure that it is positive for an inductive load.

As an example, we will solve for the power in the circuit of Fig. 13–17. The input admittance is

$$Y = 1 - j \text{ mhos.}$$

The current is

$$I_{\mathrm{rms}} = E_{\mathrm{rms}} Y = (1 - j) \text{ amp.}$$

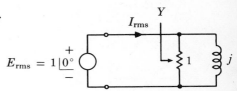

Figure 13–17. An example for admittance-power calculations.

Vector power. The basic formula for the vector power is

$$P_v = E_{\mathrm{rms}} I_{\mathrm{rms}}^* = (1 \,\underline{|0°})(1 + j) = (1 + j) \text{ va.}$$

An alternative formula, from the admittance-power triangle, is

$$P_v = |E_{\mathrm{rms}}|^2 (G - jB) = (1 \,\underline{|0°})(1 + j) \text{ va.}$$

Real power. The real power can be obtained from the vector power in the form

$$P = \mathrm{Re}\,(E_{\mathrm{rms}} I_{\mathrm{rms}}^*) = |E_{\mathrm{rms}}|\,|I_{\mathrm{rms}}| \cos \theta = 1 \text{ watt.}$$

It can also be obtained from the power triangle in the form

$$P = |E_{\mathrm{rms}}|^2 G = \frac{|E_{\mathrm{rms}}|^2}{R} = 1 \text{ watt.}$$

Reactive power. The reactive power can be obtained from the vector power in the form

$$Q = \mathrm{Im}\,(E_{\mathrm{rms}} I_{\mathrm{rms}}^*) = |E_{\mathrm{rms}}|\,|I_{\mathrm{rms}}| \sin \theta = 1 \text{ var.}$$

It can also be obtained from the power triangle in the form

$$Q = -|E_{\text{rms}}|^2 B = -1 \times (-1) = 1 \text{ var.}$$

Power factor. The power factor is

$$\text{pf} = \cos \theta = \cos 45° = 0.707.$$

Power in terms of branch currents and voltages. The total real power in a network is

$$P = \sum_1^n P_i, \tag{13–50}$$

where P_i is the real power absorbed in the ith branch of a network. Similarly, the total reactive power in a network is

$$Q = \sum_1^n Q_i, \tag{13–51}$$

where Q_i is the reactive power absorbed in the ith branch of a network.

As an example of the branch method of computing power, we shall consider the "power-factor-correction" problem. Most industrial loads are inductive, and since the power company charges for the reactive power consumed, it may be desirable for the user to buy a large capacitance and to connect it in parallel with the inductive load to supply some of the reactive power. Consider the circuit shown in Fig. 13–18. The inductive load draws 400 watts of real power and 300 vars of reactive power. The problem is to find the values of capacitive reactance which will bring the power factor of the combined load (a) to unity and (b) to 0.9.

Solution a. For unity power factor, the branch reactive power of the capacitance must be equal to the reactive power of the load. Thus

$$Q_C = -300 \text{ vars.}$$

From the admittance-power triangle

$$Q_C = -E_{\text{rms}}^2 B_C = -100^2 B_C.$$

Thus

$$B_C = \frac{300}{10,000}.$$

The reactance of the pure capacitance is the reciprocal of its susceptance and therefore

$$X_C = -33.3 \text{ ohms.}$$

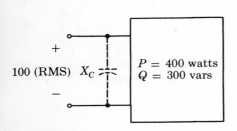

+

100 (RMS) X_C

−

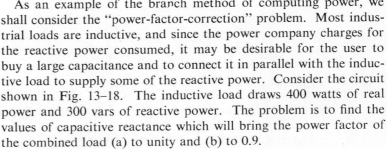

$P = 400$ watts
$Q = 300$ vars

Figure 13–18. The power-factor-correction problem.

Solution b. For a power factor of 0.9, the power-factor angle is

$$\theta = \cos^{-1} 0.9 = 26°.$$

From the power triangle, the allowable reactive power after correction is

$$Q = P \tan \theta = 400 \tan 26° = 195 \text{ vars}.$$

The capacitance must supply

$$300 - 195 = 105 \text{ vars}.$$

Thus the necessary capacitive reactance is

$$X_C = \frac{-100^2}{105} = -95 \text{ ohms}.$$

The capacitor required in the second solution is about $\frac{1}{3}$ the size, and therefore about $\frac{1}{3}$ the cost, of the capacitor required to bring the power factor up to a value of unity. The saving in power cost might not warrant the use of the larger capacitance.

Power matching. When maximum power is drawn by a load, it is said to be matched to its source. Matching is important in communications systems where the power levels are small, where the efficiency is not important, and where the maximum value of an output signal is the sole criterion of usefulness.

The general situation is shown in Fig. 13–19. A source of constant voltage has an internal impedance of $R_s + jX_s$, and the load connected to it has a value of $Z_L = R_L + jX_L$. We will consider two cases. In the first, the source and its internal impedance are given, and both the load resistance and load reactance can be varied independently.

Case 1: both R_L and X_L variable. The current in the circuit is

$$I = \frac{E}{(R_s + R_L) + j(X_s + X_L)}. \qquad (13\text{–}52)$$

The power in the load resistance is given by

$$P_L = |I_{\text{rms}}|^2 R_L = \frac{E^2 R_L}{(R_s + R_L)^2 + (X_s + X_L)^2}.$$

To find the maximum which can be obtained by varying X_L, we take the derivative with respect to it:

$$\frac{dP_L}{dX_L} = E^2 R_L \left[\frac{-2(X_s + X_L)}{(R_s + R_L)^2 + (X_s + X_L)^2} \right]. \qquad (13\text{–}53)$$

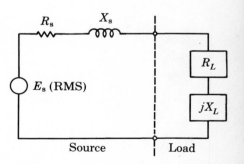

Figure 13–19. Matching for maximum power transfer.

For a maximum the derivative of Eq. (13–53) must be zero, which results in

$$X_L = -X_s. \tag{13–54}$$

This condition could have been obtained by simple reasoning. A maximum current occurs in the circuit at resonance, and maximum power is produced in the load. With $X_s = -X_L$, we will proceed to find the value of the load resistance R_L which results in maximum power in the load. The power is now given by

$$P_L = \frac{E^2 R_L}{(R_s + R_L)^2},$$

from which

$$\frac{dP_L}{dR_L} = E^2 \left[\frac{(R_s + R_L)^2 - 2R_L(R_s + R_L)}{(R_s + R_L)^4} \right]. \tag{13–55}$$

For maximum power the numerator of Eq. (13–55) is zero, and we obtain

$$R_L = R_s. \tag{13–56}$$

We see therefore that the condition for maximum power transfer when the resistance and reactance of the load are separately variable is that the reactances in the circuit should resonate and the resistances should be equal.

Case 2: only Z_L variable. If we are producing matching with a transformer, we have control only of the magnitude of the reflected load impedance. Let us denote the reflected load impedance as

$$Z_L = A \,\underline{|\theta°}. \tag{13–57}$$

Then the resistance is $A \cos \theta$ and the reactance is $A \sin \theta$. The current in the circuit is

$$I = \frac{E}{(R_s + A \cos \theta) + j(X_s + A \sin \theta)}, \tag{13–58}$$

and the power in the resistive component of the load is

$$P = |I_{\mathrm{rms}}|^2 R = \frac{E^2 A \cos \theta}{(R_s + A \cos \theta)^2 + (X_s + A \sin \theta)^2}. \tag{13–59}$$

We will differentiate the expression with respect to A in order to find the maximum value of P as A is varied:

$$\frac{dP}{dA} = E^2 \left[\frac{\begin{array}{c}[(R_s + A \cos \theta)^2 + (X_s + A \sin \theta)^2] \cos \theta - 2A \cos \theta \\ \times [(R_s + A \cos \theta) \cos \theta + (X_s + A \sin \theta) \sin \theta]\end{array}}{[(R_s + A \cos \theta)^2 + (X_s + A \sin \theta)^2]^2} \right].$$
$$\tag{13–60}$$

The condition for a maximum is that the numerator of Eq. (13–60) be zero;

$$(R_s + A \cos \theta)^2 + (X_s + A \sin \theta)^2 - 2A \cos \theta (R_s + A \cos \theta)$$
$$- 2A \sin \theta (X_s + A \sin \theta) = 0,$$

from which

$$A^2 = R_s^2 + X_s^2,$$

and

$$A = \sqrt{R_s^2 + X_s^2}. \tag{13–61}$$

Equation (13–61) shows that the condition for matching when only the magnitude of the load impedance is variable is for the magnitude of the load impedance to be equal to the magnitude of the source impedance. The power obtained in this case is, of course, less than the power obtained for the ideal matching considered in case 1.

Summary

Basic formulas

$$p = e \times i \qquad \sum p = 0 \qquad W = \int p \, dt$$

Sources

$$p_E = e \times i = E \times i$$

$$p_I = e \times i = e \times I$$

The elements

	Power	*Energy*

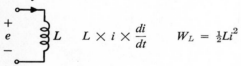

R $i^2 R = \dfrac{E^2}{R}$ $W_R = \displaystyle\int_0^t p_R \, dt$

L $L \times i \times \dfrac{di}{dt}$ $W_L = \tfrac{1}{2} L i^2$

C $C \times e \times \dfrac{de}{dt}$ $W_C = \tfrac{1}{2} C e^2$

rms values

$$F_{\text{rms}} = \sqrt{\frac{1}{T} \int_0^T f^2(t) \, dt} = \sqrt{\overline{f^2(t)}}$$

where the bar denotes average value

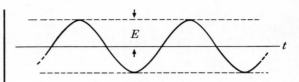

rms value $= 0.707E$

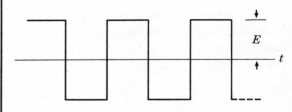

rms value $= E$

rms addition

$$F_{\text{rms}} = \sqrt{f_{1_{\text{rms}}}^2 + f_{2_{\text{rms}}}^2 + \cdots}$$

Power in the time domain

$$p = \overbrace{\frac{|E|\,|I|}{2} \cos \theta + \frac{|E|\,|I|}{2} \cos \theta \cos 2\omega t}^{p_r}$$

$$+ \overbrace{\frac{|E|\,|I|}{2} \sin \theta \sin 2\omega t}^{p_X}$$

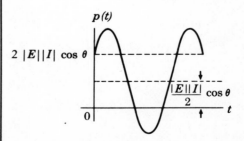

Instantaneous power

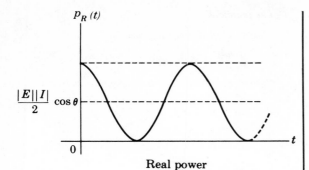

Real power

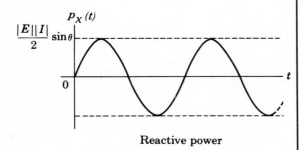

Reactive power

Three-phase power

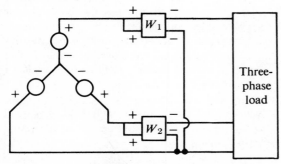

Power = $W_1 + W_2$

Power in the frequency domain

Vector power

$$P_v = E_{\text{rms}} I_{\text{rms}}^* = |I_{\text{rms}}|^2 Z$$
$$= |E_{\text{rms}}|^2 Y = |E_{\text{rms}}| |I_{\text{rms}}| (\cos \theta + j \sin \theta)$$

Real power

$$P = \text{Re} (E_{\text{rms}} I_{\text{rms}}^*)$$
$$= |I_{\text{rms}}|^2 R = |E_{\text{rms}}|^2 G = |E_{\text{rms}}| |I_{\text{rms}}| \cos \theta$$

Reactive power

$$Q = \text{Im} (E_{\text{rms}} I_{\text{rms}}^*)$$
$$= |I_{\text{rms}}|^2 X = -|E_{\text{rms}}|^2 B = |E_{\text{rms}}| |I_{\text{rms}}| \sin \theta$$

Power factor

$$\text{pf} = \cos \theta = \frac{P}{|P_v|} = \frac{R}{|Z|} = \frac{G}{|Y|}$$

Reactive factor

$$\text{rf} = \sin \theta = \frac{Q}{|P_v|} = \frac{X}{|Z|} = \frac{-B}{|Y|}$$

Impedance-power triangle

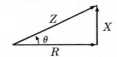

Impedance

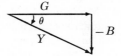

$$P_v = |I_{\text{rms}}|^2 Z \qquad Q = |I_{\text{rms}}|^2 X$$
$$P = |I_{\text{rms}}|^2 R$$

Power

Admittance-power triangle

Admittance

$$P = |E_{\text{rms}}|^2 G$$
$$P_v = |E_{\text{rms}}|^2 Y^* \qquad Q = -|E_{\text{rms}}|^2 B$$

Power

Branch power

$$P = \sum P_i$$

where P_i equals the real power in branch i

$$Q = \sum Q_i$$

where Q_i equals the reactive power in branch i

Power matching

Case 1: both R_L and X_L variable

$$X_L = X_s \quad \text{and} \quad R_L = R_s$$

Case 2: magnitude of load impedance variable

$$|Z_L| = |Z_s|$$

References

Two extreme points of view will be found in the literature on power and energy. Some authors are concerned solely with 60-cps systems, and all of their examples and exercises concern 60-cps systems. Other authors strive to be very general and treat only the general transient case. In this chapter we have tried to steer a course midway between these two extremes. References to other points of view are given below.

1. KERCHNER and CORCORAN, *Alternating Current Circuits*, 3rd ed., John Wiley, New York, 1951. This text is concerned almost completely with alternating currents and rms values. It contains a particularly good chapter on rms values and Fourier series.

2. FITZGERALD and HIGGINBOTHAM, *Basic Electrical Engineering*, 2nd ed., McGraw-Hill, New York, 1957. A concise treatment of the usual 60-cps power problems, including rms values, real and reactive power, and power factor correction.

3. E. A. GUILLEMIN, *Introductory Circuit Theory*, John Wiley, New York, 1953. Chapter 7 of this text discusses real and reactive power in the time and frequency domains. Chapter 10 gives an introduction to quadratic forms and general energy functions.

4. E. A. GUILLEMIN, *Network Synthesis*, John Wiley, New York, 1959. In this text Guillemin gives a very complete discussion of the general energy relationships of *R-L-C* networks under steady-state excitation. Excitation by damped sine waves is also included. Reference is made to original work by Otto Brune.

5. SESHU and BALABANIAN, *Network Analysis*, John Wiley, New York, 1959. This text presents a more general form of the energy relationships in the general case.

6. CLEMENT and JOHNSON, *Electrical Engineering Science*, McGraw-Hill, New York, 1960. A presentation of ac power from a middle-of-the-road point of view.

Exercises

SECTION 13-2

1. Find the power absorbed in the resistances in the circuit of Fig. 13–20. Also give that delivered by each source.

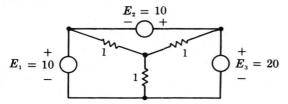

Figure 13–20

2. Find the current in each resistance in the circuit of Fig. 13–21 and the total power dissipated. Check the result by finding the power delivered by each source.

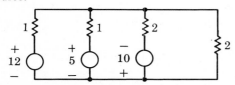

Figure 13–21

3. In the circuit of Fig. 13–22 give the energy in each inductance as a function of time. Give also the energy delivered by the source as a function of time.

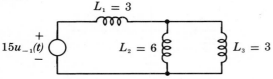

Figure 13–22

4. In the circuit of Fig. 13–23 find the energy stored on each capacitance as a function of time, and the energy delivered by the source as a function of time. Also find the power absorbed by each capacitance as a function of time, and the power supplied by the source as a function of time.

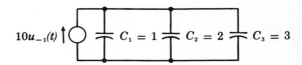

Figure 13–23

5. Find the rms value of the waveform shown in Fig. 13–24.

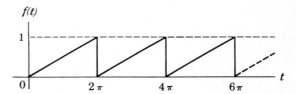

Figure 13–24

6. Find the rms value of the half-wave rectified sine wave shown in Fig. 13–25.

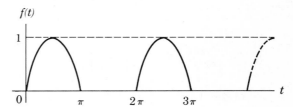

Figure 13–25

7. The waveform of Fig. 13–26 repeats with a period of 5 sec. Find its rms value.

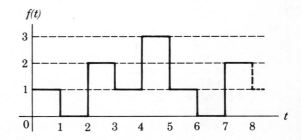

Figure 13–26

8. Find the rms value of the sum of the following three currents:

$$i_1(t) = 10,$$
$$i_2(t) = 6 \cos t + 5 \cos (3t + 45°),$$
$$i_3(t) = 5 + 6 \sin t + 5 \cos (3t - 45°).$$

SECTION 13-3

9. In the circuit of Fig. 13–27 find the energy supplied by the source, the energy stored in the inductance, and the energy lost in the resistance. What fraction of the total energy supplied is lost in the resistance?

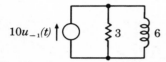

Figure 13-27

10. In the circuit of Fig. 13–28 show that the power supplied by the source is balanced at all times by the power absorbed in the capacitance and the resistance.

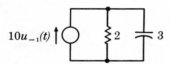

Figure 13-28

11. In the circuit of Fig. 13–29 find the energy stored in each inductance and the energy stored in the capacitance as functions of time.

12. A voltage $e(t) = 10 \cos t$ is applied to the series combination of $R = 1$ ohm and $C = 1$ f. (a) Find the instantaneous power in the form of a constant term, a cosine term of double frequency, and a sine term of double frequency. (b) Sketch $p(t)$. (c) Give P, the average power absorbed. (d) Give Q, the reactive power absorbed.

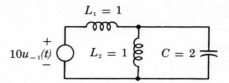

Figure 13-29

13. The switch in the circuit of Fig. 13–30 is closed at $t = 0$. Find the initial energy stored in the capacitance and the total energy lost in the resistance from $t = 0$ to $t = \infty$.

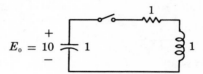

Figure 13-30

14. A voltage $e(t) = 10 \cos t$ is applied to the series combination of $R = 1$ ohm and $L = 1$ h. (a) Find the instantaneous power in the form of a constant term, a cosine term of frequency $\omega = 2$, and a sine term of frequency $\omega = 2$. (b) Sketch $p(t)$. (c) Give P, the average power absorbed. (d) Give Q, the reactive power absorbed.

15. The meter W_1 in Fig. 13–31 reads the instantaneous power $i_{aa'}e_{ab}$ and the meter W_2 reads the instantaneous power $i_{cc'}e_{cb}$. The frequency is 60-cps. (a) Show that the sum of the instantaneous readings of W_1 and W_2 equals the instantaneous power absorbed in the load. (b) Comment on the nature of the answer to part (a).

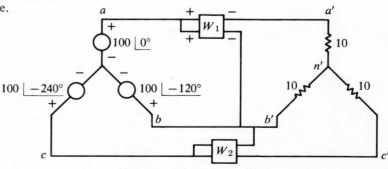

Figure 13-31

16. Show that the average power absorbed by a three-phase balance load is given by

$$P = \sqrt{3}\,|V_L|\,|I_L|\cos\theta,$$

where V_L is the line-to-line voltage, I_L is the line current, and θ is the power-factor angle of the load impedance.

SECTION 13-4

17. An rms voltage of 100 v is applied to circuit represented by a resistance of 10 ohms in parallel with a reactance of $j10$ ohms. (a) Find the vector power, real power, reactive power, and the power factor. (b) Draw the power vector diagram. (c) Solve by converting the admittance into an equivalent series impedance and finding the power in each of the two series elements.

18. For the circuit of Fig. 13-32 find the average power delivered by each source and the direction of power flow for each of the following cases:

(a) $Z = 1$ ohm
(b) $Z = j1$ ohm
(c) $Z = -j1$ ohm

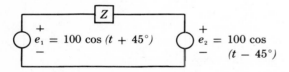

Figure 13-32

19. In Fig. 13-33 a generator with a voltage of 120 v, rms, is feeding a load through a transmission line represented by the impedance $1 + j$. The power factor of the load is known to be 0.8 and the voltage across the load is 100 volts, rms. Find the current and the power factor at the generator.

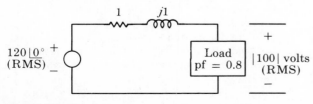

Figure 13-33

20. (a) In the circuit of Fig. 13-34 find the currents and voltages which would be compatible with an output voltage of $E = 1\,\underline{|0°}$. (b) Compute the net P and the net Q for the circuit from the branch quantities, for the conditions described. (c) Obtain the input Z from P_v. Check your answer by current and voltage computations.

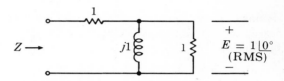

Figure 13-34

21. The circuit of Fig. 13-35 represents a generator feeding a load through a transmission line. The power factor of the load is 0.8 and the power factor at the generator is 0.5, without the capacitance. Find the capacitive reactance which then added across the generator will bring the power factor at the generator to unity.

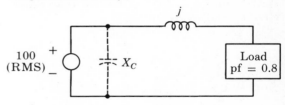

Figure 13-35

22. Both the resistive and reactive parts of the impedance in the circuit of Fig. 13-36 can be varied. (a) Find the value of Z which will absorb maximum power. (b) Give the value of the maximum power.

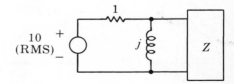

Figure 13-36

23. In the circuit of Fig. 13-37 only the turns-ratio of the ideal transformer can be varied. (a) Find the turns-ratio which gives

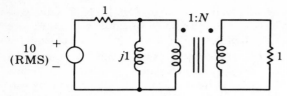

Figure 13–37

maximum power in the load resistance on the right side of the transformer. (b) Give the value of this maximum power.

24. A load which draws 100 watts and 100 vars (inductive) is to be connected in parallel with a load which draws 100 watts and 50 vars (capacitive). The voltage source remains constant in each case. (a) Give the power factor of the combined load. (b) What reactance added in parallel with the other loads will bring the power factor to unity?

Problems

1. Which of the sources in the network of Fig. 13–38 are delivering power and which are absorbing power? Give the amount in each case.

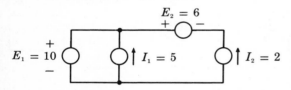

Figure 13–38

2. Compute the energy delivered to the L-C circuit of Fig. 13–39 by the voltage pulse.

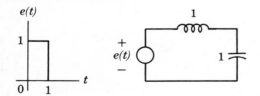

Figure 13–39

3. The switch in the circuit of Fig. 13–40 is closed at $t = 0$. Compute the energy supplied by the source, the energy lost in the resistance, the final

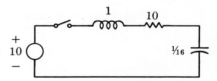

Figure 13–40

value of the energy stored in the capacitance, and verify the energy balance equation.

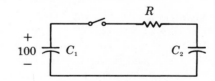

Figure 13–41

4. In the circuit of Fig. 13–41 the capacitance C_1 has a voltage of 100 v at the instant the switch is closed, and the capacitance C_2 has no voltage. (a) Find the current which flows in the circuit. (b) Find the total energy lost in the resistance. (c) Find the energy stored in C_1 and C_2 and check the energy balance equation. (d) Examine the situation as the resistance R is allowed to approach zero ohms.

5. If the voltage and the current at a terminal-pair are given by

$$e(t) = E_0 + E_1 \cos t + E_2 \cos 2t + \cdots,$$
$$i(t) = I_0 + I_1 \cos t + I_2 \cos 2t + \cdots.$$

(a) Find the rms voltage and the rms current. (b) Find the average value of the power if the instantaneous power is $e(t) \times i(t)$. (c) Show that the average power is *not* $E_{\text{rms}} \times I_{\text{rms}}$.

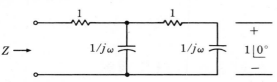

Figure 13–42

6. Find the input impedance of the circuit of Fig. 13–42 by computing the branch powers for an assumed output voltage of $E = 1\underline{\vert 0°}$.

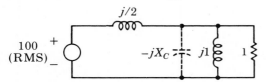

Figure 13–43

7. In the circuit of Fig. 13–43 find the value of the capacitive reactance which will give unity power factor at the terminals of the generator, although connected directly across the load.

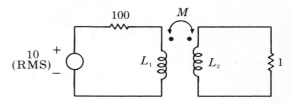

Figure 13–44

8. Matching in the circuit of Fig. 13–44 is done with a unity-coupled coil instead of an ideal transformer. At very low frequencies the power is shunted by the transformer and is not delivered to the load. The matching is adjusted to give a maximum power in the load for high frequencies, where the shunting effect of the transformer can be neglected. (a) Find the turns-ratio. The primary inductance remains at 1 h as the secondary turns are varied. Give also L_2 and M. (b) What is the half-power frequency at which the power delivered to the load is one-half of its high-frequency value?

CHAPTER 14

SIGNAL ANALYSIS IN THE FREQUENCY DOMAIN

As great Pythagoras of yore
Standing beside the blacksmith's door,
And hearing the hammers, as they smote
The anvils with a different note,
Stole from the varying tones, that hung
Vibrant on every iron tongue,
The secret of the sounding wire,
And formed the seven-chorded lyre.

LONGFELLOW

14–1 Introduction

The concept of frequency and the components of frequency arose in connection with music and musical instruments. An extension of these concepts to the analysis of more general signals first occurred in the unlikely field of heat transfer. Working in this field, Fourier announced his famous theorem stating that any signal can be resolved into sinusoidal components. Fourier's theorem is basic to most network and communications theory.

In this chapter we will consider Fourier's theorem and apply it first to periodic waves. The resulting summation of harmonic sinusoids is called a *Fourier series.*

We will then extend Fourier's theorem to nonperiodic waveforms. As the period of repetition increases without limit, the fundamental frequency of the Fourier series approaches zero, the spacing between the harmonics approaches zero, and the amplitudes of the harmonics approaches zero. The Fourier series becomes a *Fourier integral.* The frequency distribution of the harmonics in a Fourier series is a *line spectrum;* the frequency distribution in a Fourier integral is a *continuous, or band, spectrum.*

Certain convergence problems exist in Fourier integrals for step functions and other similar nonperiodic waveforms existing over infinite periods of time. These problems can be avoided if the Fourier expansions are performed in terms of rising sine waves instead of constant-amplitude sine waves. When this step is taken, the Fourier integral becomes the *Laplace integral*, or *Laplace transform.*

14–2 The Fourier theorem

In the year 1822 Fourier published his famous *Théorie Analytique de la Chaleur.* He was concerned primarily with the flow of heat, but in the course of his analysis he was led to expand arbitrary

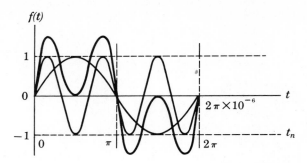

Figure 14–1. A normalized time scale.

functions in terms of infinite series of sinusoidal components. Some famous mathematicians stated categorically that this could not be done, and the mathematical storm did not subside for a hundred years.* We will consider first the case of periodic functions.

All periodic, physically realizable† functions with a period T can be expanded into a Fourier series of the form

$$f(t) = a_0 + a_1 \cos \omega_0 t + a_2 \cos 2\omega_0 t + \cdots + a_n \cos n\omega_0 t + \cdots$$
$$+ b_1 \sin \omega_0 t + b_2 \sin 2\omega_0 t + \cdots + b_n \sin n\omega_0 t + \cdots,$$
$$(14\text{–}1)$$

where $\omega_0 = 2\pi/T$ is the fundamental frequency and the a's and b's are constants which must be found. It is convenient to work in a normalized time scale in which the fundamental period of the wave is 2π units, and the corresponding normalized angular frequency is $\omega_0 = 1$. Consider the example shown in Fig. 14–1. The actual wave consists of two sinusoidal components of frequencies $\omega_0 = 10^6$ and $3\omega_0 = 3 \times 10^6$:

$$f(t) = \sin 10 \, t + \sin 3 \times 10^6 t.$$

The normalized time function is $f_n(t) = \sin t + \sin 3t$. *The actual time function can be obtained from the normalized one simply by inserting the correct fundamental frequency* in place of $\omega_0 = 1$. Thus we are perfectly general in considering the Fourier series

$$f(t) = a_0 + a_1 \cos t + a_2 \cos 2t + \cdots + a_n \cos nt + \cdots$$
$$+ b_1 \sin t + b_2 \sin 2t + \cdots + b_n \sin nt + \cdots. \quad (14\text{–}2)$$

---

* N. Wiener, *The Fourier Integral and Certain of its Applications*, Cambridge University Press, New York, 1933. See also the Dover Publications edition.

† The realizability conditions include idealized input functions such as steps, impulses, and doublets.

The coefficients of Eq. (14–2) are found by making use of the so-called "orthogonality"* properties of sinusoidal waves:

$$\int_0^{2\pi} \cos nt \, dt = \int_0^{2\pi} \sin nt \, dt$$

$$= \int_0^{2\pi} \sin nt \cos nt \, dt = 0,$$

$$\int_0^{2\pi} \cos mt \sin nt \, dt = \int_0^{2\pi} \cos mt \cos nt \, dt$$

$$= \int_0^{2\pi} \sin mt \sin nt \, dt = 0 \qquad \text{for } n \neq m,$$

$$\int_0^{2\pi} \cos^2 nt \, dt = \int_0^{2\pi} \sin^2 nt \, dt = \pi \qquad \text{for } n = m, \qquad (14\text{–}3)$$

where m and n are integers from 1 to ∞.

To find the value of the constant a_0, we integrate both sides of Eq. (14–2) over a complete period:

$$\int_0^{2\pi} f(t) \, dt = \int_0^{2\pi} a_0 \, dt + \int_0^{2\pi} a_1 \cos t \, dt + \cdots$$

$$+ \int_0^{2\pi} b_1 \sin t \, dt + \cdots.$$

From Eq. (14–3) all the integrals on the right side of the equation, except the first, are zero. Thus

$$\int_0^{2\pi} f(t) \, dt = a_0 2\pi,$$

or

$$a_0 = \frac{1}{2\pi} \int_0^{2\pi} f(t) \, dt. \qquad (14\text{–}4)$$

Note that a_0 is simply the average or dc value of the function.

To find a_1 we multiply both sides of Eq. (14–2) by $\cos t$ and integrate over one period:

$$\int_0^{2\pi} f(t) \cos t \, dt = \int_0^{2\pi} a_0 \cos t \, dt + \int_0^{2\pi} a_1 \cos^2 t \, dt$$

$$+ \int_0^{2\pi} a_2 \cos t \cos 2t \, dt + \cdots$$

$$+ \int_0^{2\pi} b_1 \cos t \sin t \, dt + \cdots.$$

----

* The name originates from a similar set of conditions which hold for the direction cosines of sets of orthogonal vectors.

From Eq. (14–3) all the integrals on the right side of this expression are zero, with the exception of that involving a_1. Thus

$$\int_0^{2\pi} f(t) \cos t \, dt = a_1 \pi,$$

or

$$a_1 = \frac{1}{\pi} \int_0^{2\pi} f(t) \cos t \, dt. \tag{14–5}$$

Equation (14–5) shows that a_1 is twice the average value of the function $f(t)$ weighted by the multiplying factor $\cos t$. By a similar process, we can obtain the other a's and b's. In summary,

$$a_n = \frac{1}{\pi} \int_0^{2\pi} f(t) \cos nt \, dt, \tag{14–6}$$

$$b_n = \frac{1}{\pi} \int_0^{2\pi} f(t) \sin nt \, dt. \tag{14–7}$$

As an example of the direct computation of the Fourier coefficients, consider the square wave of Fig. 14–2. The function $f(t)$ is defined by

$$f(t) = \begin{cases} 1 & 0 < t < \pi, \\ 0 & \pi < t < 2\pi. \end{cases}$$

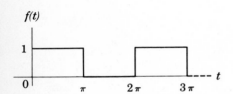

Figure 14–2. Fourier analysis of a square wave.

The computations are as follows:

$$a_0 = \frac{1}{2\pi} \int_0^{2\pi} f(t) \, dt = \frac{1}{2\pi} \int_0^{\pi} (1) \, dt + \frac{1}{2\pi} \int_{\pi}^{2\pi} (0) \, dt$$

$$= \frac{1}{2\pi} \pi + 0$$

$$= \tfrac{1}{2},$$

$$a_1 = \frac{1}{\pi} \int_0^{2\pi} f(t) \cos t \, dt = \frac{1}{\pi} \int_0^{\pi} \cos t \, dt + \frac{1}{\pi} \int_{\pi}^{2\pi} (0) \, dt$$

$$= \frac{1}{\pi} [\sin t]_0^{\pi}$$

$$= 0,$$

$$a_n = \frac{1}{\pi} \int_0^{2\pi} f(t) \cos nt \, dt = \frac{1}{\pi} \int_0^{\pi} \cos nt \, dt + \frac{1}{\pi} \int_{\pi}^{2\pi} (0) \, dt$$

$$= \frac{1}{\pi} \left[\frac{\sin nt}{n} \right]_0^{\pi}$$

$$= 0,$$

$$b_1 = \frac{1}{\pi} \int_0^{2\pi} f(t) \sin t \, dt = \frac{1}{\pi} \int_0^{\pi} \sin t \, dt + \frac{1}{\pi} \int_{\pi}^{2\pi} (0) \, dt$$

$$= \frac{1}{\pi} [-\cos t]_0^{\pi}$$

$$= \frac{2}{\pi},$$

$$b_n = \frac{1}{\pi} \int_0^{2\pi} f(t) \sin nt \, dt = \frac{1}{\pi} \int_0^{\pi} \sin nt \, dt + \frac{1}{\pi} \int_{\pi}^{2\pi} (0) \, dt$$

$$= \frac{1}{\pi} \left[\frac{-\cos nt}{n} \right]_0^{\pi}$$

$$= \begin{cases} 0 & \text{for } n \text{ even,} \\ \dfrac{2}{n\pi} & \text{for } n \text{ odd.} \end{cases}$$

The complete series is

$$f(t) = \frac{1}{2} + \frac{2}{\pi} \left(\sin t + \frac{\sin 3t}{3} + \frac{\sin 5t}{5} + \cdots \right). \qquad (14\text{–}8)$$

A sketch of the dc value, the fundamental, the third harmonic and their partial sum is given in Fig. 14–3. Even with these few terms, it is apparent that the square waveform is being approached. The addition of more terms to the partial sum causes the resultant wave to approach closer and closer to a square wave, except at the points of discontinuity.*

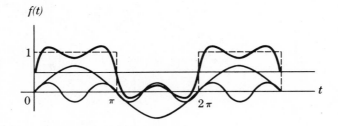

Figure 14–3. The partial sum of the Fourier series for a square wave.

Even-function symmetry. Even functions satisfy the condition $f(t) = f(-t)$. A sketch of an even function is shown in Fig. 14–4. All cosine waves are even functions, and therefore a series made up of cosine terms is an even function. Conversely, *the Fourier series for an even function has only cosine terms.* As an example of the

---

* An overshoot, called the Gibbs phenomenon, occurs at discontinuities.

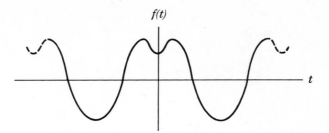

Figure 14-4. Even-function symmetry.

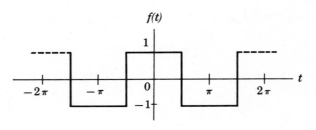

Figure 14-5. A square wave with even-function symmetry.

exploitation of even-function symmetry, consider the Fourier series of the waveform shown in Fig. 14–5. The function is defined by

$$f(t) = \begin{cases} 1 & -\pi/2 < t < \pi/2, \\ -1 & \pi/2 < t < 3\pi/2. \end{cases}$$

It possesses no dc term and no sine terms because of the even-function symmetry. For the cosine terms

$$\pi \cdot a_n = \int_{-\pi/2}^{3\pi/2} f(t) \cos nt \, dt = \int_{-\pi/2}^{\pi/2} \cos nt \, dt - \int_{\pi/2}^{3\pi/2} \cos nt \, dt$$

$$= \left[\frac{\sin nt}{n}\right]_{-\pi/2}^{\pi/2} - \left[\frac{\sin nt}{n}\right]_{\pi/2}^{3\pi/2}$$

$$= \begin{cases} (-1)^{(n+3)/2}\left[\dfrac{2}{n} - \left(-\dfrac{2}{n}\right)\right] & \\ & \text{for } n \text{ odd,} \\ 0 - 0 & \text{for } n \text{ even.} \end{cases}$$

Thus

$$a_n = \begin{cases} \dfrac{4(-1)^{(n+3)/2}}{\pi n} & \text{for } n \text{ odd,} \\ 0 & \text{for } n \text{ even.} \end{cases}$$

Note that the symmetry makes it possible to integrate over one-half the wave and to simply double the answer obtained. The complete series for the function is

$$f(t) = \frac{4}{\pi}\left(\cos t - \frac{\cos 3t}{3} + \frac{\cos 5t}{5} - \cdots\right). \tag{14-9}$$

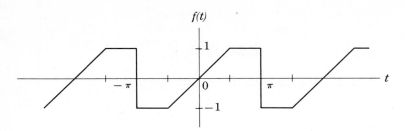

Figure 14–6. Odd-function symmetry.

Odd-function symmetry. Odd functions satisfy the condition $f(t) = -f(-t)$. A typical odd function is shown in Fig. 14–6. All sine waves are odd functions, and conversely, *the Fourier series for an odd function has only sine terms.*

If the origin of the wave in Fig. 14–5 is shifted to the left by $\pi/2$, the wave will possess odd-function symmetry. It can then be defined as

$$f(t) = \begin{cases} 1 & 0 < t < \pi, \\ -1 & \pi < t < 2\pi. \end{cases}$$

The Fourier series for this wave has only sine terms. The coefficients are given by

$$\pi \cdot b_n = \int_0^{2\pi} f(t) \sin nt \, dt = \int_0^{\pi} \sin nt \, dt - \int_{\pi}^{2\pi} \sin nt \, dt$$

$$= \left[\frac{-\cos nt}{n} \right]_0^{\pi} - \left[\frac{-\cos nt}{n} \right]_{\pi}^{2\pi}$$

$$= \begin{cases} \dfrac{2}{n} - \dfrac{-2}{n} & \text{for } n \text{ odd,} \\ 0 - 0 & \text{for } n \text{ even.} \end{cases}$$

Thus

$$b_n = \begin{cases} \dfrac{4}{\pi n} & \text{for } n \text{ odd,} \\ 0 & \text{for } n \text{ even.} \end{cases}$$

Note again that symmetry makes it possible to integrate over one-half of the period and to double the answer obtained. The complete series for the function is

$$f(t) = \frac{4}{\pi} \left(\sin t + \frac{\sin 3t}{3} + \frac{\sin 5t}{5} + \cdots \right). \qquad (14\text{–}10)$$

The waves represented by Eqs. (14–9) and (14–10) are identical except for a shift of the origin. The shift is one-quarter of the fundamental period. The shift represents $\pi/2$ radians for the fundamental term in the Fourier series but $n\pi/2$ *radians for the nth harmonic.* To change from Eq. (14–9) to (14–10), therefore, we must subtract $\pi/2$ from the fundamental, $3\pi/2$ from the fifth harmonic, and so on.

Rotation symmetry. Rotation symmetry is defined by the condition that $f(t) = -f(t + \pi)$. Waveforms of this type are produced in rotating electrical machinery when a north pole and a south pole alternately pass a given point. The coefficients of the cosine terms are given by

$$a_n = \frac{1}{\pi} \int_0^{2\pi} f(t) \cos nt \, dt$$

$$= \frac{1}{\pi} \int_0^{\pi} f(t) \cos nt \, dt + \frac{1}{\pi} \int_\pi^{2\pi} f(t) \cos nt \, dt$$

$$= \frac{1}{\pi} \int_0^{\pi} f(t) \cos nt \, dt + \frac{1}{\pi} \int_0^{\pi} f(t + \pi) \cos n(t + \pi) \, dt$$

$$= \frac{1}{\pi} \int_0^{\pi} [f(t) \cos nt + f(t + \pi)(\cos nt \cos n\pi - \sin nt \sin n\pi)] \, dt$$

$$= \frac{1}{\pi} \int_0^{\pi} [f(t) \cos nt - f(t)(\cos nt \cos n\pi)] \, dt$$

$$= \begin{cases} 0 & \text{for } n \text{ even,} \\ \dfrac{2}{\pi} \int_0^{\pi} f(t) \cos nt \, dt & \text{for } n \text{ odd.} \end{cases} \tag{14–11}$$

In a similar fashion, we obtain

$$b_n = \begin{cases} 0 & \text{for } n \text{ even,} \\ \dfrac{2}{\pi} \int_0^{\pi} f(t) \sin nt \, dt & \text{for } n \text{ odd.} \end{cases} \tag{14–12}$$

Thus we can conclude that *the Fourier series for a wave with rotation symmetry will have only odd harmonics.* An example of a typical waveform with rotation symmetry is given in Fig. 14–7.

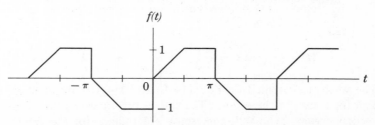

Figure 14–7. Rotation symmetry.

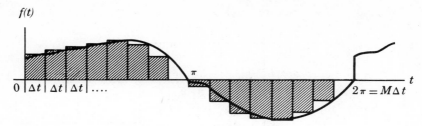

Figure 14–8. A sampled waveform.

Numerical methods. In order to proceed with numerical integration, the waveform is divided into a series of uniformly spaced sections, as shown in Fig. 14–8. Suppose that the function is sampled at the points Δt, $2\,\Delta t$, $3\,\Delta t$, . . ., $m\,\Delta t$, . . ., up to $M\,\Delta t = 2\pi$. The formula for the first coefficient in the Fourier series is

$$a_0 = \frac{1}{2\pi} \int_0^{2\pi} f(t)\, dt.$$

We replace the area under the integral by the area of the rectangles obtained by multiplying the sampled values of the function by Δt. This area is shown shaded in Fig. 14–8. The integral sign becomes a summation, and we have

$$a_0 \cong \frac{1}{2\pi} \sum_{m=1}^{M} f(m\,\Delta t)\, \Delta t. \qquad (14\text{–}13)$$

A similar process can be carried out for the other Fourier coefficients. Consider the general coefficient

$$a_n = \frac{1}{\pi} \int_0^{2\pi} f(t) \cos nt\, dt.$$

We imagine that the product $f(t) \cos nt$ is first plotted and then sampled as before. A trapezoidal wave is obtained which can be integrated by summation. Thus

$$a_n \cong \frac{1}{\pi} \sum_{m=1}^{M} f(m\,\Delta t) \cos (nm\,\Delta t)\, \Delta t. \qquad (14\text{–}14)$$

Similarly

$$b_n \cong \frac{1}{\pi} \sum_{m=1}^{M} f(m\,\Delta t) \sin (nm\,\Delta t)\, \Delta t. \qquad (14\text{–}15)$$

As an example, the first two nonzero coefficients of the Fourier series for the square wave in Fig. 14–9 will be obtained. Twelve sample points will be used, with an angle of 30° between sample

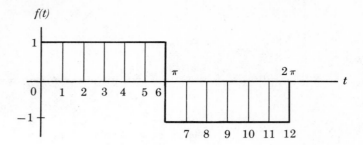

Figure 14–9. Numerical Fourier series.

points. More sample points must be used if higher harmonics are required. Shannon* has shown in a general way that any rate of sampling greater than 2 per cycle will be satisfactory. The wave has rotation symmetry and possesses only odd sine terms. The formulas for the fundamental and the third harmonic are

$$b_1 \cong \frac{2}{\pi} \sum_{m=1}^{M/2} f(m\,\Delta t)\,\sin\,(m\,\Delta t)\,\Delta t,$$

$$b_3 \cong \frac{2}{\pi} \sum_{m=1}^{M/2} f(m\,\Delta t)\,\sin\,(3m\,\Delta t)\,\Delta t.$$

A tabular solution for b_1 is given in Table 14–1, and a tabular solution for b_3 in Table 14–2. Both values agree within slide-rule accuracy with the values obtained analytically by Eq. (14–10).

TABLE 14–1

NUMERICAL EVALUATION OF FUNDAMENTAL

m	$m\,\Delta t$	$\sin m\,\Delta t$	$f(m\,\Delta t)$	$f(m\,\Delta t)\sin m\,\Delta t$
1	30	0.500	1	0.500
2	60	0.866	1	0.866
3	90	1.000	1	1.000
4	120	0.866	1	0.866
5	150	0.500	1	0.500
6	180	0.000	1	0.000
				Sum 3.732

$$b_1 = \frac{2}{\pi} \times 3.732 \times \frac{\pi}{6} = 1.24$$

---

* C. E. Shannon, *Proc. IRE*, Vol. 36, p. 1234, (Nov. 1948). Note particularly that the usual statement of the Shannon theorem, "the highest frequency sine wave must be sampled twice," is not quite correct.

TABLE 14–2

NUMERICAL EVALUATION OF THIRD HARMONIC

m	$3m\,\Delta t$	$\sin 3m\,\Delta t$	$f(m\,\Delta t)$	$f(m\,\Delta t)\sin 3m\,\Delta t$
1	90	1.00	1	1.00
2	180	0.00	1	0.00
3	270	−1.00	1	−1.00
4	360	0.00	1	0.00
5	450	1.00	1	1.00
6	540	0.00	1	0.00
			Sum	1.00

$$b_3 = \frac{2}{\pi} \times 1.00 \times \frac{\pi}{6} = 0.33$$

14–3 The Fourier integral

In this section we will extend the concept of the Fourier series for a periodic function to a Fourier integral for a single pulse of arbitrary shape. We will adopt a slightly different point of view toward a periodic wave. We will now think of it as a "repeated transient." For example, the square wave in Fig. 14–10 can be described as a square wave of period 2π, or it can be described as a pulse of width π repeated with a period of 2π. It is natural to inquire what happens to the Fourier series if we leave the pulse alone and increase the repetition period. All the harmonics will have smaller amplitudes because the integrals which describe them are averaged over the full period. The distribution of the harmonics relative to each other, however is still defined by the integration of the pulse.

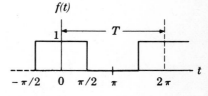

Figure 14–10. A repeated transient.

The complex Fourier series. The general Fourier series is

$$f(t) = a_0 + \sum_{n=1}^{\infty} (a_n \cos n\omega_0 t + b_n \sin n\omega_0 t),$$

where

$$a_0 = \frac{1}{T} \int_0^T f(t)\,dt,$$

$$a_n = \frac{2}{T} \int_0^T f(t) \cos n\omega_0 t\,dt, \qquad b_n = \frac{2}{T} \int_0^T f(t) \sin n\omega_0 t\,dt,$$

$$\omega_0 = \frac{2\pi}{T}.$$

Substitution of exponential expressions for the sine and cosine gives

$$f(t) = a_0 + \sum_{n=1}^{\infty} \left[a_n \frac{(e^{jn\omega_0 t} + e^{-jn\omega_0 t})}{2} + b_n \frac{(e^{jn\omega_0 t} - e^{-jn\omega_0 t})}{2j} \right]$$

$$= a_0 + \sum_{n=1}^{\infty} \left[\frac{(a_n - jb_n)}{2} e^{jn\omega_0 t} + \frac{(a_n + jb_n)}{2} e^{-jn\omega_0 t} \right]$$

$$= a_0 + \sum_{n=1}^{\infty} [c_n e^{jn\omega_0 t} + c_n^* e^{-jn\omega_0 t}],$$

where c_n^* is the complex conjugate of c_n and

$$c_n = \frac{a_n - jb_n}{2}$$

$$= \frac{2}{T} \int_0^T f(t) \left[\frac{(e^{jn\omega_0 t} + e^{-jn\omega_0 t})}{4} - j \frac{(e^{jn\omega_0 t} - e^{-jn\omega_0 t})}{4j} \right] dt$$

$$= \frac{1}{T} \int_0^T f(t) e^{-jn\omega_0 t} \, dt. \tag{14-16}$$

The expression for the Fourier series can be simplified if we note that the value of c_n given by Eq. (14–16) for $n = 0$ is identical to the value of a_0, and that the terms in the series of the form $c_n^* e^{-jn\omega_0 t}$ are identical to the terms which would have been obtained if we had taken the terms involving c_n and made n negative. Accordingly, instead of a constant term and two infinite sums from plus one to infinity, we can use a single sum from minus infinity to plus infinity. The result is the complex Fourier series

$$f(t) = \sum_{n=-\infty}^{\infty} c_n e^{jn\omega_0 t}, \tag{14-17}$$

where

$$c_n = \frac{1}{T} \int_0^T f(t) e^{-jn\omega_0 t} \, dt. \tag{14-18}$$

The complex Fourier series of Eq. (14–17) expresses a periodic function of time as a sum of positive and negative exponentials. The actual sinusoidal harmonics in the series are composed of pairs of positive and negative terms at each frequency. The amplitude of an actual harmonic is twice the amplitude of either of the corresponding exponential terms, that is, twice the magnitude of c_n. The phase is the angle of c_n.

Example. As an example of the complex Fourier series, consider the waveform of Fig. 14–11. The coefficients c_n are given by

$$c_n = \frac{1}{2\pi} \int_0^{2\pi} f(t)e^{-jnt}\, dt = \frac{1}{2\pi} \int_0^{\pi} e^{-jnt}\, dt$$

$$= \frac{1}{2\pi} \left[\frac{e^{-jnt}}{-jn} \right]_0^{\pi}$$

$$= \begin{cases} \dfrac{1}{2\pi} \cdot \dfrac{2}{jn} & \text{for } n \text{ odd,} \\ 0 & \text{for } n \text{ even.} \end{cases} \qquad (14\text{--}19)$$

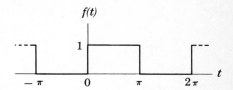

Figure 14–11. An example for the complex Fourier series.

The expression is indeterminate for $n = 0$, and the dc value is more easily determined by inspection. Here it is $a_0 = \frac{1}{2}$. The amplitude and phase spectra of the c_n's are plotted in Fig. 14–12. The actual Fourier series is given by

$$f(t) = \sum_{n=-\infty}^{+\infty} c_n e^{jn\omega_0 t}$$

$$= \cdots - \frac{1}{3\pi j} e^{-j3t} - \frac{1}{\pi j} e^{-jt} + \frac{1}{2} + \frac{1}{\pi j} e^{jt} + \frac{1}{3\pi j} e^{3jt} + \cdots.$$

Combining the positive and negative exponentials in pairs, we obtain

$$f(t) = \frac{1}{2} + \frac{2}{\pi} \left(\sin t + \frac{\sin 3t}{3} + \frac{\sin 5t}{5} + \cdots \right),$$

as in Eq. (14–8).

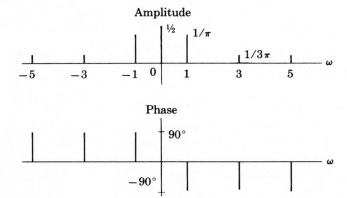

Figure 14–12. Amplitude and phase spectra.

The mathematical expressions for the complex Fourier series are beautifully simple and symmetrical. The simplicity is, however, deceptive. If the problem is merely to find the terms in a Fourier series, it is usually easier to use the trigonometric formulas. We have developed the complex form of the series, because it is a logical stepping stone toward the Fourier integral and it adds a great deal to the understanding of the integral.

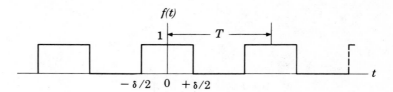

Figure 14-13. Repeated pulses.

The Fourier integral. The formal extension from the complex Fourier series to the Fourier integral is quite simple. The limiting processes cannot be rigorously justified, however, and mathematicians prefer to postulate the Fourier integral and derive its properties. The straightforward process, however, lends more insight into Fourier methods, and we will follow it. We will view the complex Fourier series as a representation of a set of repeated transients, and then we will let the period of the repetition tend to infinity. The fundamental frequency of the wave approaches zero, and so do the values of the harmonics. Let us begin with the example shown in Fig. 14-13. The complex Fourier series has coefficients given by

$$c_n = \frac{1}{T} \int_{-\delta/2}^{+\delta/2} f(t) e^{-jn\omega_0 t}\, dt$$

$$= \frac{1}{T} \int_{-\delta/2}^{\delta/2} e^{-jn\omega_0 t}\, dt = \frac{1}{T} \left[\frac{e^{-jn\omega_0 t}}{-jn\omega_0} \right]_{-\delta/2}^{\delta/2}$$

$$= \frac{1}{T} \frac{\delta}{2} \frac{e^{jn\omega_0 \delta/2} - e^{-jn\omega_0 \delta/2}}{jn\omega_0 \delta/2}$$

$$= \frac{\delta}{T} \frac{\sin n\omega_0 \delta/2}{n\omega_0 \delta/2}, \qquad \text{where } T = \frac{2\pi}{\omega_0}. \qquad (14\text{-}20)$$

As T is made larger the harmonics given by Eq. (14-20) come closer together and decrease in amplitude. In order to focus on the relative distribution of the harmonics we will multiply c_n by T, and obtain a new distribution function $F(n\omega_0)$.*

---

* In a Fourier series the harmonics are finite and have a definite power associated with them. As $T \to \infty$ the harmonics approach zero amplitude and zero power but they still represent a finite amount of energy. $F(n\omega_0)$ is the *phasor* function, which gives the amplitude and phase distribution of these harmonics.

Here we have

$$F(n\omega_0) = T \cdot c_n = \delta \frac{\sin n\omega_0\delta/2}{n\omega_0\delta/2}. \qquad (14\text{–}21)$$

A plot of $F(n\omega_0)$ is given in Fig. 14–14. The limiting value of $(\sin x)/x$ as x approaches zero is unity. The zeros of the envelope occur when

$$\frac{\omega\delta}{2} = k\pi \qquad \text{for} \quad k = 1, 2, 3, \ldots.$$

The first zero occurs at $\omega = 2\pi/\delta$. The envelope oscillates about the zero line with a period of $4\pi/\delta$ and a gradually decreasing amplitude.

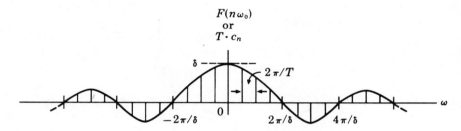

Figure 14–14. The spectrum of a single pulse.

The fundamental frequency of the Fourier series is $\omega_0 = 2\pi/T$. The components for the Fourier series are obtained by sampling the envelope waveform and dividing by the period T. As T is increased, the fundamental frequency, $\omega_0 = 2\pi/T$, decreases, the lines in the band spectrum come closer together, and the harmonic amplitudes decrease to zero. For $T \cdot c_n$ the amplitude does not decrease to zero however. It is this distribution function which is used in Fourier integral analysis. As the period approaches infinity, the sampling points come closer and closer together and the spectrum becomes more and more nearly continuous. As soon as the harmonics are so close that we cannot separate them, we use the envelope and say that the "line" spectrum of the Fourier series has become the "band" spectrum of a Fourier integral.

In the general case the complex Fourier series is

$$f(t) = \sum_{n=-\infty}^{\infty} c_n e^{jn\omega_0 t}, \qquad (14\text{–}22)$$

with

$$c_n = \frac{1}{T} \int_{-T/2}^{T/2} f(t)e^{-jn\omega_0 t}\, dt. \qquad (14\text{–}23)$$

The phasor distribution function $F(n\omega_0)$ is

$$F(n\omega_0) = c_n T = \int_{-T/2}^{T/2} f(t)e^{-jn\omega_0 t}\,dt, \qquad (14\text{–}24)$$

and in terms of it the Fourier series is

$$f(t) = \sum_{n=-\infty}^{\infty} \frac{F(n\omega_0)}{T}\, e^{jn\omega_0 t}. \qquad (14\text{–}25)$$

When we let the period approach infinity, the frequency, ω_0, of the fundamental becomes $\Delta\omega$. We do not let it become zero, because we want to think of some high harmonic, given by $n\omega_0$ as occurring at a finite frequency ω. The period of this harmonic is approaching zero, but we can let the number of harmonics approach infinity. A further consequence of the limiting process is that the summation in Eq. (14–25) becomes an integral. In summary,

$$T \to \infty,$$

$$\omega_0 = 2\pi/T \to \Delta\omega \to d\omega,$$

$$n\,\Delta\omega \to \omega,$$

and Eqs. (14–24) and (14–25) become

$$F(\omega) = \int_{-\infty}^{\infty} f(t)e^{-j\omega t}\,dt, \qquad (14\text{–}26)$$

$$f(t) = \int_{-\infty}^{\infty} \frac{F(\omega)}{2\pi}\, e^{j\omega t}\, \omega_0$$

$$= \frac{1}{2\pi} \int_{-\infty}^{\infty} F(\omega)e^{j\omega t}\,d\omega. \qquad (14\text{–}27)$$

Equations (14–26) and (14–27) are the *Fourier transforms.** Equation (14–26) tells us how to find the harmonic components or the frequency components of a single transient pulse. Equation (14–27) expresses a time function as an infinite sum of infinitesimal harmonics. The amplitude of a frequency component is $F(\omega)\,d\omega/2\pi$. Since the sinusoidal wave is made up of two exponential terms, the sine-wave terms have amplitudes of twice this value. Further-

---

* Some authors call $F(\omega)$ *the* Fourier transform. We prefer to call $F(\omega)$ the direct transform and $f(t)$, in Eq. (14–27), the inverse transform. The factor 2π is treated differently by some authors. Equations (14–26) and (14–27) follow Laplace transform practice.

more, the phase of the harmonic term is given by the angle of $F(\omega)$, considered as a phasor at that frequency.

The transform which gives the frequency components in terms of the time integral is called the *direct transform*. In practice, it is somewhat more important than the other or *inverse transform*.

As an example of the resolution of a pulse into its Fourier components, let us return to the square wave of Fig. 14–15. The direct transform, or frequency spectrum, of the pulse is given by

$$F(\omega) = \int_{-\infty}^{\infty} f(t)e^{-j\omega t}\, dt = \int_{-\delta/2}^{\delta/2} e^{-j\omega t}\, dt$$

$$= \left[\frac{e^{-j\omega t}}{-j\omega}\right]_{-\delta/2}^{\delta/2} = \frac{e^{j\omega\delta/2} - e^{-j\omega\delta/2}}{j\omega}$$

$$= 2\frac{\sin \omega\delta/2}{\omega} = \delta\frac{\sin \omega\delta/2}{\omega\delta/2}. \qquad (14\text{–}28)$$

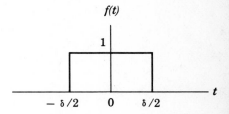

Figure 14–15. A single pulse.

The "Fourier series" for the pulse of Fig. 14–15 is now a Fourier integral:

$$f(t) = \int_{-\infty}^{\infty} 2\frac{\sin \omega\pi/2}{2\omega\pi}\, d\omega e^{j\omega t}.$$

The exponential terms combine in pairs to give real cosines with zero phase angle and amplitudes of

$$2\frac{\sin \omega\pi/2}{\pi\omega}\, d\omega.$$

Between $t = -\delta/2$ and $t = +\delta/2$ the infinitesimal cosine waves are sufficiently in phase to add up to the pulse. Beyond these points they are completely out of phase and add up to zero!

It should be observed that the Fourier integral spectrum as given by Eq. (14–28) is the envelope of the Fourier series spectral distribution curve $T \cdot c_n$ as given by Eq. (14–21).

Cosine and sine transforms. The complex integrals for the Fourier transforms can be replaced by real integrals for computational purposes.

First, let us look at the direct transform,

$$F(\omega) = \int_{-\infty}^{\infty} f(t)e^{-j\omega t}\, dt.$$

If the function $f(t)$ is zero for negative t, we can take advantage of the even- and odd-function symmetry of the cosine and sine functions. We resolve $f(t)$ into two functions. For t greater than zero,

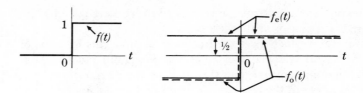

Figure 14-16. Even and odd functions of time.

each of them will be equal to one-half of $f(t)$. Thus together they add up to give $f(t)$. For t negative, however, they must add up to zero. Hence one of the functions is taken to be even, and the other odd. A resolution of a time function into even and odd components is shown in Fig. 14-16. Analytically, we write

$$f(t) = f_e(t) + f_o(t),$$

where $f_e(t)$ is an even function of t equal to $f(t)/2$ for $t > 0$, and $f_o(t)$ is an odd function of t equal to $f(t)/2$ for $t > 0$. In terms of the even and odd functions of time,

$$F(\omega) = \int_{-\infty}^{\infty} \{[f_e(t) + f_o(t)](\cos \omega t - j \sin \omega t)\}\, dt$$

$$= \int_{-\infty}^{\infty} [f_e(t) \cos \omega t - jf_o(t) \sin \omega t + f_o(t) \cos \omega t$$
$$- jf_e(t) \sin \omega t]\, dt. \qquad (14\text{-}29)$$

The product of an even function by an even function is even; the product of an odd function by an odd function is even; and the product of an odd and an even function is odd. Thus the first two integrals in Eq. (14-29) are even and the second two are odd. The integral of an odd function over all time is zero and the integral of an even function over all time is twice the value of the integral from zero to infinity. Accordingly, we obtain

$$F(\omega) = 2\int_{0}^{\infty} [f_e(t) \cos \omega t - jf_o(t) \sin \omega t]\, dt.$$

For the particular case of $f(t) = 0$ for t less than zero,

$$f_e(t) = f_o(t) = \frac{f(t)}{2} \qquad \text{for } t > 0,$$

and

$$F(\omega) = \int_{0}^{\infty} f(t) \cos \omega t\, dt - j\int_{0}^{\infty} f(t) \sin \omega t\, dt. \qquad (14\text{-}30)$$

The real part of $F(\omega)$ is the cosine transform, and the imaginary part is the sine transform. As an example of the use of the formula of Eq. (14–30), we will compute the Fourier transform of a step function. We let

$$f(t) = u_{-1}(t).$$

Then

$$F(\omega) = \int_0^\infty \cos \omega t \, dt - j \int_0^\infty \sin \omega t \, dt$$

$$= \left[\frac{\sin \omega t}{\omega}\right]_0^\infty - j \left[\frac{-\cos \omega t}{\omega}\right]_0^\infty. \qquad (14\text{–}31)$$

Strictly speaking Eq. (14–31) does not converge. If we view it as a limiting case, we can neglect the values at infinity. The first integral is zero and the second gives

$$F(\omega) = \frac{-j}{\omega} = \frac{1}{j\omega}. \qquad (14\text{–}32)$$

A similar set of simplifications can be effected in the inverse transformation. The general expression for the inverse transform is

$$f(t) = \frac{1}{2\pi} \int_{-\infty}^\infty F(\omega) e^{j\omega t} \, d\omega. \qquad (14\text{–}33)$$

The function $F(\omega)$, as can be seen from Eq. (14–30), has a real and an imaginary part. The real part is an even function of ω, since the ω term enters only in the cosine. The imaginary part is an odd function of ω, since the ω term enters only in the sine term. Thus

$$F(\omega) = R(\omega) + jI(\omega),$$

where $R(\omega)$ is an even function of ω, and $I(\omega)$ is an odd function of ω. Equation (14–33) can now be written in the form

$$f(t) = \frac{1}{2\pi} \int_{-\infty}^\infty \{[R(\omega) + jI(\omega)](\cos \omega t + j \sin \omega t)\} \, d\omega$$

$$= \frac{1}{2\pi} \int_{-\infty}^\infty [R(\omega) \cos \omega t - I(\omega) \sin \omega t] \, d\omega$$

$$+ j\frac{1}{2\pi} \int_{-\infty}^\infty [R(\omega) \sin \omega t + I(\omega) \cos \omega t] \, d\omega.$$

Since $f(t)$ is a real function, the second integral must vanish, and since both terms in the first integral are even functions of ω, we can write

$$f(t) = \frac{1}{\pi} \int_0^\infty [R(\omega) \cos \omega t - I(\omega) \sin \omega t] \, d\omega. \qquad (14\text{–}34)$$

One further simplification is possible if the function $f(t)$ is zero for t less than zero. The first integral in Eq. (14–34) is an even function of t, and the second integral is an odd function of t. If the function of t is to vanish for t negative, the even and the odd portions must be equal for t greater than zero. Hence either the cosine integral or the sine integral may be used to obtain $f(t)$:*

$$f(t) = \frac{2}{\pi} \int_0^\infty R(\omega) \cos \omega t \, d\omega = \frac{-2}{\pi} \int_0^\infty I(\omega) \sin \omega t \, d\omega. \qquad (14\text{–}35)$$

As an example of the use of Eq. (14–35) we will obtain the inverse transformation of the function $F(\omega)$ for the unit step, as obtained in Eq. (14–32). We let

$$F(\omega) = \frac{1}{j\omega} = \frac{-j}{\omega}.$$

Then

$$f(t) = \frac{-2}{\pi} \int_0^\infty I(\omega) \sin \omega t \, d\omega = \frac{-2}{\pi} \int_0^\infty \frac{-\sin \omega t}{\omega} \, d\omega.$$

This integral is tabulated. It has a value of $-\pi/2$ for $t > 0$. Hence

$$f(t) = \left(-\frac{2}{\pi}\right) \times \left(-\frac{\pi}{2}\right) = 1 \qquad \text{for } t > 0.$$

14–4 The Laplace transform

All real physical periodic functions can be expanded in Fourier series, and similarly all real physical pulses can be expanded in Fourier integrals. In some cases, however, we want to use idealized pulses which last forever. The unit step function is one such pulse. The Fourier integral does not converge for a pulse which is finite at $t = \infty$. Because of their utility, we would like to be able to include these pulses in our Fourier analysis. We will never be able to expand them in steady-state sine waves, but we may be able to expand them in a similar type of series using rising sine waves. Mathematically, it is very easy to obtain rising sine waves from undamped sine waves. We simply replace the usual exponential frequency variable $e^{j\omega t}$ by e^{st}, where $s = \sigma + j\omega$. When we make this substitution in the integral series we obtain the complex Fourier transform, which is often known as the *Laplace transform*. Naturally enough we pay some price for the convergence which we obtain. If we select a value of σ to make our integrals converge for positive

---

* For the singularity functions $R(\omega)$ is apparently zero, but it can be shown to contain an impulse, so that both integrals still hold.

values of time, they will grow infinitely large for negative values of time. Fortunately, many problems start at $t = 0$, and we are not interested in investigating the functions for negative time. For such problems the convergence factor in the Laplace transform is very useful.

An example of a pulse which cannot be expanded directly in a Fourier series is the unit step $f(t) = u_{-1}(t)$. The formal transform for the frequency components is

$$F(\omega) = \int_{-\infty}^{\infty} f(t)e^{-j\omega t}\, dt = \int_{0}^{\infty} e^{-j\omega t}\, dt$$

$$= \int_{0}^{\infty} (\cos \omega t - j \sin \omega t)\, dt. \qquad (14\text{–}36)$$

Neither the real nor the imaginary integral in Eq. (14–36) converges at $t = \infty$. The integral under a sinusoidal wave will vary from zero to $2/\omega$, depending on where the integration is stopped. Infinity gives us no information on where to stop. Similar troubles occur with most functions which have values over an infinite range.

If we decide to settle for a resolution into rising sine waves instead of undamped sine waves, we need merely to change the $j\omega$ in Eq. (14–36) to $\sigma + j\omega = s$. Formally, then,

$$F(s) = \int_{0}^{\infty} f(t)e^{-st}\, dt = \int_{0}^{\infty} e^{-st}\, dt$$

$$= \left[\frac{e^{-st}}{-s}\right]_{0}^{\infty} = \left[\frac{e^{-\sigma t}e^{-j\omega t}}{-(\sigma + j\omega)}\right]_{0}^{\infty}. \qquad (14\text{–}37)$$

The expression of Eq. (14–39) converges at infinity for any value of σ greater than zero, and we are left with

$$F(s) = \frac{1}{s}. \qquad (14\text{–}38)$$

Equation (14–38) gives us the value of the coefficients in the series of rising sine waves into which we can resolve the unit step function. Its generality is perhaps a little frightening! We can pick any damping constant we like, provided it is greater than zero, and Eq. (14–38) will give us the corresponding series.

The boundary on the value of σ above which we must go in order to obtain a convergent series is called *the abscissa of absolute convergence* of the function. For the unit step function, the abscissa of absolute convergence is zero. A list of the values which would be obtained if we integrated other functions is given in Table 14–3. For the function e^{-at} the abscissa of absolute convergence is negative. This function decays to zero by itself and presents no con-

TABLE 14–3

ABSCISSAE OF ABSOLUTE CONVERGENCE

$f(t)$	Abscissa of absolute convergence
$u_{-1}(t)$	0
$(\sin \omega t)u_{-1}(t)$	0
e^{-at}	$-a$
e^{at}	$+a$
e^{t^2}	None

vergence problems for a Fourier series. Not only can it be expanded in a summation of undamped sine waves, but even in a series of damped sine waves, up to a damping constant of a. On the other hand the function e^{at} does present convergence problems for the Fourier summation. It cannot be expanded in a summation of undamped sine waves. The waves must be positively damped, or increasing, with a damping constant of at least $+a$. As the last function in Table 14–3 shows, it may not be possible to expand a function in damped sine waves under any conditions. Such functions are rather rare and never occur in physical problems.

We will summarize the foregoing discussion by writing down the transforms for complex frequency:

$$F(s) = \int_0^\infty f(t)e^{-st}\, dt, \tag{14-39}$$

$$f(t) = \frac{1}{2\pi} \int_C F(\sigma + j\omega)e^{(\sigma + j\omega)t}\, d\omega. \tag{14-40}$$

Equation (14–39) has limits which run only from zero to plus infinity. It is assumed that the function $f(t)$ is either zero, or at least of no interest, for negative time. It is necessary to cut off the function at zero, in this way, in order to avoid convergence problems at $t = -\infty$. Equation (14–40) represents a summation of damped sine waves with a damping constant σ and a radian frequency ω. The contour C along which the integration should be carried out can be described as having a constant value of σ and a value of frequency running from $-\infty$ to $+\infty$. Since σ is a constant, the derivative of $s = \sigma + j\omega$ is $j\, d\omega$ and the integral of Eq. (14–40) can be written

$$f(t) = \frac{1}{2\pi j} \int_{-j\infty + \sigma_C}^{+j\infty + \sigma_C} F(s)e^{st}\, ds. \tag{14-41}$$

The path of integration of Eq. (14–41) is along a line parallel to the $j\omega$ axis and displaced from it by the abscissa of absolute convergence σ_C.

An integration or summation along the $j\omega$ axis in Fig. 14–17 would result in the usual Fourier components, or a series in terms of un-damped sine waves. An integration along a path to the left of the $j\omega$ axis, such as path B, represents a summation of damped sine waves. In general, a function must be zero, or must converge rapidly, at infinity to be representable by such a sum. An integration along a path C to the right of the $j\omega$ axis represents a summation of rising sine waves. Such a summation can represent functions which are constant at infinity, or even infinite.

The integrals of Eqs. (14–39) and (14–40) are called the *Laplace transforms*. Equation (14–39) is the direct transform. It resolves the function $f(t)$ in terms of a summation of damped sinusoids. It is a real integration and relatively easy to perform. Equation (14–41) is the inverse transform. It expresses the function as the summation of its frequency components. It is a complex integral and relatively difficult to evaluate. Usually, the direct transform is tabulated, and since there is a one-to-one correspondence between the function and its frequency components, tables are used instead of the integral for the inverse transformation.

The function $f(t)$ is said to be *in the time domain*. The function $F(s)$, which represents the frequency components of $f(t)$ resolved into some sort of Fourier summation, is said to be *in the frequency domain*. The nomenclature here is an extension of the one used for steady-state sine waves. The meaning of the abscissa of absolute convergence in the frequency domain is easy to determine. Consider for example the function $f(t) = e^{at}$. The integral for $F(s)$ is

$$F(s) = \int_0^\infty e^{at} e^{-st}\, dt$$

$$= \left[\frac{e^{(-\sigma+a)t} e^{-j\omega t}}{-(s-a)}\right]_0^\infty. \qquad (14\text{–}42)$$

Obviously, Eq. (14–42) will not converge unless σ is greater than a. Thus $\sigma = a$ is the abscissa of absolute convergence. The integral then vanishes at infinity and

$$F(s) = \frac{1}{s-a}.$$

In the frequency domain, the function becomes infinite at $s = a$. Clearly, we must avoid this point! One way of doing so is to use a damping constant which is greater than a. On the other hand, $F(s)$ is perfectly well defined for any value except $s = a$, and we can

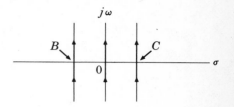

Figure 14–17. Paths for integration in the complex s-plane.

bend our contour in various ways so long as we do not pass through $s = a$, and so long as we go to the right of it eventually.* Any point where $F(s)$ goes to infinity, as at the point $s = a$ here, is called a *pole of the function.*

The meaning of a pole, or infinity, in the spectrum of an excitation function is not too difficult to discover. In a continuous (or band) spectrum the amplitudes of the individual frequency components are vanishingly small. Essentially, we are adding up an infinite number of infinitesimal harmonics, with practically no spacing between them, to form the function $f(t)$. In order to focus our attention on the distribution of the harmonics, we multiplied their amplitudes by the value of the period which we then allowed to approach infinity. If there had been any finite components in the spectrum, corresponding to lines in a line spectrum, they would likewise have been multiplied by T, and they would appear as infinities in the distribution function for the band spectrum. The meaning of the poles, or infinities, in the band spectrum is thus clear. They are line-spectrum components in the input wave. We might be encouraged to look for all these line spectral components, and to try to expand the input function in terms of a finite number of these instead of an infinite number of components in some arbitrary band spectrum.†

We will close this chapter on signal analysis by calculating one more Laplace transform, and by giving a short table of transforms for some of the most frequently occurring functions. Consider the function

$$f(t) = (\cos at)u_{-1}(t).$$

Because it is cut off for $t < 0$, the Fourier spectrum is not a simple cosine wave, and we must use the transform method. The result is a band spectrum given by

$$F(s) = \int_0^\infty \cos at \cdot e^{-st}\, dt = \int_0^\infty \frac{e^{jat} - e^{-jat}}{2} e^{-st}\, dt$$

$$= \frac{1}{2}\left[\frac{e^{(ja-s)t}}{ja - s} + \frac{e^{(-ja-s)t}}{-ja - s}\right]_0^\infty.$$

The abscissa of absolute convergence is chosen to make the integrals

---

*The selection of the best contour for integration in the complex plane is a mathematical subject which is still occupying some of the finest mathematicians of our time.

† The mathematical technique of expanding an excitation function in terms of its inherent line spectra is called the calculus of residues.

vanish for $t = \infty$. Then

$$F(s) = \frac{1/2}{s + ja} + \frac{1/2}{s - ja} = \frac{s}{s^2 + a^2}. \qquad (14\text{–}43)$$

So long as we stay away from the points in Eq. (14–43) which make $F(s) = \infty$, the function is well defined. Note that we cannot obtain a Fourier integral for this function because the poles are on the $j\omega$ axis. If we attempt an expansion with $s = j\omega$ we encounter these discontinuities. Table 14–4 lists a number of common transforms.

The method of partial fractions. Inverse Laplace transforms are almost always obtained from tables and not by direct integration. Since it is not practical to print tables containing all possible transforms, we must inquire into methods for extending the use of a small number of basic transforms. The principal tool which we will use is called the partial fraction expansion. The method of partial fractions is essentially the inverse operation of bringing terms over a common denominator. We will restrict our discussion to functions which can be expressed as the ratio of two polynomials in s:

$$F(s) = \frac{P(s)}{Q(s)}$$

$$= \cdots + b_2 s^2 + b_1 s + b_0 + \frac{a_1}{s - s_1} + \frac{a_2}{s - s_2} + \cdots.$$
$$(14\text{–}44)$$

This equation is assumed to be an identity, and therefore true for all values of s and for all similar operations performed on either side of the equation.* The terms involving the b's occurred because the numerator $P(s)$ was of higher order than the denominator. They can be removed by ordinary division until a remainder function is obtained with a numerator of lower order than the denominator. The partial fraction expansion involves the a's. If all the terms involving a are brought to a common denominator, the order of the numerator will be less than the denominator. Thus the partial fraction expansion is performed only for a function whose numerator is at least one degree less than the denominator. As an example of the removal of higher-order powers from the numerator, consider the reduction

$$F(s) = \frac{s^3 + 2s^2 + 2s + 2}{s^2 + s + 1} = s + 1 + \frac{1}{s^2 + s + 1},$$

---

* A rigorous justification of Eq. (14–44) requires some knowledge of functions of a complex variable and the calculus of residues.

TABLE 14–4

A SHORT TABLE OF
LAPLACE TRANSFORMS

$f(t)$	$F(s)$
$u_{-1}(t)$	$\dfrac{1}{s}$
e^{at}	$\dfrac{1}{s - a}$
e^{-at}	$\dfrac{1}{s + a}$
$\cos \beta t$	$\dfrac{s}{s^2 + \beta^2}$
$\sin \beta t$	$\dfrac{\beta}{s^2 + \beta^2}$
t or $u_{-2}(t)$	$\dfrac{1}{s^2}$
$u_0(t)$	1
t^n	$\dfrac{n!}{s^{n+1}}$
$e^{-at} \sin \beta t$	$\dfrac{\beta}{(s + a)^2 + \beta^2}$
$e^{-at} \cos \beta t$	$\dfrac{s + a}{(s + a)^2 + \beta^2}$

which results from the following division:

$$
\begin{array}{r}
s + 1 \\
s^2 + s + 1 \overline{\smash{\big)}\, s^3 + 2s^2 + 2s + 2} \\
\underline{s^3 + s^2 + s} \\
s^2 + s + 2 \\
\underline{s + s + 1} \\
1
\end{array}
$$

The terms involving the b's in Eq. (14–44) are removed by division. The remainder function is used to obtain the a's. We will consider first the case of no repeated roots. No restriction is made as to whether the roots are real or complex.

Case 1. No repeated roots. If there are no repeated roots and if the numerator is of lower order than the denominator, we can write $F(s)$ as

$$
\begin{aligned}
F(s) &= \frac{P(s)}{Q(s)} \\
&= \frac{a_1}{s - s_1} + \frac{a_2}{s - s_2} + \cdots + \frac{a_n}{s - s_n}.
\end{aligned} \tag{14–45}
$$

Since Eq. (14–45) is an identity, it is true for all values of s. We could select n values at random and by substituting them into the equation obtain n independent simultaneous equations for the a's. A much simpler way, however, is to evaluate each term by itself in the neighborhood of the point where the function becomes infinite. Near $s = s_1$ for example, both sides of Eq. (14–45) become infinite. The only term which contributes much on the right-hand side is the first term. Thus in the neighborhood of $s = s_1$, $F(s)$ is approximately equal to $a_1/(s - s_1)$. To exploit this fact we multiply both sides by $(s - s_1)$, and obtain

$$
\frac{P(s)(s - s_1)}{Q(s)} = a_1 + (s - s_1) \left(\frac{a_2}{s - s_2} + \cdots + \frac{a_n}{s - s_n} \right). \tag{14–46}
$$

It is clear that if we then let $s = s_1$ in Eq. (20–46), all the terms on the right side will be zero with the exception of a_1, which can then be written in the form

$$
a_1 = \left[\frac{P(s)(s - s_1)}{Q(s)} \right]_{s = s_1}.
$$

Similarly,

$$
a_n = \left[\frac{P(s)(s - s_n)}{Q(s)} \right]_{s = s}. \tag{14–47}
$$

Example. As an example of the use of Eq. (14–47) we will expand the following function $F(s)$ into partial fractions:

$$F(s) = \frac{s}{(s + 1)(s + 2)} = \frac{a_1}{s + 1} + \frac{a_2}{s + 2},$$

$$a_1 = \left[\frac{s}{s + 2}\right]_{s=-1} = \frac{-1}{1} = -1,$$

$$a_2 = \left[\frac{s}{s + 1}\right]_{s=-2} = \frac{-2}{-1} = 2.$$

Hence

$$F(s) = \frac{-1}{s + 1} + \frac{2}{s + 2}.$$

As a check

$$F(s) = \frac{-1(s + 2) + 2(s + 1)}{(s + 1)(s + 2)} = \frac{s}{(s + 1)(s + 2)}.$$

Case 2. Repeated roots. Repeated roots are never possible in a real physical problem. No two things in nature are ever quite identical. In our idealized networks, however, we may find it convenient to postulate identical roots. They can arise if we drive a circuit at exactly its resonant frequency, or if we cascade two identical networks with an ideal vacuum tube or transistor between them. We will first consider repeated roots with no other roots. Later we will extend the argument to include both repeated and nonrepeated roots. For a root $s = s_1$ which occurs k times, we write

$$F(s) = \frac{P(s)}{(s - s_1)^k}$$

$$= \frac{K_1}{(s - s_1)^k} + \frac{K_2}{(s - s_1)^{k-1}} + \cdots + \frac{K_k}{(s - s_1)}. \quad (14\text{–}48)$$

The highest-order term is easy to find. Both sides of the equation are multiplied by $(s - s_1)^k$, giving

$$P(s) = K_1 + K_2(s - s_1) + \cdots + K_k(s - s_1)^{k-1}. \quad (14\text{–}49)$$

The substitution of $s = s_1$ in Eq. (20–49) gives

$$K_1 = \left[\frac{P(s)}{(s - s_1)^k} (s - s_1)^k\right]_{s=s_1}.$$

Obviously some trick must be used to obtain the other terms. We might subtract the term involving K_1, and repeat the process with the remainder. Another procedure is to differentiate both sides of Eq. (14-49), giving

$$\frac{d}{ds} P(s) = 0 + K_2 + 2(s - s_1)K_3 + \cdots + K_k(k - 1)(s - s_1)^{k-2}.$$

Now the substitution of $s = s_1$ gives

$$K_2 = \left[\frac{d}{ds} \left(\frac{P(s)(s - s_1)^k}{(s - s_1)^k} \right) \right]_{s=s_1}.$$

Since the process can be repeated, the next term is

$$K_3 = \frac{1}{2!} \left[\frac{d^2}{ds^2} \left(\frac{P(s)(s - s_1)^k}{(s - s_1)^k} \right) \right]_{s=s_1},$$

and

$$K_r = \frac{1}{(r - 1)!} \left[\frac{d^{r-1}}{ds^{r-1}} \left(\frac{P(s)(s - s_1)^k}{(s - s_1)^k} \right) \right]_{s=s_1}.$$

The general term is useful in theoretical work, but in a numerical example it is easier to follow the process by which we arrived at the general term.

Example. As an example of repeated roots, consider the function

$$F(s) = \frac{s^2}{(s + 1)^3} = \frac{K_1}{(s + 1)^3} + \frac{K_2}{(s + 1)^2} + \frac{K_3}{(s + 1)}.$$

We first multiply both sides of the equation by $(s + 1)^3$, obtaining

$$s^2 = K_1 + (s + 1)K_2 + (s + 1)^2 K_3.$$

At $s = -1$,

$$K_1 = [s^2]_{s=-1} = (-1^2) = 1.$$

By differentiation,

$$2s = 0 + K_2 + 2(s + 1)K_3.$$

At $s = -1$,

$$K_2 = [2s]_{s=-1} = -2.$$

A second differentiation gives

$$2 = 0 + 0 + 2K_3,$$

from which

$$K_3 = 1.$$

In summary,

$$\frac{s^2}{(s + 1)^3} = \frac{1}{(s + 1)^3} + \frac{-2}{(s + 1)^2} + \frac{1}{(s + 1)},$$

as can be verified easily by recombining the terms. The same process can be used when there are both repeated and nonrepeated roots.

The basic transforms which occur in partial fraction expansions are given in Table 14–5. The powers of s in the table are used to transform the b terms in Eq. (14–44). They correspond to the singularity functions in the time domain. The constant term in the frequency domain is analogous to the unit impulse in the time domain.

The basic transform of the partial fraction part of Eq. (14–44) is represented by $1/(s + a)$ when there are no repeated roots, and its value in the time domain is e^{-at}. This transform occurs most frequently, and can be used to transform the majority of the terms which occur in practical problems. When there are repeated roots in the transform, the time function is multiplied by a power of t which is one less than the number of repeated roots, divided by the factorial of the same power.

Inverse transforms. Example 1. Two simple poles on the negative real axis. The first example we will consider of the inverse transformation of a function by means of partial fractions will be the simple case of two roots on the negative real axis. The function is, from the previous section,

$$F(s) = \frac{s}{(s + 1)(s + 2)} = \frac{-1}{s + 1} + \frac{2}{s + 2}.$$

The corresponding time function is

$$f(t) = -e^{-t} + 2e^{-2t}.$$

Example 2. The special case when one of the roots is at the origin. For this example we will consider the function

$$F(s) = \frac{1}{s(s + 2)} = \frac{a_1}{s} + \frac{a_2}{s + 2},$$

where

$$a_1 = \left[\frac{1}{s + 2}\right]_{s=0} = \frac{1}{2},$$

$$a_2 = \left[\frac{1}{s}\right]_{s=-2} = -\frac{1}{2}.$$

Thus

$$F(s) = \frac{1/2}{s} + \frac{-1/2}{s + 2},$$

and the corresponding time function is

$$f(t) = \tfrac{1}{2}(1 - e^{-2t}) \quad \text{for} \quad t > 0.$$

TABLE 14–5

LAPLACE TRANSFORMS USED WITH PARTIAL FRACTION EXPANSIONS

$F(s)$	$f(t)$
$\dfrac{1}{s}$	$u_{-1}(t)$
1	$u_0(t)$
s	$u_1(t)$
s^n	$u_n(t)$
$\dfrac{1}{s^2}$	$u_{-2}(t) = t$
s^{-n}	$u_{-n}(t) = \dfrac{t^{n-1}}{(n-1)!}$
$\dfrac{1}{s + a}$	e^{-at}
$\dfrac{1}{(s + a)^2}$	$e^{-at}(t)$
$\dfrac{1}{(s + a)^n}$	$e^{-at}\left[\dfrac{t^{n-1}}{(n-1)!}\right]$

Since Laplace transforms are defined only for $t > 0$, it is understood that the time functions are zero for negative t without explicitly stating the fact in each equation.

Example 3. *Imaginary roots.* A simple case involving imaginary roots is

$$F(s) = \frac{1}{s^2 + 1} = \frac{a_1}{s - j} + \frac{a_2}{s + j},$$

where

$$a_1 = \left[\frac{1}{s + j} \right]_{s=j} = \frac{1}{2j},$$

$$a_2 = \left[\frac{1}{s - j} \right]_{s=-j} = \frac{-1}{2j}.$$

We can write

$$F(s) = \frac{1/2j}{s - j} + \frac{-1/2j}{s + j}.$$

The corresponding time function is

$$f(t) = \frac{e^{jt} - e^{-jt}}{2j} = \sin t.$$

An alternative way to handle the case of complex roots is to notice that the coefficients of the complex conjugate root must be complex conjugates. Hence it is not necessary to find the second term; it will be the complex conjugate of the first term. Furthermore, the corresponding time functions are also complex conjugates, and the sum of a number and its complex conjugate is two times the real part of the number. Thus

$$f(t) = 2 \operatorname{Re} \left[\frac{e^{jt}}{2j} \right] = \sin t.$$

This second method is preferable when there is a phase angle in the coefficient a_1, because it saves a good deal of complex algebra.

Example 4. *Complex conjugate roots.* The easiest method of handling complex conjugate roots is an extension of the method just discussed. For example,

$$F(s) = \frac{1}{s^2 + s + 1}$$

$$= \frac{1}{(s + 0.5 + j0.866)(s + 0.5 - j0.866)}$$

$$= \frac{a_1}{s + 0.5 - j0.866} + \frac{a_2}{s + 0.5 + j0.866}.$$

The constants a_1 and a_2 are complex conjugates, as we can see by writing

$$a_1 = \left[\frac{1}{(s + 0.5 + j0.866)}\right]_{s=-0.5+j0.866} = \frac{1}{2j0.866},$$

$$a_2 = \left[\frac{1}{(s + 0.5 - j0.866)}\right]_{s=-0.5-j0.866} = \frac{-1}{2j0.866}.$$

The time functions are also complex conjugates, having the form

$$f(t) = \frac{1}{2j0.866} e^{-0.5t} e^{j0.866t} + \frac{-1}{2j0.866} e^{-0.5t} e^{-j0.866t}.$$

Thus the function $f(t)$ can be obtained as twice the real part of the first term. That is, we may write

$$f(t) = 2 \operatorname{Re}\left[\frac{1}{2j0.866} e^{-0.5t} e^{j0.866t}\right] = 1.15 e^{-0.5t} \sin 0.866t.$$

It can be seen from the example that it is not even necessary to find a_2. Now that we can resolve arbitrary input waveforms into sinusoidal and damped sinusoidal components we can apply them to networks using the same theory which we used for steady-state analysis. Each component of the input waveform is multiplied by the corresponding steady-state transfer function of the network, and the output component at that frequency is obtained. The summation of the output components represents the output waveform, as we shall see in the next chapter.

Summary

Fourier's theorem (normalized to base period of 2π)

$$f(t) = a_0 + a_1 \cos t + a_2 \cos 2t + \cdots$$
$$+ b_1 \sin t + b_2 \sin 2t + \cdots$$

where

$$a_0 = \frac{1}{2\pi} \int_0^{2\pi} f(t)\, dt$$

$$a_n = \frac{1}{\pi} \int_0^{2\pi} f(t) \cos nt\, dt$$

$$b_n = \frac{1}{\pi} \int_0^{2\pi} f(t) \sin nt\, dt$$

provided

$$\int_0^{2\pi} |f(t)|\, dt \qquad \text{is finite}$$

Examples of Fourier series

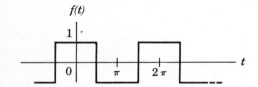

Square wave

$$f(t) = \frac{4}{\pi} \left(\cos t - \tfrac{1}{3} \cos 3t + \tfrac{1}{5} \cos 5t - \cdots \right)$$

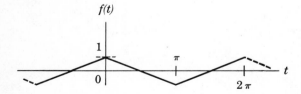

Triangular wave

$$f(t) = \frac{8}{\pi^2} \left(\cos t + \tfrac{1}{9} \cos 3t + \tfrac{1}{25} \cos 5t + \cdots \right)$$

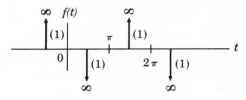

Impulse train

$$f(t) = \frac{-2}{\pi} \left(\sin t - \sin 3t + \sin 5t - \cdots \right)$$

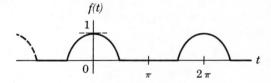

Saw-tooth wave

$$f(t) = \frac{2}{\pi} \left(\sin t - \tfrac{1}{2} \sin 2t + \tfrac{1}{3} \sin 3t - \cdots \right)$$

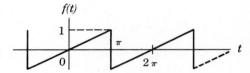

Half-wave rectified sine wave

$$f(t) = \frac{1}{\pi} \left(1 + \frac{\pi}{2} \cos t + \tfrac{2}{3} \cos 2t \right.$$
$$\left. - \tfrac{2}{15} \cos 4t + \cdots \right)$$

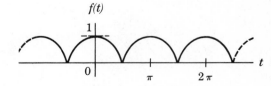

Full-wave rectified sine wave

$$f(t) = \frac{2}{\pi} \left(1 + \tfrac{2}{3} \cos 2t - \tfrac{2}{15} \cos 4t + \cdots \right)$$

Symmetry in Fourier series

1. Even function: $f(t) = f(-t)$
   (Only cosine terms)

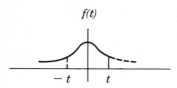

2. Odd function: $f(t) = -f(t)$
   (Only sine terms)

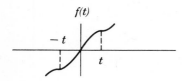

3. Rotation: $f(t) = -f(t + \pi)$
   (Only odd harmonics)

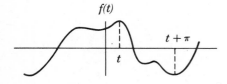

Numerical Fourier series

$$a_0 = \frac{1}{2\pi} \sum_{m=1} f(m\,\Delta t)\,\Delta t$$

$$a_n = \frac{1}{\pi} \sum_{m=1} f(m\,\Delta t) \cos(nm\,\Delta t)\,\Delta t$$

$$b_n = \frac{1}{\pi} \sum_{m=1} f(m\,\Delta t) \sin(nm\,\Delta t)\,\Delta t$$

Sampling theorem

To expose the nth harmonic of the fundamental frequency, the waveform must be sampled more than $2n$ times per period of the fundamental.

Complex Fourier series

$$f(t) = \sum_{-\infty}^{\infty} c_n e^{jn\omega_0 t} = \sum_{-\infty}^{\infty} \frac{F(n\omega_0)}{T} e^{jn\omega_0 t}$$

$$c_n = \frac{1}{T} \int_{-T/2}^{T/2} f(t) e^{-jn\omega_0 t}\,dt$$

$$F(n\omega_0) = T \cdot c_n = \int_{-T/2}^{+T/2} f(t) e^{-jn\omega_0 t}\,dt$$

Example

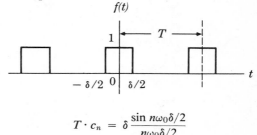

$$T \cdot c_n = \delta \frac{\sin n\omega_0 \delta/2}{n\omega_0 \delta/2}$$

Fourier integrals (Fourier transforms)

$$f(t) = \frac{1}{2\pi} \int_{-\infty}^{\infty} F(\omega) e^{j\omega t}\,d\omega$$

$$F(\omega) = \int_{-\infty}^{\infty} f(t) e^{-j\omega t}\,dt$$

Fourier sine and cosine transforms

When $f(t) = 0$ for $t < 0$

$$F(\omega) = \int_{0}^{\infty} f(t) \cos \omega t\,dt - j \int_{0}^{\infty} f(t) \sin \omega t\,dt$$

$$= R(\omega) + jI(\omega)$$

$$f(t) = \frac{2}{\pi} \int_{0}^{\infty} R(\omega) \cos \omega t\,d\omega$$

$$= \frac{-2}{\pi} \int_{0}^{\infty} I(\omega) \sin \omega t\,d\omega$$

Example

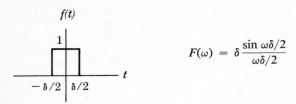

$$F(\omega) = \delta \frac{\sin \omega\delta/2}{\omega\delta/2}$$

Laplace transforms

$$f(t) = \frac{1}{2\pi j} \int_{-j\infty+\sigma_C}^{+j\infty+\sigma_C} F(s)e^{st}\, ds$$

$$F(s) = \int_0^\infty f(t)e^{-st}\, dt$$

$F(s)$	$f(t)$
1	$u_0(t)$
$\dfrac{1}{s}$	$u_{-1}(t)$
$\dfrac{1}{s^2}$	$u_{-2}(t)$ or t
$\dfrac{n!}{s^{n+1}}$	$u_{-(n+1)}t$ or t^n
$\dfrac{1}{s+\alpha}$	$e^{-\alpha t}$
$\dfrac{s}{s^2+\beta^2}$	$\cos\beta t$
$\dfrac{\beta}{s^2+\beta^2}$	$\sin\beta t$
$\dfrac{s+\alpha}{(s+\alpha)^2+\beta^2}$	$e^{-\alpha t}\cos\beta t$
$\dfrac{\beta}{(s+\alpha)^2+\beta^2}$	$e^{-\alpha t}\sin\beta t$

Repeated root transforms

$F(s)$	$f(t)$
s^n	$u_n(t)$
$1/s^n$	$u_{-n}(t) = \dfrac{t^{n-1}}{(n-1)!}$
$1/(s+\alpha)^n$	$e^{-\alpha t}\left[\dfrac{t^{n-1}}{(n-1)!}\right]$
$\dfrac{1}{(s+\alpha\pm j\beta)^n}$	$e^{-\alpha t}e^{\mp j\beta t}\left[\dfrac{t^{n-1}}{(n-1)!}\right]$

Partial fractions

(a) *No repeated roots*

$$\frac{P(s)}{Q(s)} = \frac{a_1}{s-s_1} + \frac{s_2}{s-s_2} + \cdots$$

$$a_1 = \left[\frac{P(s)}{Q(s)}(s-s_1)\right]_{s=s_1} \quad \text{etc.}$$

(b) *Repeated roots*

$$\frac{P(s)}{(s-s_1)^k} = \frac{K_1}{(s-s_1)^k} + \cdots + \frac{K_k}{(s-s_1)}$$

$$K_1 = \left[\frac{P(s)}{(s-s_1)^k}(s-s_1)^k\right]_{s=s_1}$$

$$K_r = \frac{1}{(r-1)!}\left[\frac{d^{r-1}}{ds^{r-1}}\left(\frac{P(s)(s-s_1)^k}{(s-s_1)^k}\right)\right]_{s=s_1}$$

References

In the literature there are three quite different approaches to the Fourier integral and the Laplace transform:

1. The operational calculus introduced by Heaviside.
2. The integral transform introduced by Laplace.
3. Signal analysis introduced by Fourier.

In this text we are following the signal-analysis point of view. Complex signals are resolved into their frequency components, the output response for each component is obtained, and then the total output is obtained by summing the separate components. References for the other approaches are given below.

1. VALLEY and WALLMAN, "Vacuum-Tube Amplifiers," *Radiation Laboratory Series*, Vol. 18, McGraw-Hill, New York, 1948. The first chapter of this volume presents an excellent discussion of the Laplace transform as an integral transform.

2. E. A. GUILLEMIN, *The Mathematics of Circuit Analysis*, John Wiley, New York, 1948. This volume is the standard reference for the signal-analysis point of view. It covers Fourier series and Fourier integrals but does not cover Laplace transforms.

3. V. BUSH, *Operational Circuit Analysis*, John Wiley, New York, 1929. Bush presents the Heaviside operational methods in a framework of transients in electric circuits.

4. GARDNER and BARNES, *Transients in Linear Systems*, John Wiley, New York, 1942. This popular text presents the Laplace transform from a point of view midway between that of an integral transform and that of Fourier signal analysis.

5. KERCHNER and CORCORAN, *Alternating Current Circuits*, John Wiley, New York, 3rd ed., 1951. Kerchner and Corcoran give an excellent discussion of Fourier series, complex waveforms, and symmetry conditions.

6. S. FICH, *Transient Analysis in Electrical Engineering*, Prentice-Hall, New York, 1951. Fich gives a good discussion of the Fourier series and the Fourier integral spectra, and of the relationship between them.

7. CAMPBELL and FOSTER, "Fourier Integrals for Practical Applications," *Bell System Monograph Series*, No. B-584, 1931. In addition to the theory of the Fourier integral, Campbell and Foster give an extensive table of transforms.* A reprint (D. Van Nostrand, New York, 1950) is also available.

8. M. SCHWARTZ, *Information Transmission, Modulation, and Noise*, McGraw-Hill, New York, 1959. In order to treat noise and random signals Schwartz develops the Fourier integral at some length, including power and energy.

---

* These tables and many others in the literature include a factor of 2π which does not appear in our table of Fourier transforms, which we have normalized to agree with the more common Laplace transforms.

Exercises

SECTION 14–2

1. (a) Find the Fourier series for the waveform of Fig. 14–18. (b) If the period of the waveform in Fig. 14–18 is 1μ sec, instead of 2π sec, what is the Fourier series?

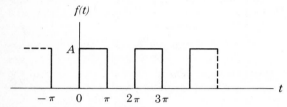

Figure 14–18

2. (a) Find the Fourier series for the waveform of Fig. 14–19. (b) If the period of the waveform in Fig. 14–19 is 100 sec instead of 2π sec, what is the Fourier series?

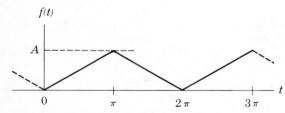

Figure 14–19

3. The impulse train shown in Fig. 14–20 is important in the theory of Class C amplifiers and in many modulation problems. Find its Fourier series, and show that each frequency component is present with the same strength. Comment on the convergence.

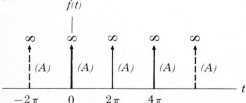

Figure 14–20

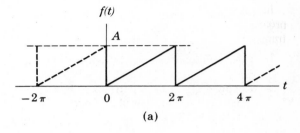

(a)

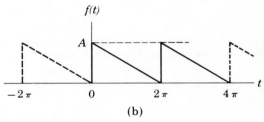

(b)

Figure 14–21

4. The waveforms of Fig. 14–21 are used as "sweeps" in radar and television circuits. Find the Fourier series, and compare them.

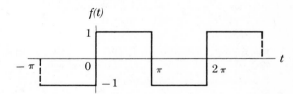

Figure 14–22

5. Sketch the integral from 0 to t of the waveform in Fig. 14–22 and also sketch the derivative of the waveform. Find the Fourier series for each of the three waveforms. Show that the original function has terms which decrease in amplitude as $1/n$, where n is the order of the harmonic; that the integral waveform has terms which decrease in amplitude as $1/n^2$; and that the derivative has terms which remain of the same order of magnitude out to the nth harmonic.

6. The waveform of Fig. 14–23 exists in the region from $t = 0$ to $t = \pi$. Complete the waveform over

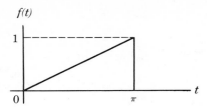

Figure 14–23

a period of 2π and write the Fourier series if (a) $f(t)$ is an even function and (b) $f(t)$ is an odd function.

7. The waveform of Fig. 14–24 has quarter-wave symmetry and hence the Fourier series is of the form

$$f(t) = a_1 \cos t + a_3 \cos 3t + a_5 \cos 5t + \cdots.$$

The wave is sampled every $30°$ $(\Delta t = \pi/6)$ starting at $t = \pi/6$. The sampled wave has half-wave symmetry, but not quarter-wave symmetry. Hence

$$a_1 = \frac{2}{\pi} \sum_{m=1}^{6} f(m\,\Delta t) \cos\,(m\,\Delta t)\,\Delta t,$$

and so on. Find a_1 and a_3 by approximate numerical integration.

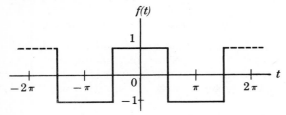

Figure 14–24

8. Use 24 sampling points per period and take advantage of the symmetry to find the first three harmonics of the waveform in Fig. 14–25.

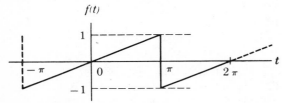

Figure 14–25

SECTION 14–3

9. In the waveform of Fig. 14–26 the period T has been increased from its normalized value of 2π, but the width of the pulse has been left at the original value of δ. Find the complex Fourier series for this waveform. Sketch the amplitude and phase spectra of c_n for $T = 2\delta$, 5δ, and 10δ. For each of the above cases sketch also the spectra of $c_n \times T$.

Figure 14–26

10. (a) Find the Fourier integral of a single pulse of the waveform of Fig. 14–26. Sketch the magnitude and the phase of the frequency distribution function $F(\omega)$ for $\delta = 1$ sec and for $\delta = 1\mu$ sec. (b) What bandwidth is required in a circuit to pass all the frequency components in the waveforms of part (a) out to the first zero in the spectrum, for $\delta = 1$ sec and for $\delta = 1\mu$ sec. (c) A criterion often used for the bandwidth required to pass a pulse is $f_0 = 2/\delta$, where f_0 is the bandwidth (in cycles) required and δ is the width of the pulse in seconds. How much of the spectrum is passed by this criterion?

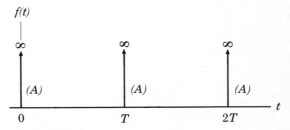

Figure 14–27

11. Find the complex Fourier series of the impulse train shown in Fig. 14–27. Sketch the line spectra of the amplitude and the phase of c_n as functions of $\omega = n\omega_0$ for $T = 1$ sec, $1/10$ sec, and $1/100$ sec. Sketch also the spectra for $c_n \times T$. Finally, obtain the Fourier integral of a single impulse and compare its spectra with those of $c_n \times T$.

12. (a) Find the complex Fourier series for the waveform of Fig. 14–28. Plot the spectra of c_n as functions of $n\omega_0$ and also plot $c_n \times T$. (b) Find the Fourier integral for a single pulse of the waveform of Fig. 14–28. Sketch the amplitude and phase spectra.

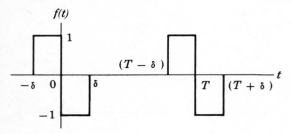

Figure 14–28

13. Find the Fourier transforms for each of the functions shown in Fig. 14–29. Show that the time functions in parts (b) and (c) are the even and odd parts of the time function in part (a), and that the sum of the Fourier transforms for parts (b) and (c) gives the transform of part (a).

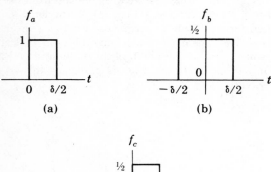

(a)   (b)

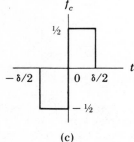

(c)

Figure 14–29

14. (a) Show that for an even function the Fourier transform will be a pure real number. Evaluate the transform of the function shown in Fig. 14–30.

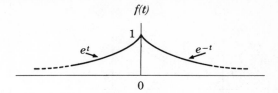

Figure 14–30

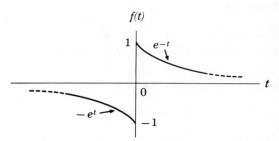

Figure 14–31

(b) Show that for an odd function of time the Fourier transform is a pure imaginary quantity. Find the Fourier transform for the function shown in Fig. 14–31.

15. A Fourier transform is given by $F(\omega) = 1/(1 + \omega^2)$. Show that the corresponding time function is an even function of t, and find an analytic expression for it. Sketch the function.

16. A Fourier transform is given by $F(\omega) = -j\omega/(1 + \omega^2)$. Show that the corresponding time function is an odd function of t, and find an analytic expression for it. Sketch the function.

SECTION 14–4

17. For the following functions of time which are all zero for $t < 0$ (a) give the abscissa of absolute convergence, (b) find the Laplace transform, and (c) give the poles of the transform in the frequency domain.

(i) $f(t) = \sin \beta t$ (ii) $f(t) = e^{-\alpha t} \sin \beta t$
(iii) $f(t) = te^{-\alpha t} \sin \beta t$ (iv) $f(t) = te^{\alpha t}$
(v) $f(t) = (1 - \cos \beta t)$

18. The following functions of time are zero for negative values of t. For each function find (a) the abscissa of absolute convergence, (b) the Laplace transform, and (c) the poles of the transform.

(i) $(1 - e^{-\alpha t})$

(ii) $\sinh \beta t$

(iii) $\cosh \beta t$

(iv) $\sin (\beta t + \theta)$

(v) $\cos (\beta t + \theta)$

19. Find the abscissa of absolute convergence and the Laplace transform of each of the following functions ($\alpha < \beta$).

(a) a^t

(b) $\dfrac{e^{-\alpha t} - e^{-\beta t}}{t}$

(c) $\sin \beta t / t$

(d) e^{t^2}

20. For the function sketched in Fig. 14–32: (a) Find the Laplace transform. (b) Find the abscissa of absolute convergence. (c) Find the poles in the complex frequency domain.

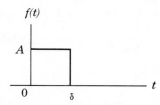

Figure 14–32

21. Expand the following functions into partial fraction form and verify the result by recombination of the terms:

(a) $F(s) = \dfrac{1}{s(s + 1)(s + 2)}$,

(b) $F(s) = \dfrac{s^3 + 3s^2 + 2s + 1}{s^3 + 3s^2 + 2s}$,

(c) $F(s) = \dfrac{s^3}{s^3 + 6s^2 + 11s + 6}$,

(d) $F(s) = \dfrac{s}{s^2 + s + 1}$,

(e) $F(s) = \dfrac{s^4 + s^3 + s^2 + s + 1}{s^2 + s + 1}$.

22. Find a partial fraction for the following functions in which the numerator of each term is a constant:

(a) $F(s) = \dfrac{s}{(s + 1)^3}$,

(b) $F(s) = \dfrac{s^3}{(s + 1)^3}$,

(c) $F(s) = \dfrac{s^2 + 2}{(s + 1)(s + 2)^2}$,

(d) $F(s) = \dfrac{s}{(s^2 + 2s + 2)^2}$,

(e) $F(s) = \dfrac{s}{(s + 1)(s^2 + 2s + 2)^2}$.

23. Find the inverse transforms of

(a) $F(s) = \dfrac{1}{s(s + 1)(s + 2)}$,

(b) $F(s) = \dfrac{s}{s^2 + 1}$,

(c) $F(s) = \dfrac{s}{s^2 + s + 1}$,

(d) $F(s) = \dfrac{s}{(s + 1)^3}$.

24. Using the method of partial fractions verify the following Laplace-transform pairs:

(a) $\dfrac{1}{(s + a)(s + b)(s + c)} \sim \dfrac{e^{-at}}{(b - a)(c - a)}$

$+ \dfrac{e^{-bt}}{(a - b)(c - b)} + \dfrac{e^{-ct}}{(a - c)(b - c)}$,

(b) $\dfrac{1}{s(s^2 + 2as + \omega^2)} \sim \dfrac{1}{\omega^2}$

$+ \dfrac{1}{\beta\omega} e^{-at} \sin (\beta t - \theta)$,

where

$\beta^2 = \omega^2 - a^2$ and $\theta = \tan^{-1} \beta/-a$,

(c) $\dfrac{1}{s^2(s + a)} \sim \dfrac{e^{-at} + at - 1}{a^2}$,

(d) $\dfrac{1}{s^2(s^2 + \beta^2)} \sim \dfrac{t}{\beta^2} - \dfrac{\sin \beta t}{\beta^3}$,

(e) $\dfrac{s^2}{(s^2 + \beta^2)^2} \sim \dfrac{1}{2\beta} (\sin \beta t + \beta t \cos \beta t)$.

Problems

1. (a) Find the Fourier series for the full-wave rectified sine wave shown in Fig. 14–33. (b) Find the Fourier series of the half-wave rectified sine wave shown in Fig. 14–34.

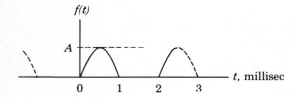

Figure 14–33

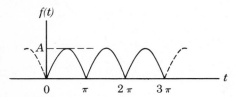

Figure 14–34

2. Convergence problems occur because of the idealized nature of the impulse function. The pulse train shown in Fig. 14–35 is more representative of the waveform which could be generated in a physical problem. (a) Show that the Fourier series for this waveform is

$$f(t) = \frac{\delta E}{2\pi} + \frac{\delta E}{\pi} \sum_{n=1,2,3\ldots}^{\infty} \left(\frac{\sin n\delta/2}{n\delta/2}\right) \cos nt.$$

(b) Show that for large n this series converges more rapidly than the known convergent series $(1 - \frac{1}{2} + \frac{1}{3} - \frac{1}{4} + \frac{1}{5} + \cdots)$. (c) What hap-

pens as E approaches infinity and δ approaches zero leaving a constant area under the impulse?

3. Sketch periodic functions over a range of one period when the Fourier series of the functions have the following properties:
(a) Only sine terms, but all harmonics present.
(b) Only cosine terms, but all harmonics present.
(c) Only odd sine terms present.
(d) Only odd cosine terms present.
(e) Only odd harmonics, but both sine and cosine terms present.
(f) Only even harmonics, but both sine and cosine terms present.
(g) The odd harmonics are sines, and the even are cosines.
(h) The even harmonics are sines, and the odd are cosines.

4. The waveforms given below are not symmetrical in the form shown. Removing the dc terms and shifting the origin will expose some hidden symmetries. Discuss each case.
(a) $f(t) = 2 + \cos(t + 45°) + \sin(3t + 15°) + \cos 5t + \cdots$
(b) $f(t) = 2 + \cos(t + 45°) + \cos(3t + 135°) + \cos(5t + 225°) + \cdots$
(c) $f(t) = 2 + \cos(t + 45°) - \sin(3t + 45°) + \sin(5t - 45°) + \cdots$
(d) $f(t) = \cos(t + 15°) - \cos(2t - 150°) - \sin(3t - 45°) + \sin(4t + 150°) + \cdots$
(e) $f(t) = \cos t + \sin t + \sin 2t - \cos 3t + \sin 3t - \cos 4t + \cdots$

5. Find the complex Fourier series for the waveform of Fig. 14–36. Plot the amplitude and phase spectra as functions of positive and negative frequency. Reduce the series to a sine-cosine series.

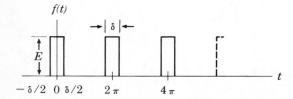

Figure 14–35

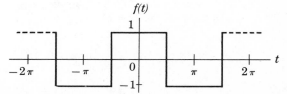

Figure 14–36

6. Find the Fourier integral of the pulse shown in Fig. 14–37. Show that if δ is allowed to approach zero, the pulse becomes a unit doublet. By letting δ approach zero in the Fourier transform, find the transform of a unit doublet function.

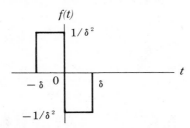

Figure 14–37

7. Whenever a constant final value of a function exists it can be obtained from the Laplace transform by the formula

$$f(\infty) = [sF(s)]_{s\to0}.$$

If there are no impulses at the origin the initial value of a function at $t = 0^+$ can be obtained from the Laplace transform according to the formula

$$f(0^+) = [sF(s)]_{s\to\infty}.$$

Verify the formulas and apply them to the following cases.

(a) $\dfrac{1}{s^2 + s + 1}$ (b) $\dfrac{s^2 + 1}{(s^2 + s + 1)s}$

(c) $\dfrac{s^2}{s^2 + s + 1}$ (d) $\dfrac{1}{s^2 + 1}$

(e) $\dfrac{s^2}{s^2 + 1}$

8. By means of a partial fraction expansion verify the following transform pairs:

(a) $\dfrac{1}{s(s + a)^2} \sim \dfrac{1}{a^2} - \dfrac{e^{-at}}{a^2}(1 + at)$,

(b) $\dfrac{(s + a)^2 - \beta^2}{[(s + a)^2 + \beta^2]^2} \sim te^{-at} \cdot \cos \beta t.$

CHAPTER 15

TRANSFORM NETWORKS AND THE s-PLANE

I often say that when you can measure what you are speaking about, and express it in numbers, you know something about it; but when you cannot express it in numbers, your knowledge is of a meager and unsatisfactory kind; it may be the beginning of knowledge, but you have scarcely, in your thoughts, advanced to the stage of a science, whatever the matter may be.

LORD KELVIN

15–1 Introduction

The "science" of electrical networks is based on the ease with which the sinusoidal network responses can be obtained in the laboratory and the generality which they possess for theoretical work. The laboratory data consists of magnitude and phase curves as functions of frequency. These curves can be used to predict the behavior of the network for any sinusoidal input function. In addition, as we have seen in the previous chapter, more general input signals can be resolved into sinusoidal components. The same network response curves predict the output from these components, and the total output is the sum of the component outputs. There are four explicit steps in the process:

Step 1. The input function is resolved into a summation of sinusoidal components. This step has been considered in detail in the previous chapter on signal analysis. It is a transformation from the time domain into the frequency domain.

Step 2. The general response of the network is obtained to sinusoids of all frequencies. In a linear system each frequency can be considered separately and the network merely changes the amplitude and the phase. Analytically the network is transformed to the frequency domain and the output phasor is computed for an input of $1 \underline{|0°}$ and a general frequency of ω.

Step 3. The output summation of frequency components is obtained by multiplying each component of the input by the appropriate amplitude and phase as found in Step 2.

Step 4. The output frequency components are summed to obtain an explicit function of time. This step represents the inverse transform which was considered in the previous chapter.

Fourier Series, Fourier Integrals, and Laplace transforms involve the same four steps. Ordinary phasor networks suffice for Fourier Series and Fourier Integrals, but transform networks must be used for Laplace transforms.

15–2 Transform networks

Laplace transforms involve a resolution of time functions into damped sinusoids. Frequency-domain phasors can be used to represent the damped sinusoids but the frequency-domain networks must be altered to encompass the damping factors.

A damped sinusoidal wave is expressed trigonometrically as

$$f(t) = |F|e^{\sigma t} \cos (\omega t + \theta). \qquad (15\text{–}1)$$

By Euler's formula we can write Eq. (15–1) in algebraic form and obtain

$$\begin{aligned} f(t) &= \mathrm{Re}\,[|F|e^{\sigma t}e^{j(\omega t+\theta)}] \\ &= \mathrm{Re}\,[|F|e^{j\theta}e^{(\sigma t+j\omega t)}] \\ &= \mathrm{Re}\,[Fe^{st}], \qquad (15\text{–}2) \end{aligned}$$

where F is a frequency-domain phasor with a magnitude of $|F|$ and an angle of θ. Thus

$$F = |F|\,\underline{/\theta}. \qquad (15\text{–}3)$$

The phasor F is identical to the phasor which would have been obtained from an undamped sine wave. The frequency variable $j\omega$, however, has been replaced by a new variable s, defined as

$$s = \sigma + j\omega. \qquad (15\text{–}4)$$

The real part of the complex frequency is a damping term, while the imaginary part is the usual angular frequency. There is nothing mysterious about a complex frequency. It is simply a convenient method of keeping track of the damping constant and the frequency in a single complex number.

Equation (15–2) represents a phasor of length $|F|$ which starts at an angle θ and rotates with an angular velocity of ω, and at the same time decays in length (for a negative value of σ). The actual damped sine wave is the projection of this rotating and decaying phasor on the real axis, as shown in Fig. 15–1. All the phasors in a given prob-

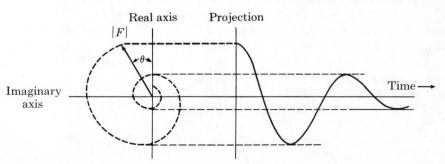

Figure 15–1. A phasor which rotates and decays in length.

lem rotate and decay at the same rate and maintain their relative positions and lengths, so that we can ignore the rotation and contraction until we wish to obtain the answer as a function of time. The "complex-frequency domain" is a combination of a merry-go-round which is rotating and an Alice-in-wonderland domain which is shrinking. *The frequency-domain calculations*, as in the case of undamped sine waves, *are performed with the phasors as they appear at $t = 0$.*

The frequency-domain networks are transformed to the complex-frequency domain by changing the frequency variable $j\omega$ to $s = \sigma + j\omega$. Resistance, inductance, and capacitance are shown in Fig. 15–2. The complex impedances are now functions of s. Thus

$$Z_R = R, \quad Z_L = Ls, \quad Z_C = 1/Cs. \quad (15\text{--}5)$$

It is, of course, a simple matter to change these impedances back to the steady-state sinusoidal form, by replacing s by $j\omega$. The form with s is simpler, however, as far as computations in the frequency domain are concerned.

As examples of the computation of response functions in terms of a complex-frequency variable, we will obtain the input impedances of the two networks in Fig. 15–3. The impedance of the series circuit of Fig. 15–3(a) is

$$Z(s) = Ls + R + \frac{1}{Cs} = \frac{L[s^2 + (R/L)s + 1/LC]}{s}, \quad (15\text{--}6)$$

and the impedance of the parallel circuit of Fig. 15–3 (b), is

$$Z(s) = \frac{1}{Cs + 1/R + 1/Ls} = \frac{s}{C[s^2 + (1/RC)s + 1/LC]}. \quad (15\text{--}7)$$

Equations (15–6) and (15–7) are examples of the response functions of networks in the complex-frequency domain. They represent the behavior of the networks of Fig. 15–3 for all frequencies and for all damping constants.

Networks in the complex frequency domain are called *transform networks*. They are used to obtain the response functions when the input time function has been transformed into the frequency domain

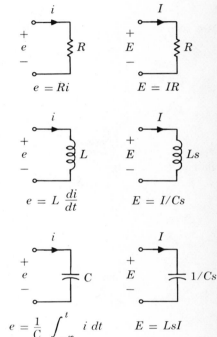

Time domain	Complex-frequency domain

$e = Ri$　　$E = IR$

$e = L\dfrac{di}{dt}$　　$E = I/Cs$

$e = \dfrac{1}{C}\displaystyle\int_{-\infty}^{t} i\,dt$　　$E = LsI$

Figure 15–2. Resistance, inductance, and capacitance in the complex-frequency domain.

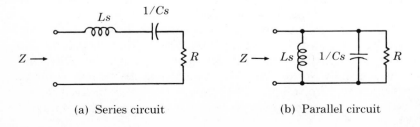

(a) Series circuit　　　(b) Parallel circuit

Figure 15–3. Impedances in the complex-frequency domain.

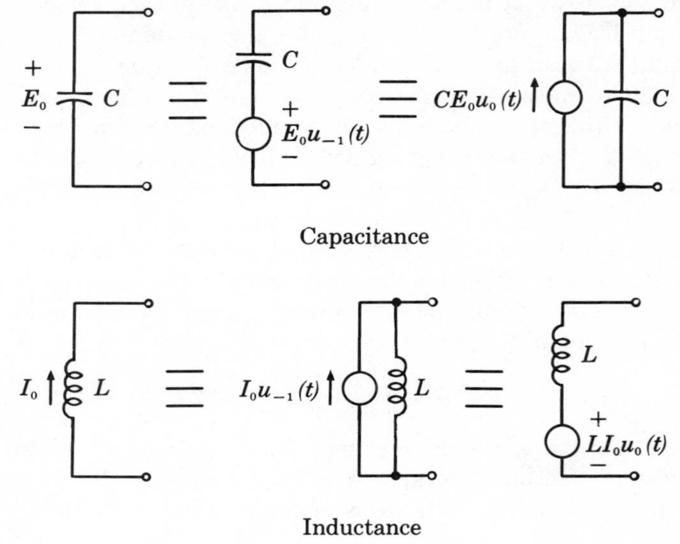

Capacitance

Figure 15-4. Equivalent networks for initial energy storage.

Inductance

by means of the Laplace transform. Transform networks are particularly simple in form and have most of the properties of resistive networks. All of the methods and theorems of resistive circuits apply directly to them.

The only new problem involves the storage of initial energy in inductances or capacitances. If we transform this energy to equivalent sources we can include them by means of superposition.

The equivalent sources for initial energy storages, as shown in Fig. 15-4, are called into being at $t = 0$. They represent the accumulated energy from the past which is present in the storage element at $t = 0$, and their presence in the circuit expresses the effect of this energy storage for $t > 0$. Since these functions are zero for negative time, they can be resolved into damped spectra by means of the Laplace transform.

The initial energy storage on a capacitance can be considered as a step source of voltage in series with the capacitance, or an impulse current source in parallel with the capacitance. Similarly, the initial energy stored in an inductance can be considered as a step current source in parallel with the inductance, or as an impulse voltage source in series with the inductance.

The frequency-domain circuits, including both sources and networks, are shown in Fig. 15-5. It is interesting to note that the two frequency-domain circuits in each case are related by Thévenin's theorem or by Norton's theorem. For example, let us apply Norton's theorem to the first frequency-domain circuit for the charged capacitor. We must compute the short-circuit current and the impedance

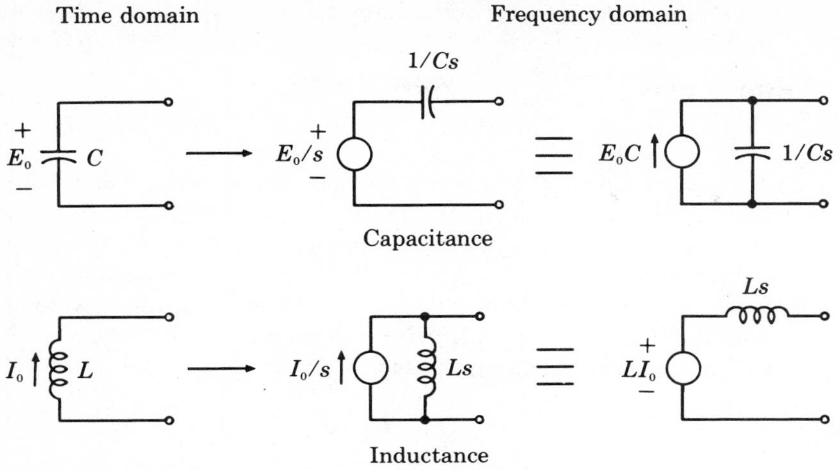

Time domain   Frequency domain

Capacitance

Inductance

Figure 15–5. Frequency-domain circuits for initial energy storage.

looking back into the network. The short-circuit current is

$$I_{\text{sc}} = \frac{E(s)}{Z(s)} = \frac{E_0}{s} \times \frac{1}{1/Cs} = E_0 C,$$

and the impedance looking back, with the voltage source shorted, is

$$Z_{\text{eq}} = \frac{1}{Cs}.$$

The short-circuit current in parallel with the network impedance is identical to the network which we would have obtained if we had transformed the impulse form of the equivalent source.

System functions. In the complex frequency domain the stimulus and the response are related by an algebraic expression which is called the system function. A time-domain circuit is shown in Fig. 15–6(a) and the corresponding frequency-domain circuit in Fig. 15–6(b). The input function $f_1(t)$ is resolved into damped sinusoids and the function $F_1(s)$ represents the corresponding phasors. The network is transformed into the complex frequency domain by replacing the elements by impedance operators, that is L becomes LS, C becomes $1/CS$, and R remains R. The output

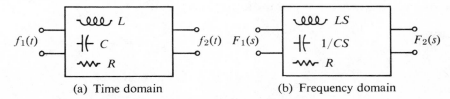

(a) Time domain   (b) Frequency domain

Figure 15–6. Frequency domain system functions.

phasor function $F_2(s)$ is computed by the ordinary rules of resistive circuits and is related to $F_1(s)$ by an algebraic expression $H(s)$, the *system function*. Thus

$$F_2(s) = H(s)F_1(s). \tag{15–8}$$

The system function $H(s)$ is characteristic of the network and is the same for all stimulus-response pairs. It expresses the amount by which the network attenuates and phase-shifts each component of the input spectrum. The function $F_2(s)$ can be computed directly from the frequency-domain network without separating its components $H(s)$ and $F_1(s)$. If $H(s)$ is desired it can be obtained by letting $F_1(s)$ be the constant phasor $1 \underline{|0°}$, since

$$H(s) = F_2(s) \qquad \text{for} \quad F_1(s) = 1 \underline{|0}. \tag{15–9}$$

Equation (15–9) expresses mathematically the fact that $H(s)$ is the frequency-response function for the network. It directs us to hold the amplitude of the input function at unity, to vary its frequency s, and to measure the corresponding output, $H(s)$. Since the frequency s is complex, we must carry out this process analytically and not experimentally.

The inverse Laplace transform of a constant is an impulse function. Hence the equivalent time-domain operation to Eq. (15–9) is the application of an impulse to the network, and the system function $H(s)$ is the Laplace transform of the impulse response $h(t)$ of the network. At times, when the interior of the network is not accessible, we may wish to obtain the system function from the impulse response. For example, the transfer functions of human operators are often obtained in this fashion. The relationships are summarized in Fig. 15–7. In the frequency domain the system function $H(s)$ connects the input and the output directly. In the time domain the relationship is much more complicated.* As an example of a system function consider the circuit of Fig. 15–8. The voltage $E_2(s)$ is given by

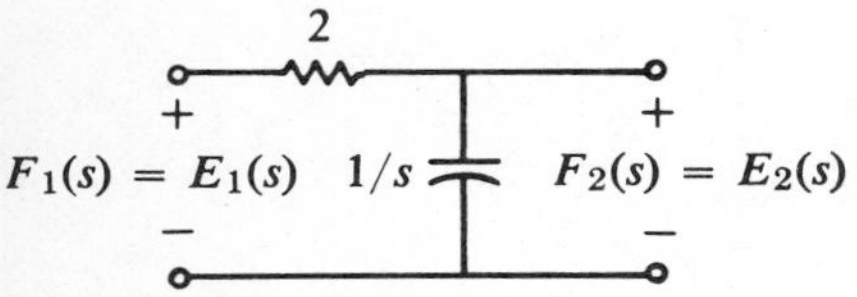

$$E_2(s) = \frac{1/s}{2 + 1/s} E_1(s),$$

and the system function is

$$H(s) = \frac{E_2(s)}{E_1(s)} = \frac{1}{1 + 2s} = \frac{1/2}{s + 1/2}.$$

$f_1(t) \circ$ ─────── $\circ f_2(t)$

$h(t)$

$H(s)$

$F_1(s) \circ$ ─────── $\circ F_2(s)$

Figure 15–7. Network system functions.

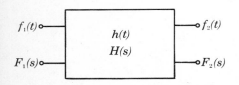

$$F_1(s) = E_1(s) \quad 1/s \quad F_2(s) = E_2(s)$$

Figure 15–8. A system function.

---

* Actually $f_2(t)$ is the convolution of $f_1(t)$ and the impulse response,

$$f_2(t) = \int_0^t f_1(t - T)h(T) \, dT.$$

The inverse transform of $H(s)$ is

$$h(t) = 1/2e^{-t/2},$$

which is also the impulse response produced at $e_2(t)$ by a unit impulse at $e_1(t)$.

15–3 Laplace transform solutions

There are four steps in the solution of a general problem by means of Laplace transforms. The process is illustrated in Fig. 15–9, and the steps are the following:

Step 1. The input time function is resolved into a sum of damped sine waves in the complex frequency domain:

$$F_1(s) = \int_0^\infty f_1(t)e^{-st}\, dt.$$

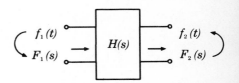

Figure 15–9. The general Laplace transform solution.

Step 2. The network transfer function $H(s)$ is obtained in the complex frequency domain ($j\omega$ is replaced by s):

$$H(s) = \frac{F_2(s)}{F_1(s)} \left[= F_2(s) \quad \text{for} \quad F_1(s) = 1 \,\underline{|0^\circ} \right].$$

Step 3. The output frequency spectrum of damped sine waves is obtained in the complex frequency domain:

$$F_2(s) = H(s) \times F_1(s).$$

Step 4. The output function is transformed back to the time domain. Tables are used or the integral:

$$f_2(t) = \frac{1}{2\pi j} \int_{-\infty + \sigma_c}^{\infty + \sigma_c} F_2(s)e^{st}\, ds.$$

Transients. *Example 1.* We will now consider an example of the Laplace method for solving a transient problem, utilizing the circuit of Fig. 15–10(a).

Step 1. The frequency spectrum of the input function is

$$F_1(s) = \int_0^\infty f_1(t)e^{-st}\, dt = \frac{1}{s} \cdot \quad \text{(See Table 14–4.)}$$

Step 2. The network response function is obtained by applying an input of $1\,\underline{|0^\circ}$ and computing the output in the frequency-domain circuit of Fig. 15–10(b). It is

$$H(s) = \frac{1\,\underline{|0^\circ}}{1 + 1/s} \times 1 = \frac{s}{s+1} \cdot$$

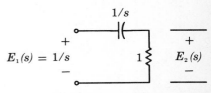

(a) Time-domain circuit

(b) Frequency-domain circuit

Figure 15–10. An example of a problem solved by the Laplace transform.

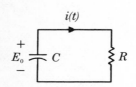

(a) Time-domain circuit

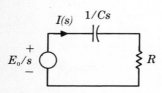

(b) Frequency-domain circuit

Figure 15–11. An R-C problem solved with the Laplace transform.

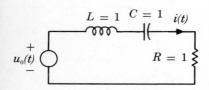

(a) Time-domain circuit

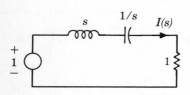

(b) Frequency-domain circuit

Figure 15–12. Two-energy-storage circuit driven by an impulse.

Step 3. The output for an input of $F_1(s)$ is

$$F_2(s) = F_1(s) \times H(s) = \frac{1}{s+1}.$$

Step 4. The time function corresponding to $F_2(s)$ is obtained from Table 14–4. It is

$$f_2(t) = e^{-t}.$$

It is worth noting that Steps 2 and 3 can be combined. Rather than finding the response for unit input and then multiplying it by the actual input, we can find the output for the actual input directly. Thus

$$F_2(s) = \frac{1}{1 + 1/s} \times \frac{1}{s} = \frac{1}{s+1}.$$

Example 2. A series R-C circuit has an initial voltage of E_0 on the capacitance. The time-domain circuit is shown in Fig. 15–11(a) and the frequency-domain circuit in Fig. 15–11(b). The current in the frequency-domain circuit, produced by the frequency-domain voltage source, is

$$I(s) = \frac{E_0}{s} \times \frac{1}{R + 1/Cs} = \frac{E_0 C}{1 + RCs}$$

$$= \frac{E_0}{R} \times \frac{1}{s + 1/RC}. \qquad (15\text{–}10)$$

The current as a function of time is obtained as the inverse transformation of Eq. (15–10). The basic transform for $1/(s + a)$ is e^{-at}. Thus the answer to our problem is

$$i(t) = \frac{E_0}{R} e^{-t/RC} \qquad \text{for} \qquad t > 0.$$

Example 3. The natural behavior of a two-energy-storage circuit is so much more complicated than that of a single-energy-storage circuit that it is often more convenient to solve it by the method of Laplace transforms than by the method of matching initial conditions which we discussed earlier. The transform solution will automatically tell us whether the circuit is overdamped, underdamped, or critically damped. As an example we will consider the series circuit of Fig. 15–12(a), which is driven by a unit impulse of voltage. The impulse source transforms to the frequency domain as a constant. The remainder of the transformed circuit is shown in Fig. 15–12(b). The current in the frequency domain is given by

$$I(s) = \frac{1}{s + 1 + 1/s} = \frac{s}{s^2 + s + 1}.$$

This function is not found in the usual short tables of transforms, and so we will use the method of partial fractions. The roots of the denominator are

$$s_1 = -0.5 + j0.866, \qquad s_2 = -0.5 - j0.866.$$

Thus

$$I(s) = \frac{s}{(s + 0.5 - j0.866)(s + 0.5 + j0.866)}$$

$$= \frac{a_1}{s + 0.5 - j0.866} + \text{conjugate},$$

where

$$a_1 = \left[\frac{s}{s + 0.5 + j0.866}\right]_{s=-0.5+j0.866}$$

$$= \frac{-0.5 + j0.866}{2j0.866}$$

$$= \frac{1\ \underline{|120° - 90°}}{2(0.866)}.$$

We can now write

$$I(s) = \frac{1/2(0.866)\ \underline{|30°}}{s + 0.5 - j0.866} + \text{conjugate},$$

and

$$i(t) = 2\,\text{Re}\left[\frac{1}{2(0.866)}\,e^{j30°}e^{-0.5t}e^{j0.866t}\right]$$

$$= \frac{1}{0.866}\,e^{-0.5t}\cos(0.866t + 30°).$$

In this example the student should note particularly the advantage of working with the polar form of the constant a_1, and of treating a_2 as the conjugate of a_1.

Combined steady-state and transient. We will now solve a problem in which a steady-state sinusoid is suddenly applied to a network at $t = 0$. The first thing we must observe is that a sinusoid which starts at $t = 0$ has a whole band of frequencies in it, and not just a single frequency. It is these components which excite the transient in the circuit. A steady-state cosine wave and a cosine wave sectioned at $t = 0$ are shown in Fig. 15–13.

Since the method of Laplace transforms does not consider a function for t negative, it cannot distinguish between the two types shown in Fig. 15–13. The steady-state cosine wave, from a Fourier point of view, represents a line spectrum and the output which it produces can be obtained by the usual methods of steady-state

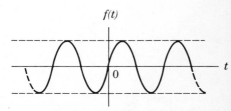

(a) Steady-state sine wave

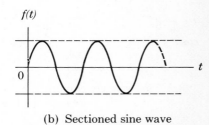

(b) Sectioned sine wave

Figure 15–13. Steady-state and sectioned sine waves.

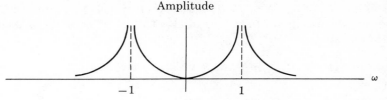

Amplitude

Figure 15-14. Amplitude spectrum for a sectioned cosine wave.

sinusoidal analysis. The sectioned wave is the only one treated by the Laplace transform. It has a transform

$$F(s) = \frac{s}{s^2 + 1}.$$

For $s = j\omega$, the function $F(s)$ is

$$F(j\omega) = \frac{j\omega}{1 - \omega^2}. \qquad (15\text{-}11)$$

The amplitude is

$$|F(\omega)| = \frac{\omega}{|1 - \omega^2|}$$

as plotted in Fig. 15-14.

The amplitude spectrum goes to infinity at $\omega = 1$. This value corresponds to the frequency of the wave, and a line spectrum at this point would be obtained if the original sinusoid ran from $-\infty$ to $+\infty$. The infinite value in the band spectrum represents a line-spectrum component, and after the transient dies out this component produces the principal response.

Let us now apply a sectioned cosine wave to a network and obtain the steady-state and transient components of the response. The network is shown in the time domain in Fig. 15-15(a), and in the frequency domain in Fig. 15-15(b). The current in the frequency domain is given by

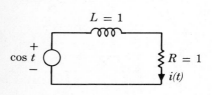

(a) Time-domain circuit

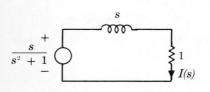

(b) Frequency-domain circuit

Figure 15-15. Circuit for steady-state and transient responses.

$$I(s) = \frac{E(s)}{Z(s)} = \frac{s}{s^2 + 1} \frac{1}{s + 1}.$$

Resolved into partial fractions, this expression becomes

$$I(s) = \frac{s}{(s + 1)(s - j)(s + j)} = \frac{a_1}{s + 1} + \frac{a_2}{s - j} + \text{conjugate},$$

where

$$a_1 = \left[\frac{s}{s^2 + 1}\right]_{s=-1} = -\tfrac{1}{2},$$

$$a_2 = \left[\frac{s}{(s + 1)(s + j)}\right]_{s=j} = \frac{j}{(1 + j)2j} = \frac{1}{2(1.414)} \underline{/-45°}.$$

Thus

$$I(s) = \frac{-\frac{1}{2}}{s+1} + \frac{1/2(1.414)\,\underline{|-45°}}{s-j} + \text{conjugate},$$

and

$$i(t) = -\tfrac{1}{2}e^{-t} + 2\,\mathrm{Re}\left[\frac{1\,\underline{|-45°}}{2(1.414)}e^{jt}\right]$$

$$= -\tfrac{1}{2}e^{-t} + 0.707\cos(t - 45°). \qquad (15\text{–}12)$$

The first term in Eq. (15–15) is the transient term. It dies out with a time constant of unity, and after about five time constants it is essentially zero. The second term is the usual steady-state response. For an input of $1\,\underline{|0°}$, the current in the frequency domain is given by

$$I(s) = \frac{1\,\underline{|0°}}{s+1} = 0.707\,\underline{|-45°}.$$

Delayed transients. All the transforms which we considered previously started at $t = 0$. It is possible to shift time functions to the right, or to delay them, and still have them exist in the region considered by the Laplace transform. Examples of time functions which have been shifted are shown in Fig. 15–16. The time expression for the delayed step function in Fig. 15–16 is

$$f(t) = u_{-1}(t - a). \qquad (15\text{–}13)$$

The time expression for the delayed sine wave is

$$f(t) = \sin(t - a)u_{-1}(t - a). \qquad (15\text{–}14)$$

Because there are a number of common waveforms which can be expressed in terms of delayed time expressions, we will find it desirable to be able to obtain the Laplace transform of functions of the sort

$$g(t) = f(t - a)u_{-1}(t - a).$$

A formal expression for the transform is

$$G(s) = \int_0^\infty f(t - a)u_{-1}(t - a)e^{-st}\,dt.$$

The unit step function in the integral ensures that the integrand is zero for $t < a$, and therefore the integration need be performed only from $t = a$ to $t = \infty$. Thus

$$G(s) = \int_a^\infty f(t - a)e^{-st}\,dt.$$

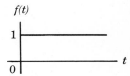

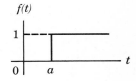

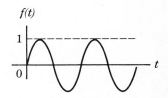

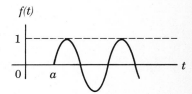

Figure 15–16. Delayed time functions.

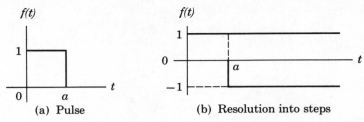

(a) Pulse   (b) Resolution into steps

Figure 15-17. A finite-width pulse.

In this integral we will now make the substitutions

$$x = (t - a), \qquad dx = dt,$$

and since $t = a$ when $x = 0$ we then obtain

$$G(s) = \int_0^\infty f(x)e^{-(a+x)s}\, dx = e^{-as}\int_0^\infty f(x)e^{-xs}\, dx.$$

The second integral is the Laplace transform of $f(t)$. The variable x is a dummy and can be changed to t without changing the value of the integral. Thus

$$G(s) = e^{-as}F(s). \tag{15-15}$$

The meaning of Eq. (15-15) is that shifting to the right by a seconds in the time domain corresponds to multiplying by the factor e^{-as} in the frequency domain.

We now make use of Eq. (15-15) to obtain the Laplace transforms of the time functions in Figs. 15-17 and 15-18. For the pulse of Fig. 15-17 the time function is

$$f(t) = u_{-1}(t) - u_{-1}(t - a).$$

The corresponding transform is

$$F(s) = \frac{1}{s} - \frac{e^{-as}}{s}. \tag{15-16}$$

For the square-wave train of Fig. 15-18 the time function is

$$f(t) = u_{-1}(t) - 2u_{-1}(t - \pi/2) + 2u_{-1}(t - 3\pi/2) - \cdots.$$

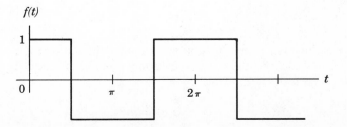

Figure 15-18. A square wave.

The corresponding transform is

$$F(s) = \frac{1}{s} - 2\frac{e^{-\pi s/2}}{s} + \frac{2e^{-3\pi s/2}}{s} - \cdots$$

$$= \frac{1}{s} - \frac{2}{s}e^{-\pi s/2}(1 - e^{-\pi s} + e^{-2\pi s} - \cdots).$$

The term within parentheses can be summed as a geometric progression. The formulas for infinite geometrical progressions can be obtained by division; that is

$$\frac{1}{1 - x} = 1 + x + x^2 + x^3 + \cdots, \qquad (15\text{–}17)$$

$$\frac{1}{1 + x} = 1 - x + x^2 - x^3 + \cdots. \qquad (15\text{–}18)$$

Using the identity of Eq. (15–18) we can write the transform of Fig. 15–18 as

$$F(s) = \frac{1}{s} - \frac{2e^{-\pi s/2}}{s(1 + e^{-\pi s})}. \qquad (15\text{–}19)$$

Now let us consider a pulse applied to an R-L circuit, as shown in Fig. 15–19(a). The current is to be found. The circuit in the frequency domain is shown in Fig. 15–19(b). The exciting function is a positive step at $t = 0$ followed by a negative step at $t = a$. The frequency-domain function is

$$E(s) = \frac{1 - e^{-as}}{s}.$$

The current in the frequency domain is

$$I(s) = \frac{E(s)}{Z(s)} = \frac{1 - e^{-as}}{s(s + 1)}. \qquad (15\text{–}20)$$

It is not possible to expand Eq. (15–20) directly into partial fractions, because the numerator is of higher order than the denominator. (The factor e^{-as} contains all powers of s from zero to infinity.) We must seek another interpretation of the transform. For this purpose we write

$$I(s) = \frac{1}{s(s + 1)}(1 - e^{-as}). \qquad (15\text{–}21)$$

Written in the form of Eq. (15–21), $I(s)$ can be interpreted as the sum of the inverse transform of the function

$$\frac{1}{s(s + 1)}$$

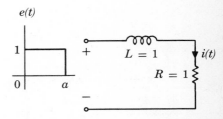

(a) Time-domain circuit

(b) Frequency-domain circuit

Figure 15–19. A pulse applied to a series R-L circuit.

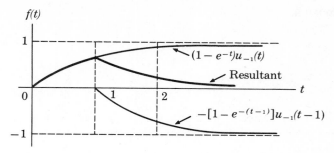

Figure 15–20. The response to a delayed step plus a step.

and the same function delayed by a seconds in the time domain. The time function is

$$i(t) = (1 - e^{-t})u_{-1}(t) - [1 - e^{-(t-a)}]u_{-1}(t - a). \qquad (15\text{–}22)$$

A sketch of Eq. (15–22) is shown in Fig. 15–20.

A second example will be given for the network of Fig. 15–21(a). The input wave can be written in the time domain as

$$e(t) = u_{-1}(t) - u_{-1}(t - 1) + u_{-1}(t - 2) - u_{-1}(t - 3) + \cdots .$$

The corresponding frequency-domain form is

$$E(s) = \frac{1}{s}(1 - e^{-s} + e^{-2s} - e^{-3s} + \cdots) = \frac{1}{s(1 + e^{-s})}.$$

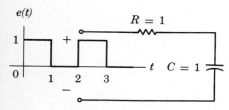

(a) Time-domain circuit

The frequency-domain current is

$$I(s) = \frac{1}{s(1 + e^{-s})} \frac{s}{s + 1} = \frac{1}{(s + 1)(1 + e^{-s})}. \qquad (15\text{–}23)$$

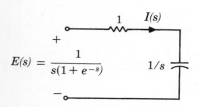

(b) Frequency-domain circuit

Figure 15–21. The square-wave response of a network.

Equation (15–23) can be interpreted in terms of Fourier series components by expanding the function in partial fraction form. The first step in this process is the determination of the roots of the denominator of $I(s)$. The first of these occurs at $s = -1$. The others occur at the roots of

$$1 + e^{-s} = 0$$

or

$$e^{-s} = -1 = e^{\pm jn\pi} = (\cos n\pi \pm j \sin n\pi) \qquad \text{for} \quad n \text{ odd}.$$

The s-values which give zeros in the denominator are

$$s = \pm jn\pi \qquad \text{for} \quad n \text{ odd}.$$

There are an infinite number of roots and therefore an infinite number of terms in the partial fraction expansion. The roots are pure imaginary, and occur in complex conjugate pairs. Each pair of roots corresponds to an undamped sine wave in the time domain, and therefore to a term in the Fourier series of the output response. The partial fraction expansion is of the form

$$I(s) = \frac{1}{(s+1)(1+e^{-s})} = \frac{a_0}{s+1} + \frac{a_1}{s-j\pi} + \text{conjugate}$$

$$+ \frac{a_3}{s-j3\pi} + \text{conjugate} + \cdots, \qquad (15\text{-}24)$$

where

$$a_0 = \left[\frac{1}{1+e^{-s}}\right]_{s=-1} = \frac{e}{e+1}, \qquad (15\text{-}25)$$

$$a_1 = \left[\frac{s-j\pi}{(s+1)(1+e^{-s})}\right]_{s=j\pi}. \qquad (15\text{-}26)$$

Equation (15-26) is indeterminate, since both numerator and denominator go to zero at $s = j\pi$. The expression can be evaluated by differentiating the numerator and the denominator before making the substitution. Thus

$$a_1 = \left[\frac{1}{(s+1)(-e^{-s}) + (1+e^{-s})}\right]_{s=j\pi}$$

$$= \frac{1}{1+j\pi} = (1+\pi^2)^{-1/2} \, \lfloor -\tan^{-1}\pi.$$

Similarly

$$a_n = [1+(n\pi)^2]^{-1/2} \, \lfloor -\tan^{-1} n\pi. \qquad (15\text{-}27)$$

The time function corresponding to Eq. (15-24) is

$$i(t) = \frac{e}{e+1} e^{-t} + 2\,\text{Re}\,[(1+\pi^2)^{-1/2} e^{j\pi t} e^{j(-\tan^{-1}\pi)}] + \cdots$$

$$= \frac{e}{e+1} e^{-t} + \frac{2}{(1+\pi^2)^{1/2}} \cos(\pi t - \tan^{-1}\pi) + \cdots$$

$$+ \frac{2}{[1+(n\pi)^2]^{1/2}} \cos(n\pi - \tan^{-1} n\pi) + \cdots. \qquad (15\text{-}28)$$

Equation (15-28) represents the sum of the transient and the steady-state responses. The first term is the transient. The remaining terms are the Fourier series terms in the output. As a check we will compute the response for the fundamental term in the Fourier series of the square wave which produced Eq. (15-28). The input voltage at the fundamental frequency has the value

$$e_1(t) = \frac{2}{\pi} \sin \pi t \qquad \text{or} \qquad E_1(s) = \frac{2}{\pi} \, \lfloor -90°.$$

The impedance at frequency $\omega = \pi$ is $1 - j/\pi$. The output current at this frequency is

$$I_1(s) = \frac{2/\pi \;\underline{|-90°}}{1 - j/\pi} = \frac{2}{1 + j\pi} \cdot$$

The corresponding time-domain expression is

$$i_1(t) = \frac{2}{(1 + \pi^2)^{1/2}} \cos(\pi t - \tan^{-1}\pi). \qquad (15\text{–}29)$$

Equation (15–29) agrees with the first term in the steady-state response of Eq. (15–28). We have thus verified the fact that the partial fraction expansion for delayed functions gives the Fourier series for the corresponding time functions.

15–4 The s-plane

The "system function" of a network relates the output frequency-domain function to the input frequency-domain function. Thus

$$F_2(s) = H(s)F_1(s), \qquad (15\text{–}30)$$

in which $H(s)$ is the system function of the network. In the analysis problem we did not find it necessary to compute $H(s)$ directly. Rather, it was easier to compute the output for the given input and to bypass the calculation of $H(s)$. Now, however, we would like to examine the $H(s)$ function. If the input and the output quantities are measured at the same pair of terminals, $H(s)$ is a driving-point admittance or impedance.

For driving-point impedances the current is the stimulus, and the voltage is the response. Some typical driving-point impedances are as follows: For the network of Fig. 15–22(a),

$$H(s) = Z(s) = Ls + R = L\left(s + \frac{R}{L}\right) \cdot$$

For the network of Fig. 15–22(b),

$$H(s) = Z(s) = R + \frac{1}{Cs} = \frac{R(s + 1/RC)}{s} \cdot$$

For the network of Fig. 15–22(c),

$$H(s) = Z(s) = R + Ls + \frac{1}{Cs} = \frac{L[s^2 + (R/L)s + 1/LC]}{s} \cdot$$

Driving-point admittances are the reciprocals of driving-point impedances, and for them the voltage is the stimulus and the current is the response.

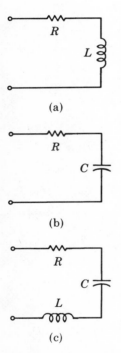

Figure 15–22. Typical driving-point impedances.

(a)

(b)

(c)

There are four types of transfer functions. If the input is a current and the output a voltage, the transfer function is an impedance. If the input is a voltage and the output a current, the transfer function is an admittance. If the input is a voltage and the output a voltage, or if the input is a current and the output a current, the ratio is dimensionless. Examples of the four types of transfer functions are shown in Fig. 15–23. The network of Fig. 15–23(a) is driven by a current source and the output is a voltage. The transfer function is an impedance given by

$$H(s) = \frac{E_2}{I_1} = \frac{R_1 R_2}{R_1 + R_2 + Ls}$$

$$= \frac{R_1 R_2}{L} \frac{1}{s + (R_1 + R_2)/L}. \qquad (15\text{–}31)$$

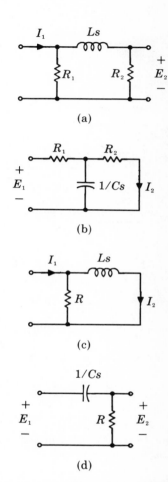

(a)

(b)

(c)

(d)

Figure 15–23. Examples of transfer functions.

The network of Fig. 15–23(b) is driven by a voltage source and the output is a current. The transfer function is an admittance given by

$$H(s) = \frac{I_2}{E_1} = \frac{1}{R_2} \frac{R_2/(1 + R_2 Cs)}{R_1 + R_2/(1 + R_2 Cs)}$$

$$= \frac{1}{R_1 R_2 C} \frac{1}{s + (R_1 + R_2)/R_1 R_2 C}. \qquad (15\text{–}32)$$

The network of Fig. 15–23(c) is driven by a current and the output is a current. The transfer function is a dimensionless ratio given by

$$H(s) = \frac{I_2}{I_1} = \frac{R}{Ls + R} = \frac{R}{L} \frac{1}{s + R/L}. \qquad (15\text{–}33)$$

The network of Fig. 15–23(d) is driven by a voltage source and the output is a voltage. The transfer function is a dimensionless ratio given by

$$H(s) = \frac{E_2}{E_1} = \frac{R}{R + 1/Cs} = \frac{s}{s + 1/RC}. \qquad (15\text{–}34)$$

From the examples which we have seen we can infer that all system functions can be written in the form

$$H(s) = \frac{K(s - s_1)(s - s_3) \ldots}{(s - s_2)(s - s_4) \ldots}, \qquad (15\text{–}35)$$

where K is a constant, $s_1, s_3, \ldots$ are the zeros of the system function, and $s_2, s_4, \ldots$ are the poles of the system function. Apart from the constant K the poles and zeros completely characterize the network, both from a transient point of view and a steady-state point of view.

Poles and zeros and the transient response. We can investigate the meaning of the poles and zeros by exciting the network with an impulse function and observing the transient response which is obtained. With impulse excitation, there is no steady-state, and the entire behavior can be classified as "transient." First, let us excite the network represented by Eq. (15–35) with an impulse. The output is

$$H(s) = \frac{K(s - s_1)(s - s_3)\ldots}{(s - s_2)(s - s_4)\ldots} = \frac{a_2}{(s - s_2)} + \frac{a_4}{(s - s_4)} + \cdots,$$

and the corresponding time function is

$$e(t) = a_2 e^{s_2 t} + a_4 e^{s_4 t} + \cdots. \qquad (15\text{–}36)$$

When the values of the poles in Eq. (15–35) are real, the transient response will contain exponential terms. When the roots are pure imaginaries, the transient response will consist of pure sine waves, and when the roots are complex the transient response will contain damped sine waves. The complex numbers representing the poles give the damping constant and the natural frequency of the transient. From this argument we conclude that the poles of a network function are the transient natural frequencies of the network.

To be more specific, let us consider a driving-point impedance function given by the following function of the complex frequency s:

$$Z(s) = \frac{A(s - s_1)(s - s_3)\ldots}{(s - s_2)(s - s_4)\ldots},$$

where $s_1, s_2, \ldots$ are the zeros, and $s_2, s_4, \ldots$ are the poles.

If we drive the impedance with the current source shown in Fig. 15–24(b) we will obtain a voltage response which is given by

$$E = \frac{IA(s - s_1)(s - s_3)\ldots}{(s - s_2)(s - s_4)\ldots}. \qquad (15\text{–}37)$$

The natural transients occur at the pole frequencies. The current source has an infinite internal impedance and is an open circuit so far as the natural transients are concerned. Hence we have shown that

the poles of the impedance function are the natural transient frequencies of the circuit with an open circuit across the terminals where the impedance is measured.

If we drive with a voltage source, as shown in Fig. 15–24(a), the current response will be

$$I = \frac{E(s - s_2)(s - s_4)\ldots}{A(s - s_1)(s - s_3)\ldots}. \qquad (15\text{–}38)$$

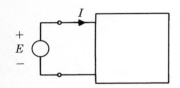

(a) Voltage source drive

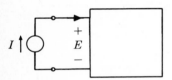

(b) Current source drive

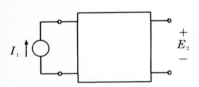

(c) Transfer impedance

Figure 15–24. Complex impedance and transient natural frequencies.

The natural transients now occur at the values of exciting frequency s given by the zeros of the original impedance function. So far as the natural transient frequencies are concerned the voltage source represents a short circuit across the terminals. We have therefore shown that

> *the zeros of the impedance function are the natural transient frequencies of the circuit with a short circuit across the terminals where the impedance is measured.*

A transfer function poses a slightly different problem. A transfer impedance of the form

$$Z_{12} = \frac{E_2}{I_1} = \frac{A(s - s_1)(s - s_3)\ldots}{(s - s_2)(s - s_4)\ldots} \qquad (15\text{–}39)$$

has poles and zeros just as a driving-point impedance does. If a current is applied at the input terminals, as shown in Fig. 15–24(c), the response E_2 is measured at the output terminals. The situation is essentially no different from the driving-point impedance so far as the poles are concerned. The natural resonant frequencies of the circuit are excited by the current source at I_1 for both cases. For the driving-point impedance the response is observed at the same pair of terminals, while for the transfer impedance it is measured at a different pair of terminals. Thus

> *the poles of a transfer impedance are the same as the poles of a driving-point impedance, and represent the natural frequencies of the network with the input terminals open-circuited.*

The zeros of the transfer function have no simple interpretation in terms of the natural transient frequencies of the network. They represent frequencies at which no output is obtained even when an input is present. They are related to the topology of the network. A series impedance which goes to infinity at the complex frequency s will produce a zero in the transfer function. Similarly, a shunt element which goes to zero at frequency s will produce a zero in the output. A bridge which is balanced at the given frequency will likewise produce a zero of transmission. Hence

> *the zeros of a transfer impedance are frequencies at which zero output is obtained, and are not related to the natural transients of the circuit.*

A similar argument would show that the poles of an admittance transfer function are the short-circuit transient natural frequencies of a network, while the zeros are simply zeros of transmission.

Poles and zeros and the steady-state response. When we replace s by $j\omega$ in a system function we obtain the usual steady-state sinusoidal response function. If the poles and zeros are plotted in the s-plane some interesting relationships appear. Consider the system function

$$H(s) = \frac{A(s - s_1)(s - s_3) \cdots}{(s - s_2)(s - s_4) \cdots}. \qquad (15\text{–}40)$$

As a function of $s = j\omega$, for steady-state sinusoidal excitation, it is

$$T(j\omega) = \frac{A(j\omega - s_1)(j\omega - s_3) \cdots}{(j\omega - s_2)(j\omega - s_4) \cdots}. \qquad (15\text{–}41)$$

The values $s_1, s_3, \ldots$ are complex numbers representing the zeros of the system function, and the values of $s_2, s_4, \ldots$ are complex numbers representing the poles of the system function. If we view the term $j\omega$ as a complex number, then each of the factors in Eq. (15–41) is simply the difference of two complex numbers. Alternatively, since complex numbers are in a one-to-one correspondence with two-dimensional vectors, each term is the difference of two vectors, which is the vector joining the tips of the two original vectors. The length of this difference vector is the magnitude of the corresponding term in Eq. (15–41), and the angle of this vector is the angle of the term in Eq. (15–41). The magnitude of the over-all response is the product of the lengths of the vectors in the numerator divided by the product of the lengths of the vectors in the denominator, and the phase of the response is the sum of the angles of the vectors in the numerator, less the sum of the angles of the vectors in the denominator. Of course, the whole calculation must be repeated for each value of ω, but a sketch of the vectors in the s-plane makes the process rather easy.

The poles and zeros are plotted in the s-plane. The poles are marked with crosses and the zeros with circles. The point $s = j\omega$ which is common to all the vectors is shown with a dot at a representative point on the $j\omega$ axis. A plot is shown in Fig. 15–25 for a typical function

$$T(j\omega) = \frac{(j\omega - s_1)}{(j\omega - s_2)(j\omega - s_4)}. \qquad (15\text{–}42)$$

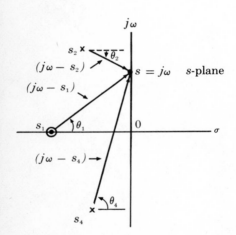

Figure 15–25. The s-plane vectors for $T(j\omega) = (j\omega - s_1)/[(j\omega - s_2)(j\omega - s_4)]$.

The magnitude of the numerator in Eq. (15–41) is the length of the vector from s_1 to the point $j\omega$. The angle of the numerator is the angle θ_1 which this vector makes with the positive axis. The magnitudes of the two terms in the denominator of Eq. (15–41) are the lengths of the two vectors from s_2 and s_4 to the point $j\omega$, and the corresponding angles are the angles θ_2 and θ_4 which the vectors make with the real axis. The over-all magnitude is the length of the numerator vector divided by the product of the lengths of the two denominator vectors, and the over-all phase angle is the numerator-vector angle minus the two angles of the denominator vectors.

The s-plane vectors do not contain any information about the constant multiplier, A, in Eq. (15–39). If the constant is known it is a simple matter to multiply by it. Alternatively, it may be given by a known value of the complete response function at some frequency.

As an example of an s-plane plot we will obtain the magnitude and phase response curves for the current in the R-L-C circuit of Fig. 15–26. As a function of the complex-frequency variable s, the impedance is

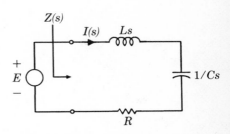

$$Z(s) = Ls + R + \frac{1}{Cs} = L\frac{s^2 + (R/L)s + 1/LC}{s}. \qquad (15\text{--}43)$$

We can put Eq. (15–43) in the standard form by factoring the numerator. Thus

$$Z(s) = L\frac{(s - s_1)(s - s_3)}{(s - 0)}, \qquad (15\text{--}44)$$

Figure 15–26. A series R-L-C circuit driven by a voltage with a complex frequency.

where

$$s_1 = -\alpha + j\omega_d,$$

$$s_3 = -\alpha - j\omega_d,$$

$$\alpha = \frac{R}{2L},$$

$$\omega_0^2 = \frac{1}{LC},$$

$$\omega_d = \sqrt{\omega_0^2 - \alpha^2}.$$

The s-plane vectors for Eq. (15–44) are plotted in Fig. 15–27. The point $s = j\omega$, which represents the frequency of the driving source, is taken to be in the vicinity of the resonant frequency s_1, and it is supposed that the circuit has a value of α which is much less than the value of ω_0. Under these assumptions, the length of the vector $(j\omega - s_1)$ is very much less than the length of the vector $(j\omega - s_3)$ or $(j\omega - 0)$. Indeed, with $j\omega$ in the vicinity of s_1, the two vectors $(j\omega - s_3)$ and $(j\omega - 0)$ are practically in the same direction, and the length of $(j\omega - s_3)$ is practically equal to twice the length of $(j\omega - 0)$. If we write

$$(j\omega - s_3) \cong 2(j\omega - 0), \qquad (15\text{--}45)$$

an approximate expression for the impedance is

$$Z(s) = 2L(j\omega - s_1). \qquad (15\text{--}46)$$

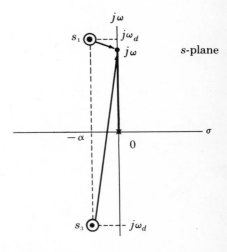

Figure 15–27. The s-plane vectors for
$$Z(s) = L\frac{(s + \alpha - j\omega_d)(s + \alpha + j\omega_d)}{s - 0}.$$

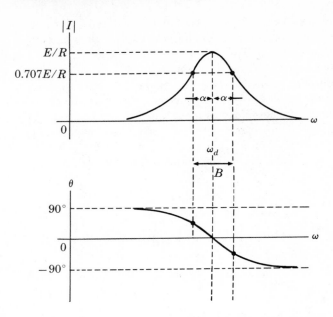

Figure 15–28. Magnitude and phase responses obtained from the s-plane vector for $I = E/[2L(s + \alpha - j\omega_d)]$.

As long as the frequency is near the resonant frequency s_1, the current will be given by

$$I = \frac{E}{2L(j\omega - s_1)}. \qquad (15\text{–}47)$$

The maximum value of current occurs when the point $s = j\omega$ is directly opposite the position of s_1. This condition is called resonance in the circuit. It occurs at a frequency of ω_d, but since α is much less than ω_0 there is very little difference between ω_0 and ω_d. The minimum length of the vector $(j\omega - s_1)$ is α, and the maximum current is

$$I_{\max} = \frac{E}{2L\alpha} = \frac{E}{R}. \qquad (15\text{–}48)$$

A sketch of the response current as a function of frequency is shown in Fig. 15–28. The current is down to 0.707 of its maximum value when the impedance is 1.414 of its minimum value. The impedance increases by 1.414 when the vector $(j\omega - s_1)$ increases by 1.414. From the geometry of Fig. 15–27 it is obvious that the vector which joins the point s_1 to the point on the $j\omega$-axis will have a value of 1.414α when it stands at an angle of $\pm45°$. One of the frequencies on the $j\omega$-axis will be below the center frequency by α, and the other will be above the center frequency by α. These two frequencies are the lower and upper half-power frequencies. At the lower half-power frequency, we find

$$(j\omega - s_1) = \sqrt{2}\,\alpha\,\underline{|-45°},$$

and

$$I = \frac{E}{2L\sqrt{2}\,\alpha\,\underline{|-45°}} = \frac{E}{\sqrt{2}\,R}\,\underline{|45°}. \qquad (15\text{–}49)$$

At the upper half-power frequency, we find

$$(j\omega - s_1) = \sqrt{2}\,\alpha\,\underline{|45°},$$

and

$$I = \frac{E}{2L\sqrt{2}\,\alpha\,\underline{|45°}} = \frac{E}{\sqrt{2}\,R}\,\underline{|-45°}. \qquad (15\text{–}50)$$

The *bandwidth* is the distance between the two half-power frequencies. It can be seen from the geometry of Fig. 15–27 that the bandwidth is

$$B = 2\alpha = \frac{R}{L}. \qquad (15\text{–}51)$$

The ratio of the center frequency to the bandwidth is

$$Q\ (\text{series}) = \frac{\omega_d}{B} = \frac{\omega_d L}{R}. \qquad (15\text{–}52)$$

The concept of the quality factor Q is somewhat more general than the definition given in Eq. (15–52). Whenever the resonance is produced by a single pole or zero in the s-plane the Q will be the reciprocal of twice the radian angle between the pole or the zero vector and the $j\omega$-axis.

The poles of $H(s)$ are its natural transient frequencies. The s-plane vectors which connect the driving frequency to the poles are a measure of the degree of resonance. If the driving frequency coincides with a pole, either because the pole is on the $j\omega$-axis, or because the driving frequency is made a damped sinusoid, the vector in the denominator vanishes and the response becomes infinite. Such an infinite response is called a resonance. Thus the complex resonant frequencies are the natural transients in the circuit. Indeed the s-plane vectors predict the steady-state behavior of a circuit at any frequency in terms of the vector distance between this frequency and the natural transient frequencies of the circuit. The s-plane vectors are thus a bridge between the steady-state and the transient responses.

Summary

Complex frequency $(s = \sigma + j\omega)$

  Time domain

$$f(t) = |F|e^{\sigma t} \cos(\omega t + \theta)$$

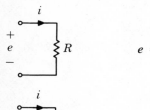

$$e = iR$$

$$e = L\frac{di}{dt}$$

$$e = \frac{1}{C}\int_{-\infty}^{t} i\,dt$$

  Complex-frequency domain

$$F = |F|e^{j\theta} = F\underline{|\theta}$$

$$E = IR$$

$$E = ILs$$

$$E = \frac{I}{Cs}$$

Initial energy storage

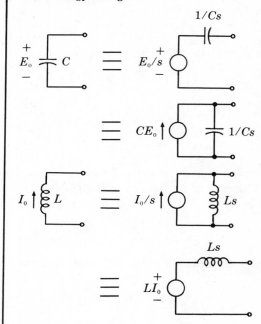

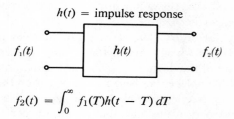

System functions

  Time domain

$$h(t) = \text{impulse response}$$

$f_1(t)$ $h(t)$ $f_2(t)$

$$f_2(t) = \int_0^{\infty} f_1(T)h(t - T)\,dT$$

  Frequency domain

$$H(s) = \text{system function}$$

$F_1(s)$ $H(s)$ $F_2(s)$

$$F_2(s) = F_1(s)H(s)$$

Laplace transform solutions

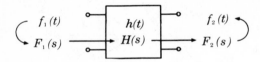

Transient solution

Time domain

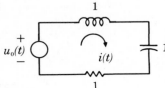

Frequency domain

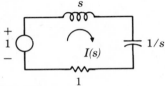

Transient plus steady-state

Time domain

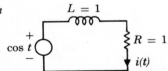

Frequency domain

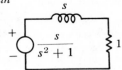

Delayed factors

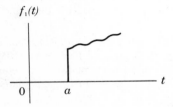

$$f_1(t) = f(t - a)u_{-1}(t - a)$$
$$F_1(s) = e^{-as}F(s)$$

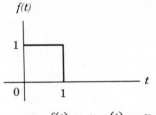

$$f(t) = u_{-1}(t) - u_{-1}(t - 1)$$
$$F(s) = \frac{1 - e^{-as}}{s}$$

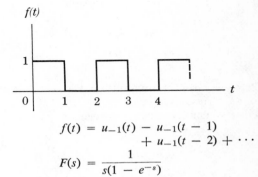

$$f(t) = u_{-1}(t) - u_{-1}(t - 1)$$
$$\qquad\qquad + u_{-1}(t - 2) + \cdots$$
$$F(s) = \frac{1}{s(1 - e^{-s})}$$

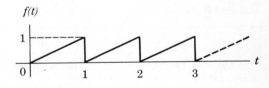

$$f(t) = tu_{-1}(t) - u_{-1}(t - 1)$$
$$\qquad\qquad - u_{-1}(t - 2) + \cdots$$
$$F(s) = \frac{1 - e^{-s} - se^{-s}}{s^2(1 - e^{-s})}$$

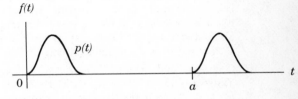

$$f(t) = p(t) + p(t - a)u_{-1}(t - a)$$
$$\qquad\qquad + p(t - 2a)u_{-1}(t - 2a) + \cdots$$
$$F(s) = \frac{P(s)}{1 - e^{-as}}$$

Driving-point impedance

$$H(s) = Z(s) = \frac{K(s - s_1)(s - s_3) \ldots}{(s - s_2)(s - s_4) \ldots}$$

$s_1, s_3, \ldots$ are zeros
$s_2, s_4, \ldots$ are poles

Zeros = short-circuit natural resonant frequencies
Poles = open-circuit natural resonant frequencies

Transfer functions

$$H(s) = \frac{K(s - s_1)(s - s_3) \ldots}{(s - s_2)(s - s_4) \ldots}$$

$s_1, s_3, \ldots$ are zeros
$s_2, s_4, \ldots$ are poles

Zeros = zeros of transmission and *not* transient resonant frequencies
Poles = natural resonant frequencies

s-plane plots

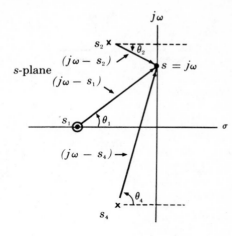

$$H(j\omega) = \frac{(j\omega - s_1)}{(j\omega - s_2)(j\omega - s_4)}$$

References

In Chapter 14 complex signals were resolved into sinusoidal components. In Chapter 15 network responses to such signals are obtained. In the end transient problems are solved by frequency-domain methods. A number of excellent texts are devoted entirely to Fourier or Laplace methods.

1. O. HEAVISIDE, *Electromagnetic Theory*, Dover, New York, 1950. The original Heaviside work is available in this excellent reprint. In addition to lumped-element problems, Heaviside applied his methods to distributed-parameter systems, such as cables and transmission lines.

2. GARDNER and BARNES, *Transients in Linear Systems*, John Wiley, New York, 1942. Gardner and Barnes apply the Laplace transform to the solution of transient problems in electrical and mechanical systems.

3. M. E. VAN VALKENBURG, *Network Analysis*, Prentice-Hall, New Jersey, 1955. Van Valken-

burg presents essentially the same material as Gardner and Barnes at a level more suitable for undergraduate students.

4. D. K. CHENG, *Analysis of Linear Systems*, Addison-Wesley, Reading, Mass., 1959. Cheng gives a slightly more modern treatment of the ground covered by Gardner and Barnes. The Laplace transform is the basic tool used, but a heuristic development of the Laplace transform from Fourier series and Fourier integrals is included.

5. R. V. CHURCHILL, *Modern Operational Methods in Engineering*, McGraw-Hill, New York, 1951. Churchill covers transform methods in detail, from the point of view of an applied mathematician.

6. S. GOLDMAN, *Transformation Calculus and Electrical Transients*, Prentice-Hall, New Jersey, 1949. The methods of Laplace transforms are

applied to lumped-parameter circuits and dis-tributed-parameter circuits. The relationship of the methods to the calculus of residues is covered in some detail.

7. E. A. Guillemin, *The Mathematics of Circuit Analysis*, John Wiley, New York, 1948. This text represents a good summary of the Fourier methods, as opposed to the Laplace methods. In particular, pulses which exist for both posi-tive and negative time are considered as excita-tions for a network.

8. J. Truxal, *Control System Synthesis*, McGraw-Hill, New York, 1955. Truxal discusses the two-sided Laplace transform which can be used for both positive and negative time.

9. Van der Pol and Bremmer, *Operational Cal-culus Based on the Two-sided Laplace Integral*, Cambridge University Press, London, 1950. This text is the original presentation of the two-sided Laplace transform, which applies to pulses defined for both positive and negative time. It is very readable and contains many examples.

10. Brenner and Javid, *Analysis of Electric Cir-cuits*, McGraw-Hill, New York, 1959. The Brenner and Javid book is an example of a modern text which presents the Heaviside opera-tional approach to the solution of transient problems.

Exercises

SECTION 15–2

1. Give the impedance of each of the networks in Fig. 15–29 as a function of complex frequency.

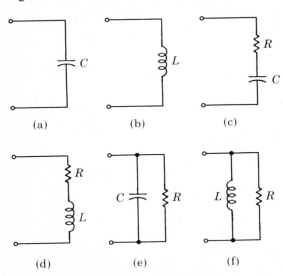

(a)   (b)   (c)

(d)   (e)   (f)

Figure 15–29

2. Find the driving-point impedance of the network in Fig. 15–30 as a function of the complex fre-quency s.

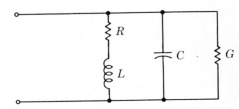

Figure 15–30

3. (a) In the circuit of Fig. 15–31 convert the initial energy storage to a step source in series with the capacitance and solve for the current in the frequency domain. (b) Repeat part (a) but convert the initial energy storage into an impulse source in parallel

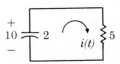

Figure 15–31

with the capacitance. (c) Show that the circuit for part (b) is the Thévenin circuit for part (a).

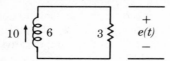

Figure 15–32

4. (a) In the circuit of Fig. 15–32 convert the initial energy stored in the inductance to a step current in parallel with the inductance and solve for the voltage in the frequency domain. (b) Repeat part (a) but represent the initial energy storage by an impulse voltage source in series with the inductance. (c) Show that the circuit for part (b) is the Norton circuit for part (a).

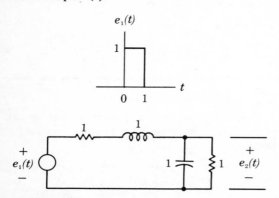

Figure 15–33

5. (a) Find $H(s)$ for the circuit of Fig. 15–33 if the input is $e_1(t)$ and the output is $e_2(t)$. (b) Find the corresponding $h(t)$.

6. The input function to a given circuit is a unit step function and the output is

$$f_2(t) = \sin 3t \cdot u_{-1}(t).$$

(a) Find the system function $H(s)$. (b) Find the output if the input is

$$f_1(t) = \sin 3t \cdot u_{-1}(t).$$

7. The input function for a certain circuit is

$$f_1(t) = (2e^{-t} - e^{-2t})u_{-1}(t).$$

The corresponding output is

$$f_2(t) = e^{-3t} \cdot u_{-1}(t).$$

(a) Find the system function $H(s)$ for the network.
(b) Find the output time function if the input is

$$f_1(t) = e^{-3t} \cdot u_{-1}(t).$$

8. (a) Find $H(s)$ for the circuit of Fig. 15–34 if the input is $e_1(t)$ and the output is $e_2(t)$. (b) Find $h(t)$.

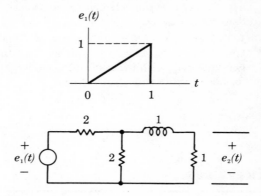

Figure 15–34

SECTION 15–3

9. In the circuit of Fig. 15–35 the stimulus is a step current of amplitude 10 amp and the desired response is the voltage $e(t)$. (a) Obtain $E(s)$ from a frequency-domain diagram. (b) Obtain $e(t)$ from $E(s)$.

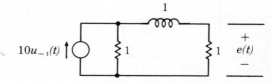

Figure 15–35

10. Find the voltage $e(t)$ in the circuit of Fig. 15–36 by the Laplace transform method.

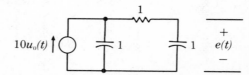

Figure 15–36

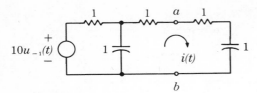

Figure 15–37

11. For the circuit of Fig. 15–37 draw the frequency-domain diagram and obtain the equivalent Thévenin circuit to the left of terminal-pair *a-b*. From the Thévenin circuit find the current $i(t)$.

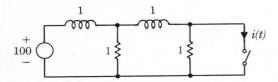

Figure 15–38

12. The switch in the circuit of Fig. 15–38 is closed at $t = 0$. (a) Make an equivalent Thévenin circuit and thus find the current $i(t)$ through the switch. (b) Replace the source and the initial energy storages by step or impulse sources and solve the complete problem for $i(t)$. (Previous to $t = 0$ a steady-state has been reached in the circuit.)

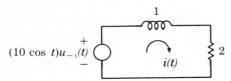

Figure 15–39

13. The voltage source in the circuit of Fig. 15–39 is suddenly applied at $t = 0$. Use the Laplace transform method to find the current which flows for $t > 0$ and separate it into its steady-state and transient components. Check the steady-state value by phasor algebra.

14. The voltage source in the circuit of Fig. 15–40 is applied at $t = 0$. Use the Laplace transform method to find the current which flows and separate it into its steady-state and transient components. Check the steady-state value by phasor algebra.

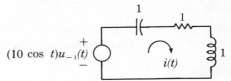

Figure 15–40

15. The voltage applied to the circuit of Fig. 15–41 is a symmetrical square wave as shown. (a) Find the component in the current which occurs at the natural frequency of the circuit. (b) Find the component of the current which occurs at the fundamental frequency of the applied square wave.

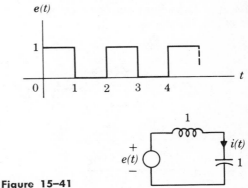

Figure 15–41

16. In the circuit of Fig. 15–42: (a) Find the Laplace transform of the current. (b) Write the time function for the current in terms of delayed functions, and sketch it. (c) By expanding the transform in partial fractions obtain the transient and steady-state components of the current.

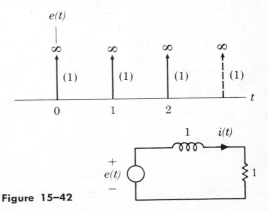

Figure 15–42

SECTION 15-4

17. (a) Find the input impedance for the network of Fig. 15–43. (b) Give the poles and zeros. (c) Give the meaning of the poles and zeros in terms of the natural transients in the circuit.

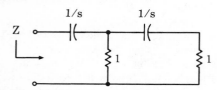

Figure 15–43

18. Find the input impedance of each of the networks of Fig. 15–44.

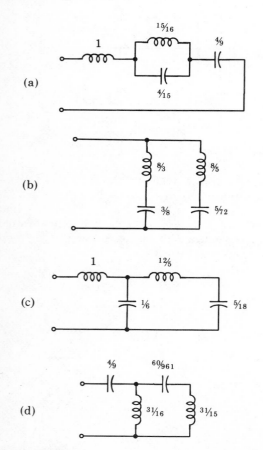

Figure 15–44

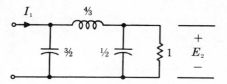

Figure 15–45

19. (a) Find the ratio of E_2/I_1, that is, Z_{12}, for the network of Fig. 15–45. (b) Give the zeros and the poles of Z_{12}.

20. The impedance of a network is given by

$$Z(s) = \frac{s + 1}{s^2 + 2s + 100}.$$

(a) Find the form of the current which will occur if the circuit is driven by a voltage step. (b) Find the form of the voltage which will occur if the circuit is driven by a current step.

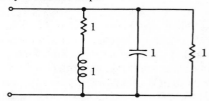

Figure 15–46

21. (a) Find the driving-point impedance of the network in Fig. 15–46. (b) Find its open-circuit transient if driven by a current impulse. (c) Find its short-circuit transient if driven by a voltage impulse.

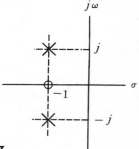

Figure 15–47

22. (a) Find the impedance represented by the *s*-plane plot of Fig. 15–47, given that the value at $s = 0$ is 1. (b) From the *s*-plane vectors evaluate

the impedance at $s = j$. (c) If a current $i(t) = 10 \cos t$ is applied to the impedance, what voltage will occur across it?

23. The impedance of a series $R\text{-}L\text{-}C$ circuit is

$$Z(s) = \frac{10(s + 1 + j10)(s + 1 - j10)}{s}.$$

(a) Make use of the s-plane vectors to obtain an approximate expression for the impedance in the vicinity of the resonance. (b) Give the frequency of the resonance. (c) What is the bandwidth? (d) What is the Q? (e) Give the impedance at

resonance. (f) Sketch the resonance curve in magnitude and phase.

24. A parallel resonant circuit has the impedance

$$Z(s) = \frac{1}{10} \frac{s}{(s + 1 + j10)(s + 1 - j10)}.$$

(a) Find an approximate form of $Z(s)$ which holds in the vicinity of resonance. (b) Give the resonant frequency. (c) What is the impedance at the resonant frequency? (d) Give the bandwidth. (e) Give the Q.

Problems

1. The series parallel circuit of Fig. 15–48 has the impedance

$$Z(s) = 10^6 \frac{(s + 1)}{(s + 1 + j100)(s + 1 - j100)}.$$

(a) Find the values of R, L, C, and G. (b) Find the element values if the resonant frequency is scaled up by a factor of 1000. (c) Sketch the poles and zeros in parts (a) and (b) and give the Q in each case.

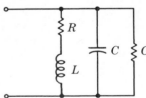

Figure 15–48

2. An impedance is given by

$$Z(s) = \frac{10(s + 1 + j100)(s + 1 - j100)}{(s + 1)}.$$

A voltage source

$$e(t) = 1.0 + \cos 50t + \cos 100t$$

is applied to the impedance. Compute the resulting current at each frequency using the s-plane.

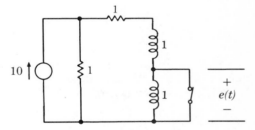

Figure 15–49

3. The switch in the circuit of Fig. 15–49 is closed and a steady-state is reached in the network. Then at $t = 0$ the switch is opened. Find the voltage across the switch for $t > 0$.

4. (a) Using delayed factors write the Laplace transform for the half-wave rectified sine wave of Fig. 15–50. (b) By resolving the transform into partial fractions obtain the Fourier series for the

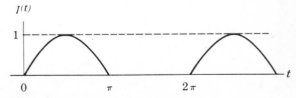

Figure 15–50

original waveform. (c) Repeat with the waveform a full-wave rectified sine wave instead of the half-wave rectified sine wave.

5. Find the current $i(t)$ in the circuit of Fig. 15–51 by means of the Laplace transform.

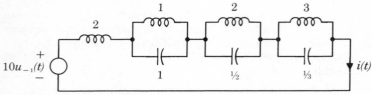

Figure 15–51

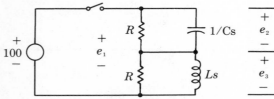

Figure 15–52

6. (a) Find the driving-point impedance of the circuit in Fig. 15–52, subject to the condition that $R^2 = L/C$. (b) A constant voltage of 100 v is ap-

plied to the circuit and allowed to remain until a steady-state is reached. It is then removed at $t = 0$. Find $e_2(t)$, $e_3(t)$, and $e_1(t)$ as functions of time.

7. (a) Give and sketch the time function whose Laplace transform is

$$F(s) = \frac{1}{s \sinh s}.$$

(b) Give and sketch the time function whose Laplace transform is

$$F(s) = \frac{1}{s \cosh s}.$$

8. The singularity functions representing the derivatives of $u_0(t)$ are equivalent to initial energy storages in a problem. From the singularity functions in the equation below compute the initial value of the current, and of its first three derivatives. Show that the same differential equation would be obtained for $t > 0$ if these initial values were used when the equation was transformed, and the singularity functions were ignored.

$$\frac{d^3 i}{dt^3} + 2\frac{d^2 i}{dt^2} + 2\frac{di}{dt} + 2i = u_0(t) + 2u_1(t) + 3u_2(t)$$

Answers to Exercises

CHAPTER 1

1. Atom, electron, electric circuit, map, economic system, inertia, particle, line, circle, energy, equator, friction.

2. War, stock boom; elections, less graft; government spending, inflation; high birth rate, expanding population; labor government, higher wages; business government, higher profits; fear and uncertainty, recession.

3. (a) Mechanical-acoustic
   (b) Mechanical-electric-acoustic
   (c) Hydraulic-mechanical-electrical
   (d) Chemical-mechanical-electrical
   (e) Chemical-mechanical-electrical
   (f) Chemical-mechanical-electrical-mechanical
   (g) Solar-electrical
   (h) Electrical-thermal-mechanical-electrical
   (i) Chemical-mechanical-electrical-light

4. Store prices are constant but stock prices rise and number of shares bought is not proportional to money spent.

5. (a) 30 amp   (b) -30 amp
   (c) Signs reverse

6. (a) 10 v   (b) -10 v
   (c) -10 v   (d) 10 v

7. (a) 100 w   (b) -100 w
   (c) -100 w

8. (b) and (d)   9. 34 ohms

10. 0.0144×10^{-6} f

11. 1 h

12. 3 amp; 18 w

13. 18×10^{-6} j; the energy remains

14. 50 j; the energy remains

15. (a) None   (b) 100 w
    (c) Infinity   (d) -10 w

16. (a) Infinity   (b) None
    (c) 100 w   (d) -10 w

17.

18. $V_{cd} = -3$ v

19. $I_{do} = -11$ amp

20. $i_{10} = i_a - i_b$; $i_{20} = i_b - i_c$; $i_{30} = i_c - i_d$; $i_{40} = i_d - i_a$

21. $e_{ba} = 6$ v; $e_{ca} = -7$ v; $e_{da} = -4$ v

22. (a) $i_1 + i_2 + i_3 - i_4 = 0$; $i_4 - i_5 = 0$; $i_1 + i_2 + i_3 + i_5 = 0$
    (b) The third one is the sum of the other two.

23. (a) $e_1 + e_2 - e_6 = -e$; $e_6 - e_3 - e_4 - e_5 = 0$; $e + e_1 + e_2 - e_3 - e_4 - e_5 = 0$
    (b) The third equation is the sum of the first two.

24. $i = 228.3$ amp

CHAPTER 2

1. (a) 2   (b) 2×10^6 (c) 1
   (d) ∞ (e) 9

2. $\frac{9}{5}$

3. (a) $\frac{1}{2}$ (b) $\frac{1}{2} \times 10^6$ (c) 0
   (d) 1   (e) 2

4. $\dfrac{R_1 R_2 R_3}{R_1 R_2 + R_2 R_3 + R_3 R_1}$;   (a) 1   (b) $\frac{1}{3}$
   (c) $\frac{1}{2}$ (d) 1   (e) $\frac{6}{11}$

5. 25 v

6. 5 amp

7. 20 v

8. 10 amp

9. $b = 8, n = 6, l = 3$, KCL Eqs. $= 5$, KVL Eqs. $= 3$, v-a Eqs. $= 8$

10. $b = 18, n = 12, l = 7$, KCL Eqs. $= 11$, KVL Eqs. $= 7$, v-a Eqs. $= 18$

11. $b = 12, n = 7, l = 6$, KCL Eqs. $= 6$, KVL Eqs. $= 6$, v-a Eqs. $= 12$

12. $b = 8, n = 7, l = 2$. All separate parts must share a common reference node.

13. (a) and (b) are planar

14. (a) $b = 1, n = 2, l = 1$
    (b) $b = 10, n = 7, l = 4$

15. $b = 6, n = 4, l = 3$

16. $b = 7, n = 5, l = 3$

17. $e_1 = 4, e_2 = 2, e_3 = 2$; $i_1 = -2, i_2 = 2$, $i_3 = 2$

18. $i_1 = -3, i_2 = 1.5, i_3 = 1.5; e_1 = 3, e_2 = 3,$
    $e_3 = 3$

19. $i_1 = 1, i_2 = -1; e_1 = 12, e_2 = 12$

20. 10 v in series with R_2

21. 10 amp in parallel with R_2

22. $e_1 = 6, e_2 = -12, e_3 = 12, e_4 = 6, e_s = 18$

23. $i_1 = -1, i_2 = -2, i_3 = 1.5, i_4 = 1.5, i_s = 3$

24. (a) 10 v in series with R_1 and R_2 in parallel
    (b) a 10-v source
    (c) a 2-amp source across R_5

CHAPTER 3

1. $e_{ab} = -11$ v

2. $i_a = \frac{30}{13}, i_b = i_c = \frac{10}{13}$

3. $e_0 = \frac{10}{21}$

4.

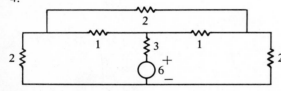

5. $i_1 = 4, i_2 = 9$

6. $i_1 = 3, i_2 = \frac{3}{4}, i_3 = \frac{15}{4}$

7. $i_1 = 6, i_2 = 4, i_3 = 3$

8. $i_1 = -5, i_2 = 2.5$

9. $e_a = 1, e_b = 0$

10. $e_a = \frac{30}{13}, e_b = e_c = \frac{10}{13}$

11. $e_a = \frac{80}{21}$

12.

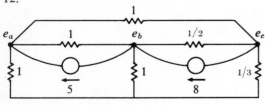

13. $e_a = -1, e_b = 3$

14. $e_a = 5, e_b = 10, e_c = 10$

15. $e_a = 10, e_b = 5, e_c = -5$

16. $e_a = -2, e_b = 10, e_c = 4$

17. Node 1: 3-amp source in, $\frac{1}{2}$ and 1 ohm to
        ground, $\frac{1}{4}$ ohm to node 2
    Node 2: 5-amp source out, $\frac{1}{3}$ and 1 ohm to
        ground, $\frac{1}{4}$ ohm to node 1

18. Node 1: dummy voltage of 5 v, 1 ohm to node 2
    Node 2: $\frac{1}{2}$ ohm to ground, 1 ohm to node 1,
        $\frac{1}{3}$ ohm to node 3
    Node 3: $\frac{1}{4}$ ohm to ground, $\frac{1}{3}$ ohm to node 2,
        $\frac{1}{5}$ ohm to node 4
    Node 4: dummy voltage of -10 v, $\frac{1}{5}$ ohm to
        node 3

19. Obtain original network

20. Node 1: 5 amp source in, $\frac{1}{3}$ ohm to ground,
        $\frac{1}{4}$ ohm to node 2
    Node 2: 1 ohm to ground, $\frac{1}{4}$ ohm to node 1,
        minus end of 2-v source
    Node 3: $\frac{1}{3}$ ohm to node 4, $\frac{1}{2}$ ohm to ground,
        plus end of 2-v source
    Node 4: $\frac{1}{3}$ ohm to node 3, $\frac{1}{5}$ ohm and $\frac{1}{4}$ ohm to
        ground

21. (a) $i = 1$
    (b) $P_R = 1$ watt, $P_e = 0$, $P_i = 1$ watt

22. $i = 17$

23. (a) $\frac{2}{11}$ (b) $\frac{200}{11}$ (c) $\frac{2}{11} \times 10^{-4}$

24. (a) $\frac{1}{2}$ (b) $\frac{1}{2} \times 10^{-3}$ (c) $\frac{1}{2} \times 10^3$

CHAPTER 4

1. 3 ohms

2. 3 ohms

3. $\frac{13}{21}$ ohms

4. (a) 12, 12, 12 ohms   (b) $\frac{19}{3}, \frac{19}{4}$, 19 ohms
    (c) $\frac{3}{2}, \frac{3}{4}, \frac{9}{8}$ ohms
    (a) $\frac{7}{3}, \frac{7}{3}, \frac{7}{3}$ ohms   (b) 1, $\frac{1}{3}, \frac{1}{2}$, ohms
    (c) $\frac{1}{11}, \frac{2}{11}, \frac{3}{11}$ ohms

5. $\frac{5}{9}, \frac{5}{9}, \frac{5}{9}$ ohms

6. $\frac{16}{3}$ ohms

7. 8 ohms

8. $\frac{13}{4}$ ohms

9. (a) $e = 5 + 10i$ (b) $e = 10 + 5i$
    (c) $e = 10 + 5i$ (d) $e = -10 + 5i$

10. (a) 5 v, $\frac{10}{3}$ ohms   (b) 0 v, 15 ohms
    (c) 66 v, 10 ohms

11. (a) 1 amp, 7 ohms   (b) 0 amp, 2 ohms
    (c) 8 amp, 5 ohms

12. $E_{oc} = 3$ v, $R_{eq} = \frac{5}{3}$ ohms, $I_{sc} = \frac{9}{5}$ amp

13. $E_{oc} = -2$ v, $R_{eq} = 2$ ohms, $I_{sc} = -1$ amp

14. $E_{oc} = \frac{65}{8}$ v, $R_{eq} = \frac{31}{8}$ ohms, $I_{sc} = \frac{65}{31}$ amp

15. $E_{oc} = 2$ v, $R_{eq} = \frac{7}{8}$ ohms, $I_{sc} = \frac{16}{7}$ amp

16. $E_{oc} = 6$ v, $R_{eq} = \frac{8}{5}$ ohms, $I_{sc} = \frac{15}{4}$ amp

17. (a) $R = 2$ ohms   (b) $E_2 = 6$ v
    (c) $E_0 = 1$ v
18. (a) $R = \frac{3}{5}$ ohm   (b) $E_2 = \frac{6}{5}$ v
    (d) $I_0 = \frac{8}{5}$ amp
19. $e_0 = 1$ v
21. $e_0 = 3$ v
23. $\frac{5}{6}$ ohm
20. $\frac{180}{37}$ ohm
22. $\frac{7}{12}$ ohm
24. $\frac{3}{4}$ ohm

CHAPTER 5

1. 10 amp
2. -4 v
3. $\frac{12}{17}$ amp
4. 10 v
5. $r_{11} = r_{22} = \frac{11}{5}, r_{12} = \frac{9}{5}$;
   T-values: $\frac{2}{5}, \frac{9}{5}, \frac{2}{5}$ ohms
   $g_{11} = g_{22} = \frac{11}{8}, g_{12} = -\frac{9}{8}$;
   π-values: $4, \frac{8}{9}, 4$ ohms
   $h_{11} = \frac{8}{11}, h_{12} = \frac{9}{11}, h_{21} = -\frac{9}{11}, h_{22} = \frac{5}{11}$
6. $r_{11} = \frac{21}{10}, r_{22} = \frac{12}{5}, r_{12} = \frac{1}{5}$;
   T-values: $\frac{19}{10}, \frac{1}{5}, \frac{11}{5}$ ohms
   $g_{11} = \frac{12}{25}, g_{22} = \frac{21}{50}, g_{12} = -\frac{1}{25}$;
   π-values: $\frac{25}{11}, 25, \frac{50}{19}$ ohms
7. $h_{12} = -\dfrac{g_{12}}{g_{11}}, \quad h_{21} = \dfrac{g_{21}}{g_{11}}$
8. $h_{11} = \dfrac{r_{11}r_{22} - r_{12}r_{21}}{r_{22}^2}, \quad h_{12} = \dfrac{r_{12}}{r_{22}},$
   $h_{21} = -\dfrac{r_{21}}{r_{22}}, \quad h_{22} = \dfrac{1}{r_{22}};$
   $h_{11} = \dfrac{1}{g_{11}}, \quad h_{12} = -\dfrac{g_{12}}{g_{11}}, \quad h_{21} = \dfrac{g_{21}}{g_{11}},$
   $h_{22} = \dfrac{g_{11}g_{22} - g_{12}g_{21}}{g_{11}^2}$
9. $r_{11} = \frac{26}{21}, r_{22} = \frac{68}{21}, r_{12} = \frac{2}{21}$;
   T-values: $\frac{8}{7}, \frac{2}{21}, \frac{22}{7}$ ohms
10. $g_{11} = \frac{34}{42}, g_{22} = \frac{13}{42}, g_{12} = -\frac{1}{42}$;
   π-values: $\frac{14}{11}, 42, \frac{7}{2}$ ohms
13. π-values: $\frac{5}{7}, \frac{15}{2}, \frac{5}{7}$ ohms
14. π-values: 2, 2, 2 ohms
15. T-values: $\frac{1}{3}, \frac{9}{2}, 1$ ohm
16. π-values: $\frac{6}{7}, 6, \frac{6}{7}$ ohms
17. (a) $r_{11} = r_{22} = 3, r_{12} = 1$;
    T-values: 2, 1, 2 ohms
    $g_{11} = g_{22} = \frac{3}{8}, \quad g_{12} = -\frac{1}{8}$;
    π-values: 4, 8, 4 ohms
   (b) $r_{12} = -1$; T-values: 4, -1, 4 ohms
    $g_{12} = \frac{1}{8}$; π-values: 2, -8, 2 ohms

18. T-values: 1, $\frac{1}{6}$, 1 ohms; π-values: $\frac{4}{3}$, 8, $\frac{4}{3}$ ohms
19. $R_x = 2, R_y = 6$
20. $R_x = \frac{2}{3}, R_y = 2$
21. $R_x = 1, R_y = \frac{4}{3}$
22. Six resistances: five of 2 ohms, one of $\frac{4}{3}$ ohms
23. T-values: $\frac{33}{7}, \frac{9}{14}, \frac{33}{7}$ ohms
24. T-values: $\frac{8}{3}, \frac{2}{3}, \frac{8}{3}$ ohms

CHAPTER 6

1. In the five intervals the derivative is 1, 0, -1, -1, 1.
2. Positive impulse at 0, negative impulse at 1, positive impulse at 2.
3. Derivative is 1; negative impulses at 1 and 3.
4. Derivative $= \cos t$
5. Derivative $= e^{-t}$
6. $f' = 2e^{2t}$; $f'' = 4e^{2t}$; $f''' = 8e^{2t}$
7. $f' = nt^{n-1}$; $f'' = n(n-1)t^{n-2}$;
   $f''' = n(n-1)(n-2)t^{n-3}$;
   $(n+1)$th derivative is zero.
8. Max $= 0.707e^{-\pi/4}$ at $t = \pi/4$
9. Peak value is 2 at $t = 3$; final value is 1.
10. From 0 to 1, a linear rise from 0 to 1; from 1 to 2, a linear drop from 1 to 0.
11. From 0 to 1, a parabolic rise from 0 to $\frac{1}{2}$; from 1 to 2, a parabolic fall from $\frac{1}{2}$ to 0; from 2 to 3, a parabolic rise from 0 to $\frac{1}{2}$.
12. $f^{-1} = t$; $f^{-2} = t^2/2$; $f^{-3} = t^3/6$
13. $f' = 2$ from 0 to 1 and $f' = -2$ from 1 to 2
14. (a) $f' = \cos t$; integral $\sin t$; inverse
   (b) Not inverse
15. $f' = -\sin t$; integral $= (-1 + \cos t)$; not inverse
16. Need an impulse at $t = 0$ of area unity.
17. Area $= 1$; f' becomes a unit impulse, $u_0(t)$.
18. (a) $13u_{-1}(t)$ (b) $13u_0(t)$ (c) $13u_{-2}(t)$
19. $f' = u_0(t) - \sin t \cdot u_{-1}(t)$
20. $u_{-1}(t) - 2u_{-1}(t-1) + u_{-1}(t-2)$;
   derivative $u_{-1} \to u_0$; integral $u_{-1} \to u_{-2}$
21. $u_{-2}(t) - 2u_{-2}(t-1) + u_{-2}(t-2)$
22. $u_{-2}(t) - 2u_{-2}(t-1) + 2u_{-2}(t-2)$
    $- 2u_{-2}(t-3) + \cdots$
23. $\sin t \cdot u_{-1}(t) - \sin t \cdot u_{-1}(t-\pi)$
24. A staircase rising one unit for each unit of time.

CHAPTER 7

1. (a) Step of height 5   (b) Ramp of slope 2
2. (a) Step of height 20   (b) Ramp of slope $\frac{5}{2}$
3. (a) $5 \sin 3t$ (b) $90 \cos 3t$
   (c) $\frac{5}{6}(1 - \cos 3t)$
4. (a) $20 \cos 2t$ (b) $\frac{5}{3} \sin 2t$
   (d) $-80 \sin 2t$
5. (a) $Q = 30, t = 0$ (b) $\lambda = 10, t = 0$
6. (a) $W(10) = 400, W(100) = 40,000$
   (b) $W(5) = 225, W(10) = 900$
7. Four series inductances of value 3, four shunt capacitances of value 2
8. Voltage = 9; current = 10; $R = \frac{1}{8}$ and $\frac{1}{3}$; $C = 7$ and 6; $L = 4$ and 5
9. (a) $C = 3, e_{oc} = 10u_{-1}(t)$
   (b) $C = 3, i_{sc} = 30u_0(t)$
10. (a) $L = 5, e_{oc} = 50u_0(t)$
    (b) $L = 5, i_{sc} = 10u_{-1}(t)$
11. Thevenin ≡ voltage source; Norton ≡ current source
12. $i = 5, i' = -\frac{5}{6}$
13. $e = 20, e' = -8$
14. Inductances: 6 v; capacitances: 6 v
15. (a) 2   (b) 2
16. (a) 2   (b) 2
17. (a) (i) $10u_{-1}(t)$ (ii) $\frac{100}{3}u_{-2}(t)$ (iii) $\frac{100}{6}u_0(t)$
    (b) (i) $300u_{-1}(t)$ (ii) $700u_0(t)$ (iii) $25u_{-2}(t)$
18. (a) $u_{-1}(t), \frac{10}{6}u_{-2}(t), 50u_0(t)$
    (b) $50u_{-1}(t), 70u_0(t), \frac{10}{3}u_{-2}(t)$
19. (a) $2u_{-1}(t) - 2u_{-1}(t-1) + 2u_{-2}(t)$
    $\qquad - 2u_{-2}(t-1) + 2u_0(t)$
    $\qquad - 2u_0(t-1)$
    (b) Same as (a)
20. (a) Parallel $R = \frac{1}{5}, L = \frac{1}{3}, C = 6$
    (b) Series $R = 3, L = \frac{1}{3}, C = \frac{8}{7}$
21. (a) (i) $10u_0(t)$ (ii) $100/3u_{-1}(t)$ (iii) $500u_1(t)$
    (b) (i) $52u_0(t)$ (ii) $65u_1(t)$ (iii) $39u_{-1}(t)$
22. (a) $5u_0(t) - 5u_0(t-1) + 2u_{-1}(t)$
    $\qquad - 2u_{-1}(t-1) + 2.5u_1(t)$
    $\qquad - 2.5u_1(t-1)$
    (b) Same as (a)
23. (a) $5u_1(t) - 5u_2(t)$ (b) $5u_1(t) - 40u_{-2}(t)$
24. (a) Parallel $R = \frac{1}{5}, C = 3, L = \frac{1}{10}$
    (b) Series $R = \frac{1}{3}, L = 7, C = 15$

CHAPTER 8

1. (a) $10, 10/e, 10/e^2, 0$ (b) 10 sec
   (c) $-e^{-t/10}$ (d) 10 sec
   (e) 10 sec
2. (a) $0, 6.32, 8.65, 10$ (b) 10 sec
   (c) $e^{-t/10}$ (d) 10 sec
   (e) 10 sec
3. $5e^{-2t/3}$
4. $-10e^{-t/2}$
5. $i = \frac{7}{3}(1 - e^{-3t/5})$
6. $e = \frac{10}{3}(1 - e^{-3t})$
7. $i = 3e^{-2t}$
8. $e = 2e^{-t/8}$
9. $6e^{-5t/2} \cdot u_{-1}(t)$
10. $160e^{-t/3} \cdot u_{-1}(t)$ for $0 < t < 3$
    $29.3e^{-(t-3)/6} \cdot u_{-1}(t-3)$ for $3 < t < \infty$
11. $6e^{-t} \cdot u_{-1}(t)$
12. $8e^{-2t/3} \cdot u_{-1}(t)$
13. (a) $2e^{-3t/4} \cdot u_{-1}(t)$ (b) Same
14. (a) $[-6 + 26(1 - e^{-5t/3})]u_{-1}(t)$ (b) Same
15. (a) $(1 + e^{-6t/5})u_{-1}(t)$ (b) Same
16. (a) $(10 - 6e^{-2t/3})u_{-1}(t)$ (b) Same
17. $5u_0(t) - 5e^{-t} \cdot u_{-1}(t)$
18. $4e^{-t/25} \cdot u_{-1}(t)$
19. (a) $3e^{-t/15} \cdot u_{-1}(t)$ (b) Same
20. $5e^{-t/15} \cdot u_{-1}(t)$
21. $\frac{5}{3}e^{-5t/12} \cdot u_{-1}(t)$
22. $(30 - 36e^{-t/6})u_{-1}(t)$
23. $(10 - 5e^{-t/10})u_{-1}(t)$
24. $(5 + 25e^{-15t})u_{-1}(t)$

CHAPTER 9

1. $0, 0$; Max = 3.5 at $t = 1.58$
2. 0.0; Max = $4/e$ at $t = 2$
3. $0.707, 0.428, 0.262, 0$; $t = 2$ sec; period = 1 sec; $f = 1$ cps; $\theta = 45°$
4. $i = 10(e^{-2t} - e^{-3t})$
5. $e = 10te^{-2t}$
6. $i = 10e^{-4t}(\cos 3t + \sin 3t)$
7. $i = 2 + \frac{2}{3}e^{-4t} - \frac{8}{3}e^{-t}$
8. (a) $e = 1 - e^{-3t}(1 + 3t)$
   (b) $i = 10(1 - e^{-0.707t} \cos 0.707t$
   $\qquad\qquad - e^{-0.707t} \sin 0.707t)$

9. (a) Sinusoidal (b) 10 (c) 1
   (d) 1 (e) 2π (f) $+45°$
   (g) Change time scale

10. $i = 1, i' = 0, \omega_0 = 8, i(t) = \cos 8t \cdot u_{-1}(t)$

11. $i(t) = 1.4 \cos (t/4 + 45°)u_{-1}(t)$

12. $i = 40, i' = 0, \omega_0 = 4, i(t) = 40 \cos 4t \cdot u_{-1}(t)$

13. $e = 10 \sin t/2 \cdot u_{-1}(t)$,
    $i = 20/3(1 - \cos t/2)u_{-1}(t)$

14. (a) $i = 0, i' = \frac{10}{3}, \omega_0 = \frac{1}{6}$
    (b) $i(\infty) = 0$
    (c) $i = 20 \sin t/6 \cdot u_{-1}(t)$
    (d) $i(t) = 10 \sin t/6 \cdot u_{-1}(t)$

15. $e = 100(1 - \cos 4t)u_{-1}(t)$

16. $i = 10(1 - \cos 16t)u_{-1}(t)$

17. (a) Damped sinusoid
    (b) $\omega = 2\pi, f = 1$, period $= 1$
    (c) $t = 1$
    (d) $+45°$

18. (a) $i = 0, i' = 1, i(\infty) = 0$
    (b) $i(t) = 10e^{-t/10} \sin t/10 \cdot u_{-1}(t)$
    (c) Damped sinusoid

19. $i = e^{-t/2}(10 \cos 0.866t - 5.77 \sin 0.866t)u_{-1}(t)$

20. $e = e^{-t/2}(6 \cos 0.866t - 3.46 \sin 0.866t)u_{-1}(t)$

21. (a) $e = 0, e' = \frac{1}{2}, e(\infty) = 0$,
    $e = 5e^{-t/10} \sin t/10 \cdot u_{-1}(t)$
    (b) $e = 7.07e^{-t/10} \cos (t/10 + 45°) \cdot u_{-1}(t)$
    (c) $e = 5e^{-t/10} \cos t/10 \cdot u_{-1}(t)$

22. (a) $i = 0, i' = 10, i(\infty) = 0$,
    $i = 11.55e^{-t/2} \sin 0.866t \cdot u_{-1}(t)$
    (b) $e = [10 - 11.55e^{-t/2} \cos (0.866t - 30°)]$
    $\times u_{-1}(t)$

23. (a) $i = 0, i' = 240, i(\infty) = 0$,
    $i = (40e^{-2t} - 40e^{-8t})u_{-1}(t)$
    (b) $e = (60 - 80e^{-2t} + 20e^{-8t})u_{-1}(t)$

24. (a) $e = 0, e' = 10, e(\infty) = 0$,
    $e = 11.55e^{-t/2} \sin (0.866t)u_{-1}(t)$
    (b) $i = [10 - 11.55e^{-t/2} \cos (0.866t - 30°)]$
    $\times u_{-1}(t)$

CHAPTER 10

1. Amp $= 100$, phase $= 30°$, frequency $= 60$ cps,
   period $= \frac{1}{60}$ sec

2. $f = 14.1 \cos (2\pi t - 45°)$

3. (a) Length 10, angle $0°$
   (b) Length 5, angle $45°$
   (c) Length 10, angle $-90°$

(d) Length 5, angle $135°$
(e) Length 10, angle $135°$

4. (a) $10 \cos t$ (b) $-10 \sin 377t$
   (c) $5 \cos (1000t - 60°)$ (d) $5 \cos (t + 53°)$
   (e) $282 \cos (t/10 + 135°)$

5. (a) $1.41 \cos (\omega t + 45°)$ (b) $5 \cos (\omega t - 53°)$
   (c) $2.82 \cos (\omega t + 225°)$ (d) $5 \cos (\omega t + 127°)$
   (e) $\cos (\omega t + 90°)$

6. (a) $1.41 \underline{|45°}$ (b) $2 \underline{|60° + \theta}$
   (c) $2.82 \underline{|90°}$ (d) $9 \underline{|35°}$
   (e) $5 \underline{|123°}$ (f) 0
   (g) 0 (h) 0
   (i) 0 (j) 0

7. (a) $5 + j0, 7.07 + j7.07, -0.866 - j1.5$,
   $10 + j0.174, 0.174 - j10$
   (b) $-10 + j0, 2.4 + j4.33, -3.1 - j9.45$,
   $-0.2 - j0.336, -7.07 + j7.07$
   (c) $6 \underline{|90°}, 2.24 \underline{|-63.5°}, -2.24 \underline{|63.5°}, 5 \underline{|53°}$,
   $-5 \underline{|-53°}$
   (d) $0.406 \underline{|32°}, 0.805 \underline{|-81.2°}, -0.637 \underline{|-88.78}$,
   $343 \underline{|0.167°}, -3.57 \times 10^6 \underline{|61°}$
   (e) $3.61, 3.61, 0.277, 13, 2.72$
   (f) $0, 0.707, 10, 0.12, -4.23$
   (g) $14.7 \underline{|61.7°}, 2 \underline{|0°}, 0.707 \underline{|45°}, 2.69 \underline{|-33.4°}$,
   $7.4 \underline{|-90°}$

8. (a) 25 (b) $0.2 \underline{|-53°}$
   (c) $9.43 \underline{|-32°}$ (d) $1 \underline{|21.6°}$
   (e) $-1 \underline{|21.6°}$ (f) $3.7 \underline{|-0.365°}$
   (g) $-0.71 \underline{|-32.2°}$ (h) $2.64 \underline{|-39.5}$
   (i) $1.74 \underline{|62°}$ (j) $1.15 \underline{|69.8°}$
   or
   (a) 25 (b) $0.12 - j0.16$
   (c) $8 - j5$ (d) $0.928 + j0.369$
   (e) $0.928 - j0.369$ (f) $3.7 - j0.0235$
   (g) $-0.598 + j0.378$ (h) $2.04 - j1.68$
   (i) $0.816 + j1.54$ (j) $0.395 + j1.08$

9. $e(t) = 141 \cos (\omega t + 15°)$

10. $e(t) = 0$

11. (a) $5 \cos (t + 82°)$
    (b) $8.66 \cos t$
    (c) $15 \cos (t + 90°)$
    (d) $9.1 \cos (13t + 24.4°)$
    (e) $0.41 \cos (3t + 90°)$

12. (a) $100 \cos (t - 90°)$ (b) $100 \cos (t + \pi)$
    (c) $100 \cos (t + \pi/2)$ (d) $100 \cos (t + \pi/2)$
    (e) $100 \cos (t - \pi/2)$

13. (a) $4 \cos (377t - 45°)$ (b) $6 \cos (t + 120°)$
   (c) $7 \cos (t + 45°)$ (d) $\cos (1000t + 120°)$
   (e) $10 \cos 3t$

14. $e_s(t) = 389 \cos (377t + 75.1°)$

15. $i_s(t) = 14.1 \cos 1000t$

16. $e_s(t) = 100 \cos (2t + 45°)$

17. $e_s = 0$

18. $i_s = 0$

19. (a) $i = 2.5 \sin 10t$ (b) Same

20. (a) $i = -2000 \sin 10t$ (b) Same

21. $I = 3.53 \underline{|-45°}$, $i(t) = 3.53 \cos (2t - 45°)$

22. $E = 7070 \underline{|-45°}$, $e(t) = 7070 \cos (1000t - 45°)$

23. $i(t) = 5.53 \cos (2t - 56.4°)$

24. $e(t) = 3.53 \cos (3t - 69.5°)$

CHAPTER 11

1. $I_1 = 3.53 \underline{|-45°}$, $I_2 = 3.53 \underline{|45°}$

2. (a) $E_a = 3.53 \underline{|-45°}$, $E_b = 3.53 \underline{|45°}$
   (b) They are duals.

3. (a) $Z = 3.53 \underline{|45°}$, $E_{oc} = 3.53 \underline{|-45°}$
   (b) $I_{sc} = 1 \underline{|-90°}$

4. (a) $I_{sc} = 5 \underline{|0}$, $Z = 1.414 \underline{|45°}$
   (b) $E_{oc} = 7.07 \underline{|-45°}$

5. (a) $R = 1, C = 1, L = 1$
   (b) $R = 1, C = 10^{-3}, L = 10^{-3}$
   (c) $R = 1, C = 10^{-6}, L = 10^{-6}$

6. (a) $E = 7.07 \underline{|45°}$
   (b) $e(t) = 7.07 \cos (t + 45°)$,
     $R = 1, L = \frac{1}{2}, C = 1$
   (c) $e(t) = 7.07 \cos (10^6 t + 45°)$,
     $R = 1, C = 10^{-6}, L = \frac{1}{2} \times 10^{-6}$

7. (a) $R = 1; C \to -j, -j; L \to j3$
   (b) $E_0 = 4.47 \underline{|153.5°}$
   (c) $e_0 = 4.47 \cos (10^6 t + 153.5°)$

8. (a) $C \to -2j/3, -2j; L \to 4j/3; R \to 1$
   (b) $E_2 = 7.07 \underline{|225°}$
   (c) $e_2(t) = 7070 \cos (10^6 t + 225°)$

9. (a) $R \to 1, C \to -j$
   (b) $Z = \frac{1}{2} - j\frac{1}{2}$
   (c) $R = \frac{1}{2}, C = 2$
   (d) $Z = (1 - j\omega)/(1 + \omega^2)$
   (e) $1/(1 + \omega^2), \omega/(1 + \omega^2)$
   (f) Elements are functions of frequency.

10. (a) $R \to 1, L \to j$ (b) $Y = \frac{1}{2} - j\frac{1}{2}$
   (c) $R = 2, L = 2$

   (d) $Y = (1 - j\omega)/(1 + \omega^2)$
   (e) $1/(1 + \omega^2), \omega/(1 + \omega^2)$
   (f) The elements are functions of frequency.

11. (a) $Z = 0.5 + j0.5$
   (b) $R = \frac{1}{2}, L = \frac{1}{2}$
   (c) $R = 1, L = 1$
   (d) $Z(\omega) = (1 + j\omega^3)/(1 + \omega^2)$

12. (a) $Z = 0.5 - j0.5$
   (b) $R = \frac{1}{2}, C = 2$
   (c) $R = 1, C = 1$
   (d) $Z = \omega^2/1 + \omega^2 + j/\omega + \omega^3$

13. $\omega_0 = 10^4, Q = 100$

14. $C = 10^{-8}, Q = 10$

15. (a) $Z = 1/[1 + j(\omega - 1/\omega)]$
   (b) $R = 1000, L = 1000, C = 10^{-3}$
   (c) $R = 1000, L = 10^{-3}, C = 10^{-9}$

16. (a) $Z = 1 + j(\omega - 1/\omega)$
   (b) $R = 1000, L = 1000, C = 10^{-3}$
   (c) $R = 1000, L = 10^{-3}, C = 10^{-9}$

17. (a) $e_a = 110 \cos \omega t$
     $e_b = 110 \cos (\omega t - 120°)$
     $e_c = 110 \cos (\omega t - 240°)$
     $E_a = 110 \underline{|0°}, E_b = 110 \underline{|-120°}$,
     $E_c = 110 \underline{|-240°}$
   (b) $e_a = 110 \cos \omega t, e_b = 110 \cos (\omega t + 120°)$,
     $e_c = 110 \cos (\omega t + 240°)$
     $E_a = 110 \underline{|0°}, E_b = 110 \underline{|120°}$,
     $E_c = 110 \underline{|240°}$
   (c) $e_a = 110 \cos \omega t, e_b = 110 \cos (\omega t - 60)$,
     $e_c = 110 \cos (\omega t - 120°)$
     $e_d = 110 \cos (\omega t - 180°)$,
     $e_e = 110 \cos (\omega t - 240°)$,
     $e_f = 110 \cos (\omega t - 300°)$,
     $E_a = 110 \underline{|0°}, E_b = 110 \underline{|-60°}$,
     $E_c = 110 \underline{|-120°}, E_d = 110 \underline{|-180°}$,
     $E_e = 110 \underline{|-240°}, E_f = 110 \underline{|-300°}$

18. (a) $E_{xy} = 173 \underline{|30°}$,   (b) $E_{xy} = 173 \underline{|-30°}$,
     $E_{yz} = 173 \underline{|-90°}$, $E_{yz} = 173 \underline{|90°}$,
     $E_{zx} = 173 \underline{|-210°}$ $E_{zx} = 173 \underline{|210°}$
   (c) $E_{xy} = 173 \underline{|210°}$,   (d) $E_{xy} = 173 \underline{|-210°}$,
     $E_{yz} = 173 \underline{|90°}$, $E_{yz} = 173 \underline{|-90°}$,
     $E_{zx} = 173 \underline{|-30°}$ $E_{zx} = 173 \underline{|30°}$

19. $I_{aa'} = 123 \underline{|-75°}, I_{bb'} = 123 \underline{|-195°}$,
   $I_{cc'} = 123 \underline{|-315°}$

20. $I_{aa'} = 334 \underline{|-45°}, I_{bb'} = 334 \underline{|-165°}$,
   $I_{cc'} = 334 \underline{|-285°}$

21. $I_{aa'} = 70.7 \underline{|-75°}$, $I_{bb'} = 70.7 \underline{|-195°}$,
    $I_{cc'} = 70.7 \underline{|-315°}$

22. $I_{aa'} = 141 \underline{|-45°}$, $I_{bb'} = 141 \underline{|-165°}$,
    $I_{cc'} = 141 \underline{|-285°}$

23. $I_{aa'} = 106 \underline{|-45°}$, $I_{bb'} = 106 \underline{|-165°}$,
    $I_{cc'} = 106 \underline{|-285°}$, $V_{a'b'} = 86.6 \underline{|30°}$,
    $V_{b'c'} = 86.6 \underline{|-90°}$, $V_{c'a'} = 86.6 \underline{|-210°}$

24. (a) $e_{bn} = 100 \cos(\omega t - 120°)$
         $+ 50 \cos(3\omega t + 30°)$
         $+ 50 \cos(5\omega t - 180°)$,
    $e_{cn} = 100 \cos(\omega t - 240°)$
         $+ 50 \cos(3\omega t + 30°)$
         $+ 50 \cos(5\omega t - 60°)$

    (b) $V_{LL}(\text{first}) = 173$, $V_{LL}(\text{third}) = 0$,
        $V_{LL}(\text{fifth}) = 86.6$

    (c) $e_{ab} = 173 \cos(\omega t + 30°)$
             $+ 86.6 \cos(\omega t + 30°)$,
        $e_{bc} = 173 \cos(\omega t - 90°)$
             $+ 86.6 \cos(\omega t - 210°)$,
        $e_{ca} = 173 \cos(\omega t - 210°)$
             $+ 86.6 \cos(\omega t - 90°)$

CHAPTER 12

1. (a) $z_{11} = z_{22} = 0$, $z_{12} = -j$
   (b) Shunt $C = -j$ ohms; series L's $= j$ ohms
   (c) $z_{11} = z_{22} = \dfrac{(\omega^2 - 1)}{j\omega(\omega^2 - 2)}$,
   $z_{12} = \dfrac{1}{j\omega(2 - \omega^2)}$

2. $y_{11} = y_{22} = 0$, $y_{12} = j$
   (b) Shunt C's $= -j$ ohms; series $L = j$ ohms
   $y_{11} = y_{22} = \dfrac{1 - \omega^2}{j\omega(2 - \omega^2)}$,
   $y_{12} = \dfrac{-1}{j\omega(2 - \omega^2)}$

3. (a) $h_{11} = j$, $h_{21} = -2$, $h_{12} = 2$, $h_{22} = 3j$
   (b) Series voltage source $-2E_2$ and j ohms,
       parallel current source $2I_1$ and $1/3j$ ohms
   (c) $h_{11} = \dfrac{-j\omega^3 + 2j\omega}{-2\omega^2 + 3}$,
   $h_{21} = \dfrac{-(\omega^2 + 3)}{-2\omega^2 + 3} = -h_{12}$,
   $h_{22} = \dfrac{3j\omega}{-2\omega^2 + 3}$

4. $z_{11} = z_{22} = \dfrac{-\omega^2 + 1}{j\omega}$, $z_{12} = \dfrac{1}{j\omega}$
   (b) $y_{11} = y_{22} = \dfrac{-\omega^2 + 1}{j\omega(-\omega^2 + 2)}$,
   $y_{12} = \dfrac{-1}{j\omega(-\omega^2 + 2)}$

5. (a) $1/(1 + j\omega)$
   (d) $R = 10^5$, $L = 10/2\pi$

6. (c) $0.172 \underline{|-59°}$, $0.172 \underline{|-121°}$

7. (a) $1/(1 + j\omega)$
   (d) $R = 10^4$, $C = 10^{-10}$

8. (a) $1/(-j\omega^3 - 2\omega^2 + 2j\omega + 1)$
   (c) $R = 10^3$, $C_1 = 1.5 \times 10^{-6}$,
       $C_2 = 0.5 \times 10^{-6}$, $L = 1.33$

9. Alone: 8, 6; series: 18, 10; parallel: $\frac{22}{9}$, $\frac{22}{5}$;
   shorted: $\frac{22}{3}$, $\frac{11}{2}$ h

10. $L_{eq} = 34$ h

11. (a) $e_1(t) = 10 \cos(t + 90°)$
    (b) $e_2(t) = 2.5 \cos(t + 90°)$

12. $E_2 = 3.9 \underline{|-11°}$

13. $E_2 = 8.15 \underline{|-99.4°}$

14. $Z = j\omega L_1 + \dfrac{\omega^2(L_1 - M)^2}{j\omega(L_1 + L_2 - 2M) + Z_2}$

15. $Z = j\omega L_1 + Z_2 - \dfrac{(j\omega M + Z_2)^2}{j\omega L_2 + Z_2}$

16. $I_R = 18.6 \underline{|3.6°}$

17. (a) $E_3 = 353 \underline{|-45°}$ (b) Same

18. (a) $E_1 = 4840 \underline{|14°}$ (b) Same

19. $I_1 = 6.7 \underline{|-42.3°}$

20. $I_1 = 7.84 \underline{|-11.3°}$

21. (a) Series $10 + j50$, shunt $j50$, series $8 + j50$,
        ideal transformer $N = \frac{1}{2}$
    (b) Ideal transformer $N = \frac{1}{2}$, Series $2.5 + j12.5$,
        shunt $j12.5$, series $2 + j12.5$

22. (a) $E_2 = 22.6 \underline{|26.5°}$ (b) Same

23. Primary: $R = 1$, $jX = j22$, $jM = j200$
    Secondary: $1100 + j2200$

24. (a) $E_2 = 72.2 \underline{|15.7°}$ (b) Same

CHAPTER 13

1. 200 w; indeterminate

2. 171 w

3. $13.5t^2$, $3t^2$, $6t^2$ j $\cdot$ $22.5t^2$ j

4. $25t^2/18$, $50t^2/18$, $75t^2/18$ j; $25t^2/3$ j; $25t/9$,
   $50t/9$, $50t/6$ w; $50t/3$ w

5. 0.577

6. 0.5

7. 1.732

8. 16.9 amp

9. 600 j; 300 j; 300 j; $\frac{1}{2}$

10. $P_S = 200(1 - e^{-t/6})$ w;
    $P_R = 200(1 - 2e^{-t/6} + e^{-t/3})$ w;
    $P_C = 200(e^{-t/6} - e^{-t/3})$ w

11. $W_{L_1} = 12.5(t^2 + 2t \sin t + \sin^2 t)$;
    $W_{L_2} = 12.5(t^2 - 2t \sin t + \sin^2 t)$;
    $W_C = 25(1 - 2 \cos t + \cos^2 t)$

12. (a) $p(t) = 25 + 25 \cos 2t - 25 \sin 2t$ w
    (c) $P = 25$ w   (d) $Q = -25$ vars

13. 50 j, 50 j

14. (a) $p(t) = 25 + 25 \cos 2t + 25 \sin 2t$ w
    (c) $P = 25$ w   (d) $Q = 25$ vars

15. (a) $P = P_1 + P_2$
    (b) P_1 or P_2 can be negative, P is positive.

16. $P = \sqrt{3} \, V_L I_L \cos \theta$

17. (a) $P_v = 500 + j500$,   pf $= 0.707$
    (c) $P_v = 500 + j500$,   pf $= 0.707$

18. (a) $P_{e_1} = 5000$ w; $P_{e_2} = 5000$ w;
        sources to resistance
    (b) $P_{e_1} = 5000$ w; $P_{e_2} = -5000$ w;
        power flows left to right
    (c) $P_{e_1} = -5000$ w; $P_{e_2} = 5000$ w;
        power flows right to left

19. $I = 14 \underline{/-38°}$,   pf $= 0.78$

20. (b) $P_v = 3 + j1$ (c) $Z = 1.5 + j0.5$

21. $X_C = -2.36$ ohms

22. (a) $Z = 0.5 - j0.5$ (b) $P_{max} = 25$ w

23. (a) $N = 1.18$ (b) $P_{max} = 20.8$ w

24. (a) pf $= 0.974$ (b) $Q = -50$ vars

CHAPTER 14

1. (a) $f(t) = \frac{A}{2} + \frac{2A}{\pi}$
   $$\times \left(\sin t + \frac{\sin 3t}{3} + \frac{\sin 5t}{5} + \cdots \right)$$
   (b) $f(t) = \frac{A}{2} + \frac{2A}{\pi}$
   $$\times \left(\sin 2\pi \times 10^6 t + \frac{\sin 6\pi \times 10^6 t}{3} + \cdots \right)$$

2. (a) $f(t) = \frac{A}{2} - \frac{4A}{\pi^2}$
   $$\times \left(\cos t + \frac{\cos 3t}{9} + \frac{\cos 5t}{25} + \cdots \right)$$
   (b) $f(t) = \frac{A}{2} - \frac{4A}{\pi^2}$
   $$\times \left(\cos \left(\frac{2\pi t}{100} \right) + \frac{\cos 6\pi t/100}{9} + \cdots \right)$$

3. $f(t) = \frac{A}{2\pi} + \frac{A}{\pi}$
   $$\times (\cos t + \cos 2t + \cos 3t + \cdots)$$

4. (a) $f(t) = \frac{A}{2} + \frac{A}{\pi}$
   $$\times \left(-\sin t - \frac{\sin 2t}{2} - \frac{\sin 3t}{3} - \cdots \right)$$
   (b) $f(t) = \frac{A}{2} + \frac{A}{\pi}$
   $$\times \left(\sin t + \frac{\sin 2t}{2} + \frac{\sin 3t}{3} + \cdots \right)$$

5. (a) $f(t) = \frac{4}{\pi} \left(\sin t + \frac{\sin 3t}{3} + \frac{\sin 5t}{5} + \cdots \right)$
   (b) $f^{-1}(t) = \frac{-4}{\pi}$
   $$\times \left(\cos t + \frac{\cos 3t}{9} + \frac{\cos 5t}{25} + \cdots \right)$$
   (c) $f'(t) = \frac{4}{\pi} (\cos t + \cos 3t + \cos 5t + \cdots)$

6. (a) $f(t) = \frac{1}{2} - \frac{4}{\pi^2}$
   $$\times \left(\cos t + \frac{\cos 3t}{9} + \frac{\cos 5t}{25} + \cdots \right)$$
   (b) $f(t) = \frac{2}{\pi} \left(\sin t - \frac{\sin 2t}{2} + \frac{\sin 3t}{3} - \cdots \right)$

7. $a_1 = 1.24$, $a_3 = -0.33$; exact values: 1.26,
   -0.42

8. $b_1 = 0.632$, $b_2 = -0.312$, $b_3 = 0.118$; exact
   values: 0.636, -0.318, 0.212

9. $c_n = \frac{\delta}{T} \frac{\sin n\omega_0 \delta/2}{n\omega_0 \delta/2}$; envelope of $c_n T$ is same.

10. (a) $F(\omega) = \frac{\delta \sin \omega \delta/2}{\omega \delta/2}$
    (b) 2π rad, $2\pi \times 10^6$ rad
    (c) To $\omega = 4\pi/\delta$ (one positive and one nega-
        tive loop)

11. $c_n = A/T = A\omega_0/2\pi$; $c_n T = A$; $F(\omega) = A$

12. (a) $c_n = (1/Tjn\omega_0)(2\cos n\omega_0\delta - 2)$;
$T \cdot c_n = (1/jn\omega_0)(2\cos n\omega_0\delta - 2)$
(b) $F(\omega) = (2\cos\omega\delta - 2)/j\omega$

13. (a) $\dfrac{1 - \cos\omega\delta/2 + j\sin\omega\delta/2}{j\omega}$

(b) $\dfrac{\delta}{2}\dfrac{\sin\omega\delta/2}{\omega\delta/2}$ (c) $\dfrac{1 - \cos\omega\delta/2}{j\omega}$

14. (a) $F(\omega) = \dfrac{2}{1 + \omega^2}$ (b) $F(\omega) = \dfrac{-2\omega j}{1 + \omega^2}$

15. $f(t) = \begin{cases} e^{-t}/2 & \text{for } t > 0 \\ e^{t}/2 & \text{for } t < 0 \end{cases}$

16. $f(t) = \begin{cases} e^{-t}/2 & \text{for } t > 0 \\ -e^{-t}/2 & \text{for } t < 0 \end{cases}$

17. (i) (a) $\sigma_c = 0$

(b) $F(s) = \dfrac{\beta}{s^2 + \beta^2}$

(c) poles at $s = \pm j\beta$

(ii) (a) $\sigma_c = -\alpha$

(b) $F(s) = \dfrac{\beta}{(s + \alpha)^2 + \beta^2}$

(c) poles at $s = -\alpha \pm j\beta$

(iii) (a) $\sigma_c = -\alpha$

(b) $F(s) = \dfrac{2\beta(s + \alpha)}{[(s + \alpha)^2 + \beta^2]^2}$

(c) poles at $s = -\alpha \pm j\beta$

(iv) (a) $\sigma_c = \alpha$ (b) $F(s) = \dfrac{1}{(s - \alpha)^2}$

(c) poles at $s = \alpha$

(v) (a) $\sigma_c = 0$ (b) $F(s) = \dfrac{\beta^2}{s(s^2 + \beta^2)}$

(c) poles at $s = 0$ and $\pm j\beta$

18. (i) (a) $\sigma_c = 0$ (b) $F(s) = \dfrac{\alpha}{s(s + \alpha)}$

(c) poles at $s = 0, -\alpha$

(ii) (a) $\sigma_c = \beta$ (b) $F(s) = \dfrac{\beta}{(s^2 - \beta^2)}$

(c) poles at $s = \pm\beta$

(iii) (a) $\sigma_c = \beta$ (b) $F(s) = \dfrac{s}{(s^2 - \beta^2)}$

(c) poles at $s = \pm\beta$

(iv) (a) $\sigma_c = 0$

(b) $F(s) = \dfrac{s\sin\theta + \beta\cos\theta}{s^2 + \beta^2}$

(c) poles at $s = \pm j\beta$

(v) (a) $\sigma_c = 0$

(b) $F(s) = \dfrac{s\cos\theta - \beta\sin\theta}{s^2 + \beta^2}$

(c) poles at $s = \pm j\beta$

19. (a) $\sigma_c = \log_e a$; $F(s) = 1/(s - \log_e a)$

(b) $\sigma_c = -\alpha$; $F(s) = \log_e\left(\dfrac{s + \beta}{s + \alpha}\right)$

(c) $\sigma_c = 0$; $F(s) = \tan^{-1}(\beta/s)$

(d) No σ_c; no $F(s)$

20. (a) $\dfrac{A(1 - e^{-\delta s})}{s}$ (b) $s = \infty$ (c) None

21. (a) $F(s) = \dfrac{\frac{1}{2}}{s} - \dfrac{1}{s + 1} + \dfrac{\frac{1}{2}}{s + 2}$

(b) $F(s) = 1 + \dfrac{\frac{1}{2}}{s} - \dfrac{1}{s + 1} + \dfrac{\frac{1}{2}}{s + 2}$

(c) $F(s) = 1 - \dfrac{\frac{1}{2}}{s + 1} + \dfrac{8}{s + 2} - \dfrac{\frac{27}{2}}{s + 3}$

(d) $F(s) = \dfrac{0.577\ \underline{|30°}}{s + \frac{1}{2} - j0.866} + \dfrac{0.577\ \underline{|-30°}}{s + \frac{1}{2} + j0.866}$

(e) $F(s) = s^2 + \dfrac{0.577\ \underline{|30°}}{s + \frac{1}{2} - j0.866}$
$+ \dfrac{0.577\ \underline{|-30°}}{s + \frac{1}{2} + j0.866}$

22. (a) $\dfrac{-1}{(s + 1)^3} + \dfrac{1}{(s + 1)^2}$

(b) $1 - \dfrac{1}{(s + 1)^3} + \dfrac{3}{(s + 1)^2} - \dfrac{3}{s + 1}$

(c) $\dfrac{3}{s + 1} - \dfrac{6}{(s + 2)^2} - \dfrac{2}{s + 2}$

(d) $F(s) = \dfrac{0.353\ \underline{|-45°}}{(s + 1 - j)^2} + \dfrac{0.353\ \underline{|45°}}{(s + 1 + j)^2}$
$+ \dfrac{0.25\ \underline{|90°}}{s + 1 - j} + \dfrac{0.25\ \underline{|-90°}}{s + 1 + j}$

(e) $F(s) = \dfrac{-1}{s + 1} + \dfrac{-0.25 - j0.25}{(s + 1 - j)^2}$
$+ \dfrac{-0.25 + j0.25}{(s + 1 + j)^2} + \dfrac{0.5 - j0.25}{s + 1 - j}$
$+ \dfrac{0.5 + j0.25}{s + 1 + j}$

23. (a) $f(t) = \frac{1}{2} - e^{-t} + \frac{1}{2}e^{-2t}$
(b) $f(t) = \cos t$
(c) $f(t) = 1.15e^{-t/2}\cos(0.866t + 30°)$
(d) $f(t) = te^{-t}(1 - t/2)$

CHAPTER 15

1. (a) $Z = 1/Cs$; pole at zero, zero at ∞
   (b) $Z = L(s)$; pole at ∞, zero at 0
   (c) $Z = R + 1/Cs$; pole at 0, zero at $-1/RC$
   (d) $Z = R + Ls$; pole at 0, zero at $-R/L$
   (e) $Z = \dfrac{R}{1 + RCs}$;
   pole at $S = -1/RC$, zero at ∞
   (f) $Z = \dfrac{RLs}{R + Ls}$;
   zero at $s = 0$, pole at $s = -R/L$

2. $Z = \dfrac{1}{C} \dfrac{s + R/L}{s^2 + s(R/L + G/C) + (1 + RG)LC}$

3. (a) $i(t) = 2e^{-t/10}$ (b) Same

4. (a) $e(t) = 30e^{-t/2}$ (b) Same

5. (a) $H(s) = \dfrac{1}{s^2 + 2s + 2}$
   (b) $h(t) = e^{-t} \sin t$

6. (a) $H(s) = \dfrac{3s}{s^2 + 9}$ (b) $e_2(t) = \dfrac{9t}{6} \sin 3t$

7. (a) $H(s) = \dfrac{(s + 1)(s + 2)}{(s + 3)^2}$
   (b) $f_2(t) = e^{-3t}(2t^2 - 3t + 1)u_{-1}(t)$

8. (a) $H(s) = \dfrac{1}{2(s + 2)}$ (b) $h(t) = \dfrac{e^{-2t}}{2}$

9. (a) $E(s) = \dfrac{10}{s(s + 2)}$
   (b) $e(t) = 5(1 - e^{-2t})$

10. $e(t) = 5(1 - e^{-2t})$

11. $E_{oc} = \dfrac{10}{s(s + 1)}$, $Z_{eq} = \dfrac{s + 2}{s + 1}$,
    $i(t) = 3.54(e^{-0.3t} - e^{-1.7t})$

12. $i(t) = 50u_{-2}(t) + 125u_{-1}(t) - 25e^{-2t} \cdot u_{-1}(t)$

13. $i(t) = 4.48 \cos (t - 26.5°) - 4e^{-2t}$

14. $i(t) = 10 \cos t - 11.5e^{-t/2} \cos (0.866t + 30°)$

15. (a) i (transient) $= 0.565 \sin (t + 28.5°)$

(b) i (steady-state) $= 2/(1 - \pi^2) \cos \pi t$

16. (a) $I(s) = \dfrac{1}{(s + 1)(1 - e^{-s})}$
    (b) $i(t) = e^{-t}u_{-1}(t) + e^{-(t-1)}u_{-1}(t - 1)$
    $\qquad\qquad + e^{-(t-2)}u_{-1}(t - 2) + \cdots$
    (c) $i(t) = 1 + \dfrac{e^{-t}}{1 - e} + \dfrac{1}{[1 + (2\pi)^2]^{1/2}}$
    $\qquad \times \cos (2\pi t - \tan^{-1} 2\pi)$
    $\qquad + \dfrac{1}{[1 + (4\pi)^2]^{1/2}}$
    $\qquad \times \cos (4\pi t - \tan^{-1} 4\pi) + \cdots$

17. (a) $\dfrac{s^2 + 3s + 1}{2s^2 + s}$
    (b) Zeros: $s = -2.62, -0.38$; poles: $s = 0$, -0.5
    (c) Zeros = short-circuit transients; poles = open-circuit transients

18. $Z = \dfrac{(s^2 + 1)(s^2 + 9)}{s(s^2 + 4)}$ for all 4 networks

19. (a) $Z_{12} = \dfrac{1}{s^3 + 2s^2 + 2s + 1}$
    (b) Zeros: 3 at ∞;
    (c) Poles: $s = -1, s = -0.5 \pm j0.866$

20. (a) Ae^{-t} (b) $Ae^{-t} \cos (10t + \theta°)$

21. (a) $Z = \dfrac{s + 1}{s^2 + 2s + 2}$
    (b) $Ae^{-t} \cos (t + \theta)$ (c) Ae^{-t}

22. $Z(s) = \dfrac{2(s + 1)}{s^2 + 2s + 2}$ (b) $Z(j) = 1.26 \underline{|-18.50}$
    (c) $e(t) = 12.6 \cos (t - 18.50)$

23. (a) $Z(s) = 20(s + 1 - j10)$
    (b) $s = j10$ (c) $B = 2$ rps
    (d) $Q = 5$ (e) $Z_R = 20$ ohms

24. (a) $Z(s) = \dfrac{1}{20(s + 1 - j10)}$
    (b) $s = j10$ (c) $Z = \frac{1}{20}$
    (d) $B = 2$ (e) $Q = 5$

Index